sl
the
Ar
Libra

Multivariate Statistical Analysis for Biologists

Multivariate Statistical Analysis for Biologists

HILARY L. SEAL
Yale University

METHUEN AND CO LTD
11 NEW FETTER LANE LONDON EC4

First published 1964

Reprinted with minor corrections, 1966
Printed in Great Britain by
Spottiswoode, Ballantyne & Co. Ltd.
London and Colchester
1·2

Contents

Introduction

Most biologists pay lip-service to the necessity of a basic knowledge of organic chemistry, inorganic chemistry, calculus, physics, and statistics. But lack of time and an indifference to the mathematical niceties of the last of these subjects leave the biologist quite unprepared to deal effectively with a problem which he faces far more frequently than he is prone to admit, namely the reduction to 'sensible' form of a mass of measured or enumerated observations.

The statistical textbook writers have done a superb job in making available to the non-mathematically attuned research worker the statistical techniques he is likely to require. Most of these attempt to provide a *rationale* of the methods they describe even though proofs have to be left to more mathematical texts. Nevertheless, it would seem that the typical biologist retains little in his mind of statistical courses he may have attended other than a vague notion that a t-test may be used to compare two means, an F-test to compare two variances, a χ^2-test to judge the hypothesis of no-correlation in a contingency table, and an 'analysis of variance' to compare several means (somewhat mysteriously) by an F-test. If the biologist has to compare several linear regressions or to analyse a complex experiment he rushes to the nearest 'tame' statistician.

Perhaps this is an inevitable state of affairs in an age of narrower and narrower specialization. But we think that the statistician hasn't (yet) got his message across to the biologist in sufficiently 'practical' terms. Isn't it time the biologist was given a clearer insight into the mathematical models the statistician expects him to use? Shouldn't the biologist himself make some attempt to judge whether the parametric models which he implicitly uses when he makes an analysis of variance have any relevance to the experiment he intended to carry out? Too often the statistician imposes his model on the biologist because its mathematics are easy.

Part A of this book is an attempt to provide the biologist with a sound working knowledge of the Least Squares technique known as Regression Analysis of a Linear Model. As adumbrated by the statistician this method seeks to 'explain' a single variate (e.g., cubic capacity of an animal skull) in terms of a number of other variables. Because of the current availability of electronic computers our procedure here is to derive the orthogonal model as a special case of the more general model encountered by the scientist who cannot control his variable values. In that general (non-orthogonal) model determinantal and matrix methods are introduced at an early stage so that the reader will understand the burden of computation he is escaping when he uses, as he must, an electronic computer.

However, Part A is restricted to the so-called 'fixed effects' model and even so omits consideration of several standard techniques. Thus, for example, curvilinear regression finds no place in the text, nor does 'degrees of freedom for non-additivity'.† The proper discussion of Latin Squares and Incomplete Blocks would have required consideration of 'random effects' models and have made the book much longer. We hope this limitation of scope will not damage its usefulness.

This brings us to Part B which really occasioned this book, namely, multivariate, as opposed to multivariable, statistical methods. Until a year or two ago the mathematical statistician could talk of Canonical Analysis, Principal Components and (even) Factor Analysis without even being able to illustrate these techniques numerically except in trivial cases. Rao's (1952) pioneering text is largely about multivariate methods, yet he could only illustrate them numerically on a sample, each unit of which was measured as to nine variates. The systematist measuring the 'whole animal' will probably want to make as many as 50 measurements (including 0, 1 variates) per animal. The analysis of such data has only recently become a feasible project.

But with this revolution in the reduction of multivariate data we see a real danger. On hearing that a set of multiple measurements can be synthesized in a matter of minutes on a large computer (once the original data are in punched-card form) the biologist will be tempted to 'have a go' without understanding too clearly what the machine is doing for him. So far no attempt has been made to explain multivariate statistical methods in relatively simple language which yet omits none of the technical details. This is the purpose of Part B of this book. While the material in this part is largely independent of that of Part A it requires – it has to require – the use of vector and matrix notation which is introduced to the reader in the earlier chapters.

The prior knowledge of statistical theory required of readers is relatively slight. It could have been obtained by a biologist who has been forced to refer to statistical texts in the course of his biological research. A more suitable preparation would be through a one semester course in basic statistics. While the reader does not have to remember the techniques there developed he should be on nodding terms with such expressions as 'probability distribution' (and the Normal, Chi-square, and F distributions in particular) and the 'mean' and 'variance' of such a distribution. He should be aware that in a sample drawn from any

† Except, *en passant*, in the footnote of p. 53.

probability distribution the calculated mean and variance are only 'estimates' of their 'true' values; and that statements of 'confidence intervals' will contain the corresponding 'true' parameters with a specified relative frequency. He should also have some familiarity with the idea of a 'test' of a given statistical hypothesis, such as that the mean of the probability distribution from which we are sampling is zero. But this is about all that is absolutely essential background information.

Note to 1966 reprint

It is gratifying to the author that the original edition of this work was exhausted within twelve months. In this reprint we have merely corrected some errors, added a few references, and expanded the discussions of pp. 79 and 115. The latter expansion appears in the form of an Addendum on p. 200.

The comments of some reviewers have led us to make the following *apologia*:

(i) We have made no attempt in this book to name the originators of the various techniques described. To have said, for example, that in 1901 Karl Pearson derived the general equations which determine the principal axes of the probability ellipsoid (given their name by Schols in 1875) would largely have missed the point. For the numerical evaluation of eigenvalues and eigenvectors has a history of its own going back to the last century, and we must not overlook the ingenious efforts by psychologists to approximate or bypass the exact solution. And while the idea of canonical variates was due to Harold Hotelling we have not used his technique of canonical correlation. In fact, as we have indicated in our references, our approach is based on Bartlett's matricial synthesis of all these earlier works.

(ii) Any user of Chapter Seven whose colleagues criticize him for not preferring 'classical discriminant analysis' may be assured, like the *bourgeois gentilhomme* was in similar circumstances, that he has been using it all the time. For the first canonical variate is (apart from a possible change of origin and scale) the 'linear discriminant function' of many statistical texts. We have, nevertheless, preferred the Hotelling-Bartlett terminology which has no emotional overtones.

As for the absence of Hotelling's T^2-test this is because it is merely a special case of the U-test. In fact T^2 is the equivalent of $U_{1,p,N-s-p}$ whose use is described on pp. 92–93 and illustrated on pp. 131–132.

(iii) It should, perhaps, be emphasized that for an electronic computer all the models of Part A are particular cases of the model described in Chapter Five (see e.g., p. 186). The proliferation of titles in Part A has been solely for the convenience of human computers who developed different numerical procedures for each special case.

(iv) In our experience biologists are confirmed 'data snoopers' and our advocacy of Scheffé's S-method (p. 19) was to permit them to doodle and yet remain technically pure. While the T-method (Scheffé, 1959, cited in Chapter One) may produce narrower confidence intervals, broadly these seem to be limited to contrasts of the type $c_1\beta_1 + c_2\beta_2$ where the sample estimate of each of the two terms has the same variance. In the more general type of contrast the S-method is usually more precise (Scheffé, *loc. cit.*, Sec. 3.7).

DEDICATION

Although the title-page neglects to mention it the sub-title of this book is: *Quotations from an Unfamiliar Bartlett.*

PART A

A Single Dependent Variate

EXHORTATION

He had bought a large map representing the sea,
  Without the least vestige of land:
And the crew were much pleased when they
    found it to be
  A map they could all understand.

CARROLL, L. (1876) *The Hunting of the Snark*, London.

CHAPTER ONE

The Linear Model and its Least Square Analysis

In order to explain the concept of the so-called linear model it is convenient to proceed by means of an illustration. We have chosen an experiment, reported by M. L. Ryder (1956), designed to assess the effect of poor nutrition on the fleece of Masham sheep. Since the growth of a lamb may be judged by the increase in size from age to age of areas of tattooed squares of skin, changes in such skin areas could be used as the criterion for estimating differential nutritional effects.

The experimental results

Two matched pairs of sheep were used in the experiment which lasted about 16 weeks. One of the sheep of each pair was regarded as a 'control' and was fed on the regular diet of concentrates (1·5 lb per sheep per day) throughout the experimental period. Five† points of time were chosen in this period for the measurement of the total skin areas which had been tattooed so far as possible in the same positions on each sheep of a matched pair.

After a preliminary 'adjustment' period of six weeks the four sheep were measured and were then continued a further three weeks on the control diet of concentrates before they were measured again. Immediately after the second set of measurements the nutritional plane of the two 'experimental' sheep was dropped and, after two weeks, all four sheep were subjected to a further set of measurements. At this point, because of the small effect of the reduced diet on the 'experimental' sheep (no fibre shedding had occurred), the nutritional plane was dropped even further. Three weeks after this second drop another set of measurements was made on all four sheep; thereafter the regular diet was given to the 'experimental' sheep. Two weeks after this resumption of normal diet a final set of measurements was made.

The experimental results are summed up in the following tattooed skin area differences in cm^2 in favour of the 'control' animals. Our purpose is to extract the greatest possible information from this set of 10 results.

† Problem 2 at the end of this chapter shows how we have tampered with Ryder's results.

Time point	First pair	Second pair	Mean
1. 6 weeks after start	0·37	−0·73	0·202
2. 3 weeks later	−0·50	1·67	
3. 2 weeks after drop	−0·70	0·58	−0·060
4. 3 weeks after further drop	1·77	4·57	3·170
5. 2 weeks after resumption of normal diet	1·31	3·78	2·545
Totals	2·25	9·87	

The conceptual model

In order to do this we will have to make a number of assumptions which differ somewhat in their degree of generality and in their influence on our conclusions. In the first place we assume that while the matching procedure has substantially reduced the inherent differences between the two sheep of each pair, nevertheless there may be a real difference between the (means of the) first pair and the second pair of sheep. Let us write $2\beta_1$ for the real, unknown difference in tattooed area between the two pairs and, conventionally, measure the 'effect' of belonging to the first pair as $+\beta_1$ and the 'effect' of belonging to the second as $-\beta_1$. This implies that we are measuring pair-effects from a point midway between the (means of the) two pairs. We must be prepared for the possibility that this β_1 is so small in relation to other effects, such as ill-matching within one or both of the pairs, that we will not find it statistically significant – or, expressing this differently, we may find that the hypothesis $\beta_1 = 0$ does no injustice to the observational results.

Turning now to the growth picture, the experimenter clearly expected to observe two positive area differentials in favour of the control sheep after the 'experimental' animals had suffered a nutritional deficiency for two weeks. In other words, he expected the reduced diet to result in a smaller growth in comparison with the 'control' during the two weeks at the end of which he recorded the measurements on line 3 of the preceding table. We will write β_2 (cm^2) for this expected differential although the *a posteriori* view is that β_2 is either zero or even negative. Similarly we write β_3 for the differential in area measurements (measured from the initial normal-diet period as base-line) after a further three weeks, and β_4 for the differential existing at the end of the experiment.

One difficulty at this point is to decide whether the experiment calls for *different* β_2-values (say) for each of the two pairs of sheep. Presumably the experimenter had no such possibility in mind. The experiment would have no general validity if the conclusion was that diet changes affected different sheep differently, over and above the general growth differential between sheep (which we have allowed for in β_1). Nevertheless the and the 'effects' of different nutritional planes can be added together to produce a total 'effect' superimposed on the general mean of the observations. Nevertheless the linear model obtained by such an aggregation is a reasonable first approximation (at least) to the truth.

Now we are attempting to 'explain' 10 observations in terms of five parameters, namely μ the general mean, β_1 the pair 'effect', and β_2, β_3, β_4 the diet 'effects'. Even if we could peer behind the veil to discover the true values of these parameters there would still be a residue of variation in the observations not accounted for by the parameters. This so-called 'error' has 10 values in the instant case for a given set of parameter values. A reasonable assumption, which has been shown to be not too sensitive in its effect on the conclusions drawn (see Chapter 10 of Scheffé, 1959), is that these 'errors' are a random sample of 10 variates from a Normal distribution with a mean of zero when the five parameters are given their true values.

It is appropriate to mention here that the *raison d'être* of the statistician is in the development of methods to deal with the variability that occurs in repeated measurements (samples) of what is apparently one and the same quantity. The statistician postulates that the size of such measurements fluctuates above and below a 'true' value which it is the experimenter's purpose to discover. A fluctuation of specified amount occurs – the statistician supposes – with a given (unknown) probability. The set of probabilities attached to every one of the possible fluctuations constitutes the 'probability distribution' of fluctuation (and thus of measurement) sizes. It is this distribution which frequently turns out to be approximately Normal.

The algebraic model

We are now ready to write out our linear model in full. We will call this model Ω.

Observation	Model	Error
0·37	$\mu+\beta_1-\beta_2-\beta_3-\beta_4$	10 'errors' which, when added to the model-values, produce the observations
−0·73	$\mu-\beta_1-\beta_2-\beta_3-\beta_4$	
−0·50	$\mu+\beta_1-\beta_2-\beta_3-\beta_4$	
1·67	$\mu-\beta_1-\beta_2-\beta_3-\beta_4$	
−0·70	$\mu+\beta_1+4\beta_2-\beta_3-\beta_4$	
0·58	$\mu-\beta_1+4\beta_2-\beta_3-\beta_4$	
1·77	$\mu+\beta_1-\beta_2+4\beta_3-\beta_4$	
4·57	$\mu-\beta_1-\beta_2+4\beta_3-\beta_4$	
1·31	$\mu+\beta_1-\beta_2-\beta_3+4\beta_4$	
3·78	$\mu-\beta_1-\beta_2-\beta_3+4\beta_4$	

statistician may be tempted to introduce some further paramete test this so-called 'interaction' effect between diet changes anc sheep themselves.

For the moment, however, we will content ourselves with the thre representing the effects of the three diet changes. Since we are measu the change in growth from a 'control' sheep fed on the 'normal' diet, five successive pairs of measurements contain the following gro differentials:

$$0, \quad 0, \quad \beta_2, \quad \beta_3, \quad \beta_4$$

As we will see later, there are computational advantages in measur these five quantites about their mean. Or, even better, let us meası them thus and multiply all results by five to clear off fractions. This effected in the following table.

Time point	Assumed dietary effect	Effect *minus* mean effect	Five times previous column
1	0	$-\beta/5$	$-\beta_2-\beta_3-\beta_4$
2	0	$-\beta/5$	$-\beta_2-\beta_3-\beta_4$
3	β_2	$\beta_2-\beta/5$	$4\beta_2-\beta_3-\beta_4$
4	β_3	$\beta_3-\beta/5$	$-\beta_2+4\beta_3-\beta_4$
5	β_4	$\beta_4-\beta/5$	$-\beta_2-\beta_3+4\beta_4$
Totals	β (say)	0	0

Although the final column appears to mingle β_2, β_3 and β_4 inextricably nevertheless the pattern becomes clear once we ask, for instance, what is the difference between an average measurement at time-point 3 and one at time-point 2. This difference is

$$(4\beta_2-\beta_3-\beta_4)-(-\beta_2-\beta_3-\beta_4) = 5\beta_2$$

Hence β_2 is one-fifth of said difference.

The foregoing is essentially what we did when considering 'pair' effects. The table above was then

Pair no.	Assumed effect	Effect *minus* mean effect
1	$2\beta_1$	$2\beta_1-\beta_1 = \beta_1$
2	0	$0-\beta_1 = -\beta_1$
Totals	$2\beta_1$	0

It is essential to arrange that at least one of the original cells has a zero value in it. Otherwise we have more 'parameters' than 'effects'.

A new difficulty is now to decide whether the 'effects' of different pairs

It is convenient to refer to the observations as a (10-component) vector of observations. Also, in order to save the repetitive printing of the β's in any one column, we may refer to the coefficients of that column as the vector of coefficients attached to that β. Although there is little uniformity of notation in this subject we will write x's for the observations and z's for the coefficients of the β's. These z's are sometimes called 'instrumental' variables to distinguish them from observed variate values. We will reserve y for linear transformations of the x's, a matter of some importance in Part B.

One other point concerning notation. It is useful to have some way of showing how a particular observational x-value arose. For example, in the nutritional experiment x_{32} would refer to the observation of the third time-point and the second pair of sheep. Algebraically, we express our 10 measurements as x_{ij} ($i = 1, 2, \ldots 5; j = 1, 2$).

We can now rewrite Ω in the following form where sometimes we will suppress the e's for conciseness.

i	j	$x_{ij} = \mu +$	$\beta_1 \times$ +	$\beta_2 \times$ +	$\beta_3 \times$ +	$\beta_4 \times$ +	e_{ij}
1	1	0·37	1	−1	−1	−1	e_{11}
	2	−0·73	−1	−1	−1	−1	e_{12}
2	1	−0·50	1	−1	−1	−1	e_{21}
	2	1·67	−1	−1	−1	−1	e_{22}
3	1	−0·70	1	4	−1	−1	e_{31}
	2	0·58	−1	4	−1	−1	e_{32}
4	1	1·77	1	−1	4	−1	e_{41}
	2	4·57	−1	−1	4	−1	e_{42}
5	1	1·31	1	−1	−1	4	e_{51}
	2	3·78	−1	−1	−1	4	e_{52}

The principle of least squares

In the foregoing set-up we have 10 observations 'explained' in terms of five unknown parameters. If we added the first and the third observation, the second and the fourth, the fifth and the seventh, the sixth and the eighth, and the ninth and the tenth observations, we would, if we ignored the presence of the 'errors', obtain five equations in five unknowns. We could thus 'solve' for the five unknown parameters. However, we instinctively feel that there must be a 'better' method of finding estimates for these parameters.

In fact, if the residuals are assumed to have been independently sampled from one and the same Normal distribution with zero mean [which we will write as $N(0, \sigma^2)$ where σ is the standard deviation of the distribution] the 'best' numerical values of the five parameters will be obtained by minimizing the sum of the squares of the 'errors' with respect to variation in μ, β_1, ... β_4. That is to say, we are to minimize

$$\mathscr{S}_\Omega \equiv \sum_{i,j} e_{ij}^2 \equiv \sum_{i,j} [x_{ij} - \{\mu + \beta_1 z_{1ij} + \beta_2 z_{2ij} + \beta_3 z_{3ij} + \beta_4 z_{4ij}\}]^2$$

for variations in the five parameters. Notice that in these expressions $\sum_{i,j}$ is short for: sum over all values of i and j. Furthermore, since there are four vectors of z's we have had to adopt a third subscript in order to state them explicitly.

□□□ The minimization of such an expression may, perhaps, be unfamiliar to some readers so we will exemplify it on a simplified case.

Consider the model

$$\begin{aligned} \Omega: \quad x_1 &= \beta_0 z_{01} + \beta_1 z_{11} + e_1 \\ x_2 &= \beta_0 z_{02} + \beta_1 z_{12} + e_2 \\ x_3 &= \beta_0 z_{03} + \beta_1 z_{13} + e_3 \end{aligned}$$

Note that if we make each of the three components of the vector $\mathbf{z}_0$ equal to unity and replace β_0 by μ we are back at our previous model with the last three of the four β's of that model identically equal to zero.

Continuing, we have

$$\mathscr{S}_\Omega \equiv (x_1 - \beta_0 z_{01} - \beta_1 z_{11})^2 + (x_2 - \beta_0 z_{02} - \beta_1 z_{12})^2 + (x_3 - \beta_0 z_{03} - \beta_1 z_{13})^2$$

Differentiating with respect to β_0

$$\begin{aligned} \frac{\partial \mathscr{S}_\Omega}{\partial \beta_0} &= 2(x_1 - \beta_0 z_{01} - \beta_1 z_{11})(-z_{01}) \\ &\quad + 2(x_2 - \beta_0 z_{02} - \beta_1 z_{12})(-z_{02}) \\ &\quad + 2(x_3 - \beta_0 z_{03} - \beta_1 z_{13})(-z_{03}) \\ &= -2[z_{01} x_1 + z_{02} x_2 + z_{03} x_3 - \beta_0(z_{01}^2 + z_{02}^2 + z_{03}^2) \\ &\quad - \beta_1(z_{01} z_{11} + z_{02} z_{12} + z_{03} z_{13})] \end{aligned}$$

with an expression of similar form (with the components of the vector $\mathbf{z}_1$ used instead of those of the vector $\mathbf{z}_0$) when we differentiate with respect to β_1. These two differential coefficients must be equated to zero simultaneously to obtain the 'stationary' values of β_0 and β_1 – call them $\hat{\beta}_0$ and $\hat{\beta}_1$ – which make $\mathscr{S}_\Omega$ a minimum with a value $\mathscr{S}_\Omega^0$, say.

A noteworthy feature about $\partial \mathscr{S}_\Omega / \partial \beta_0$ is the component-by-component multiplication of the vectors $\mathbf{z}_0$ and $\mathbf{x}$, and of the vectors $\mathbf{z}_0$ and $\mathbf{z}_1$. It will be helpful in later chapters if the reader familiarizes himself with this concept of 'vector multiplication'. If we write a three-component vector as $\mathbf{a}$ we will always understand a column vector of the form

$$\begin{bmatrix} a_1 \\ a_2 \\ a_3 \end{bmatrix}$$

On the other hand if we 'prime' the vector, namely $\mathbf{a}'$, we understand the row vector

$$\{a_1 \quad a_2 \quad a_3\}$$

(The two different uses of the brackets and the braces is a convention that is not adhered to by all authors.) Finally, the single (scalar) quantity obtained by multiplying the *row* vector $\mathbf{a}'$ by the *column* vector $\mathbf{b}$ (of the same number of components) is written $\mathbf{a}'\mathbf{b}$, i.e.,

$$\mathbf{a}'\mathbf{b} \equiv \{a_1 \quad a_2 \quad a_3\} \begin{bmatrix} b_1 \\ b_2 \\ b_3 \end{bmatrix} \equiv a_1 b_1 + a_2 b_2 + a_3 b_3$$

We will use this notation henceforth.

Reverting to our expression for $\partial \mathscr{S}_\Omega / \partial \beta_0$ and equating it to zero we obtain, in vector notation, after suppressing the -2,

$$\mathbf{z}_0'\mathbf{x} = \mathbf{z}_0'\mathbf{z}_0\hat{\beta}_0 + \mathbf{z}_0'\mathbf{z}_1\hat{\beta}_1 \tag{1}$$

and, as symmetry suggests, the second equation is

$$\mathbf{z}_1'\mathbf{x} = \mathbf{z}_1'\mathbf{z}_0\hat{\beta}_0 + \mathbf{z}_1'\mathbf{z}_1\hat{\beta}_1 \tag{2}$$

The generality of these equations (which are called the 'normal equations') is apparent and they are promptly extended to as many β's as we require. They are easily remembered. Thus the original model Ω in the nutrition experiment (ignoring 'error') was, *in (column) vector notation*:

$$\mathbf{x} = \mathbf{z}_0\beta_0 + \mathbf{z}_1\beta_1 + \mathbf{z}_2\beta_2 + \mathbf{z}_3\beta_3 + \mathbf{z}_4\beta_4$$

with $\beta_0 \equiv \mu$ and $\mathbf{z}_0$ a vector of units. Multiply through by the row vector $\mathbf{z}_0'$ to obtain

$$\mathbf{z}_0'\mathbf{x} = \mathbf{z}_0'\mathbf{z}_0\hat{\beta}_0 + \mathbf{z}_0'\mathbf{z}_1\hat{\beta}_1 + \mathbf{z}_0'\mathbf{z}_2\hat{\beta}_2 + \mathbf{z}_0'\mathbf{z}_3\hat{\beta}_3 + \mathbf{z}_0'\mathbf{z}_4\hat{\beta}_4$$

This is the first of the normal equations. Now multiply Ω through by the row vector $\mathbf{z}_1'$ to get the second normal equation, namely

$$\mathbf{z}_1'\mathbf{x} = \mathbf{z}_1'\mathbf{z}_0\hat{\beta}_0 + \mathbf{z}_1'\mathbf{z}_1\hat{\beta}_1 + \mathbf{z}_1'\mathbf{z}_2\hat{\beta}_2 + \mathbf{z}_1'\mathbf{z}_3\hat{\beta}_3 + \mathbf{z}_1'\mathbf{z}_4\hat{\beta}_4$$

and similarly

$$\mathbf{z}_2'\mathbf{x} = \mathbf{z}_2'\mathbf{z}_0\hat{\beta}_0 + \mathbf{z}_2'\mathbf{z}_1\hat{\beta}_1 + \mathbf{z}_2'\mathbf{z}_2\hat{\beta}_2 + \mathbf{z}_2'\mathbf{z}_3\hat{\beta}_3 + \mathbf{z}_2'\mathbf{z}_4\hat{\beta}_4$$
$$\mathbf{z}_3'\mathbf{x} = \mathbf{z}_3'\mathbf{z}_0\hat{\beta}_0 + \mathbf{z}_3'\mathbf{z}_1\hat{\beta}_1 + \mathbf{z}_3'\mathbf{z}_2\hat{\beta}_2 + \mathbf{z}_3'\mathbf{z}_3\hat{\beta}_3 + \mathbf{z}_3'\mathbf{z}_4\hat{\beta}_4$$
$$\mathbf{z}_4'\mathbf{x} = \mathbf{z}_4'\mathbf{z}_0\hat{\beta}_0 + \mathbf{z}_4'\mathbf{z}_1\hat{\beta}_1 + \mathbf{z}_4'\mathbf{z}_2\hat{\beta}_2 + \mathbf{z}_4'\mathbf{z}_3\hat{\beta}_3 + \mathbf{z}_4'\mathbf{z}_4\hat{\beta}_4$$

Remember that in the above five normal equations for five unknowns $\hat{\beta}_0, \hat{\beta}_1 \ldots \hat{\beta}_4$ we have to put $\hat{\beta}_0 \equiv \hat{\mu}$ and write $\mathbf{z}_0$ as a column vector of 10 units. It is usual to interchange the right- and left-hand sides of these equations and we will do this hereafter.

Numerical estimates of the β's

Reverting to the nutritional experiment we find from the layout on p. 7:

$$\begin{aligned}
\mathbf{z}_0'\mathbf{x} &= 0{\cdot}37 - 0{\cdot}73 - 0{\cdot}50 + 1{\cdot}67 \ldots \quad + 3{\cdot}78 = 12{\cdot}12\\
\mathbf{z}_1'\mathbf{x} &= 0{\cdot}37 + 0{\cdot}73 - 0{\cdot}50 - 1{\cdot}67 \ldots \quad - 3{\cdot}78 = -7{\cdot}62\\
\mathbf{z}_2'\mathbf{x} &= -0{\cdot}37 + 0{\cdot}73 + 0{\cdot}50 - 1{\cdot}67 \ldots \quad - 3{\cdot}78 = -12{\cdot}72\\
\mathbf{z}_3'\mathbf{x} &= -0{\cdot}37 + 0{\cdot}73 + 0{\cdot}50 - 1{\cdot}67 \ldots \quad - 3{\cdot}78 = 19{\cdot}58\\
\mathbf{z}_4'\mathbf{x} &= -0{\cdot}37 + 0{\cdot}73 + 0{\cdot}50 - 1{\cdot}67 \ldots + 4 \times 3{\cdot}78 = 13{\cdot}33
\end{aligned}$$

Similarly

$$\begin{aligned}
\mathbf{z}_0'\mathbf{z}_0 &= 10 \quad \text{while} \quad \mathbf{z}_0'\mathbf{z}_1 = 0 = \mathbf{z}_0'\mathbf{z}_2 = \mathbf{z}_0'\mathbf{z}_3 = \mathbf{z}_0'\mathbf{z}_4\\
\mathbf{z}_1'\mathbf{z}_1 &= 10 \quad \mathbf{z}_1'\mathbf{z}_2 = 0 = \mathbf{z}_1'\mathbf{z}_3 = \mathbf{z}_1'\mathbf{z}_4\\
\mathbf{z}_2'\mathbf{z}_2 &= 40 \quad \mathbf{z}_2'\mathbf{z}_3 = -10 = \mathbf{z}_2'\mathbf{z}_4\\
\mathbf{z}_3'\mathbf{z}_3 &= 40 \quad \mathbf{z}_3'\mathbf{z}_4 = -10 \quad \mathbf{z}_4'\mathbf{z}_4 = 40
\end{aligned}$$

Observe that, e.g., $\mathbf{z}_2'\mathbf{z}_4 = \mathbf{z}_4'\mathbf{z}_2$ and $\mathbf{z}_0'\mathbf{z}_3 = \mathbf{z}_3'\mathbf{z}_0$, which means that the normal equations are *always* symmetric about the diagonal through $\hat{\beta}_0$ in the first equation, $\hat{\beta}_1$ in the second, and so on.

In this case the five normal equations are

$$\begin{aligned}
10\hat{\beta}_0 &= 12{\cdot}12\\
10\hat{\beta}_1 &= -7{\cdot}62\\
40\hat{\beta}_2 - 10\hat{\beta}_3 - 10\hat{\beta}_4 &= -12{\cdot}72\\
-10\hat{\beta}_2 + 40\hat{\beta}_3 - 10\hat{\beta}_4 &= 19{\cdot}58\\
-10\hat{\beta}_2 - 10\hat{\beta}_3 + 40\hat{\beta}_4 &= 13{\cdot}33
\end{aligned}$$

The first two of these immediately result in

$$\hat{\beta}_0 = \frac{12{\cdot}12}{10} = 1{\cdot}212 = \hat{\mu}$$
$$\hat{\beta}_1 = -0{\cdot}762$$

It is reassuring to note that the estimate of μ is the mean of the 10 observations.

Simultaneous linear equations

The last three equations can be solved by successive elimination of 'unknowns' in the usual way. The result is

$$\hat{\beta}_2 = -0{\cdot}0525 \qquad \hat{\beta}_3 = 0{\cdot}5935 \qquad \hat{\beta}_4 = 0{\cdot}4685$$

However, because this will facilitate later discussion, we will introduce the concept of a 'determinant' and provide the general solution of simultaneous linear equations by means of determinants.

□□□ We define a 2×2 determinant as the value of the difference between the two cross-products of diagonal entries in a square expression. Thus

$$\begin{vmatrix} a & b \\ c & d \end{vmatrix} \equiv ad - bc$$

Note that by interchanging the first and second row (or the first and second column) the value of the determinant is multiplied by *minus one*. Observe, too, that if a and c have a common factor it can be extracted before the computation and applied to the result. The same is true of a and b or of b and d or of c and d. Any factor common to a row may be extracted; any factor common to a column may be extracted.

In order to extend this definition to a 3×3 determinant we define

$$\begin{vmatrix} a_1 & b_1 & c_1 \\ a_2 & b_2 & c_2 \\ a_3 & b_3 & c_3 \end{vmatrix} = a_1 \begin{vmatrix} b_2 & c_2 \\ b_3 & c_3 \end{vmatrix} - a_2 \begin{vmatrix} b_1 & c_1 \\ b_3 & c_3 \end{vmatrix} + a_3 \begin{vmatrix} b_1 & c_1 \\ b_2 & c_2 \end{vmatrix}$$

$$= a_1 M_{11} - a_2 M_{21} + a_3 M_{31}$$

where M_{11} is the (minor) determinant obtained by deleting the first row and first column of the original determinant. It is a convention that the *row* is always used as the *first* subscript in a row–column subscript. The alternate signs of the terms are negative in the foregoing rule which is easily extensible to the reduction of a fourth-order determinant to a third, etc. It can be shown that we may use the components of the first row (instead of those of the first column) as multipliers of the appropriate minors without affecting the ultimate result.

Anticipating, slightly, let us calculate the value of

$$\varDelta = \begin{vmatrix} 40 & -10 & -10 \\ -10 & 40 & -10 \\ -10 & -10 & 40 \end{vmatrix}$$

$$= 40 \begin{vmatrix} 40 & -10 \\ -10 & 40 \end{vmatrix} - (-10) \begin{vmatrix} -10 & -10 \\ -10 & 40 \end{vmatrix} + (-10) \begin{vmatrix} -10 & -10 \\ 40 & -10 \end{vmatrix}$$

$$= 40 \times 1500 + 10 \times (-500) - 10 \times 500 = 50{,}000$$

More simply, we can first extract the common factor 10 from *each* of the three columns (or rows) and obtain

$$\Delta = 10^3 \begin{vmatrix} 4 & -1 & -1 \\ -1 & 4 & -1 \\ -1 & -1 & 4 \end{vmatrix} = 10^3 \left\{ 4 \begin{vmatrix} 4 & -1 \\ -1 & 4 \end{vmatrix} + \begin{vmatrix} -1 & -1 \\ -1 & 4 \end{vmatrix} + \begin{vmatrix} -1 & -1 \\ 4 & -1 \end{vmatrix} \right\}$$

$$= 10^3(60-5-5) = 10^3 \times 50$$

Reverting now to the set of three equations for $\hat{\beta}_2$, $\hat{\beta}_3$ and $\hat{\beta}_4$ we have

$$\begin{aligned} 40\hat{\beta}_2 - 10\hat{\beta}_3 - 10\hat{\beta}_4 &= -12{\cdot}72 = \mathbf{z}_2'\mathbf{x} \\ -10\hat{\beta}_2 + 40\hat{\beta}_3 - 10\hat{\beta}_4 &= 19{\cdot}58 = \mathbf{z}_3'\mathbf{x} \\ -10\hat{\beta}_2 - 10\hat{\beta}_3 + 40\hat{\beta}_4 &= 13{\cdot}33 = \mathbf{z}_4'\mathbf{x} \end{aligned}$$

A rule known as Cramer's Rule then states that if $\Delta \neq 0$ is the determinant of the coefficients of the unknowns on the left-hand side, the value of $\hat{\beta}_2$ is obtained by dividing Δ into the determinant obtained by substituting the vector of numbers on the right of the equations for the *first* column vector in Δ, the value of $\hat{\beta}_3$ is a similar quotient where the numerator is the determinant obtained by substituting the vector on the right of the equations for the *second* column vector in Δ, and so on, generally.

In this case, for example,

$$\hat{\beta}_2 = \begin{vmatrix} -12{\cdot}72 & -10 & -10 \\ 19{\cdot}58 & 40 & -10 \\ 13{\cdot}33 & -10 & 40 \end{vmatrix} \div \begin{vmatrix} 40 & -10 & -10 \\ -10 & 40 & -10 \\ -10 & -10 & 40 \end{vmatrix}$$

$$= -0{\cdot}0525$$

The importance of the foregoing determinantal methods is not in the arithmetic – for few (human) computers nowadays try to solve by hand simultaneous linear equations with more than four unknowns – but lies in the insight it gives us into electronic machine computations for solving such equations.†

Residuals after fitting the model

Having obtained the numerical values of the $\hat{\beta}$'s our estimate of any particular x-value is given by

$$\hat{x}_{ij} = 1{\cdot}212 - 0{\cdot}762z_{1ij} - 0{\cdot}0525z_{2ij} + 0{\cdot}5935z_{3ij} + 0{\cdot}4685z_{4ij}$$

† This is not to imply that electronic computers actually use the determinantal method of solution.

On inserting the component values of the vectors **z** in this we obtain the following comparison of 'actual' and 'estimated' x-values where, for example,

$$\hat{x}_{11} = 1{\cdot}212 - 0{\cdot}762 \times (1) - 0{\cdot}0525 \times (-1) + 0{\cdot}5935 \times (-1) + 0{\cdot}4685 \times (-1)$$

i	j	x_{ij}	$\hat{x}_{ij}$	$x_{ij} - \hat{x}_{ij}$ = error of estimate or 'residual'	Square of 'residual' (to 5 decs.)
1	1	0·37	−0·5595	0·9295	0·86397
	2	−0·73	0·9645	−1·6945	2·87133
2	1	−0·50	−0·5595	0·0595	0·00354
	2	1·67	0·9645	0·7055	0·49773
3	1	−0·70	−0·8220	0·1220	0·01488
	2	0·58	0·7020	−0·1220	0·01488
4	1	1·77	2·4080	−0·6380	0·40704
	2	4·57	3·9320	0·6380	0·40704
5	1	1·31	1·7830	−0·4730	0·22373
	2	3·78	3·3070	0·4730	0·22373
	Totals	12·12	12·1200	0·0000	5·52787 $\equiv \mathscr{S}^0_\Omega$

Study of the $\hat{x}$'s and the resulting 'residuals' indicates that the model Ω has broadly fulfilled its objective, namely to 'reproduce' the observations within certain limits of error.

Estimating σ^2

The sum of the squares of the 'residuals' of the foregoing table is $\mathscr{S}^0_\Omega = 5{\cdot}52787$. It has been obtained after estimating – not merely the usual mean but – *five* parameters. Just as one 'degree of freedom' is deducted when a variance is calculated about an estimated mean, so here we deduct five degrees of freedom from the 10 observations to provide the divisor of the 'residual sum of squares'. Hence our estimate of the σ^2 which governs the distribution of the e_{ij} in the model Ω is 5·52787/5 or $1{\cdot}10557 = \hat{\sigma}^2$.

Now in the standard case with N observations

$$s^2 \equiv \hat{\sigma}^2 \equiv \frac{\Sigma\,(x-\bar{x})^2}{N-1}$$

and it is known that $\Sigma\,(x-\bar{x})^2/\sigma^2$ is distributed as χ^2 with $N-1$ degrees of freedom. The analogy here is complete, for with

$$\hat{\sigma}^2 \equiv \frac{\mathscr{S}^0_\Omega}{N-q} \qquad (N \text{ is } 10)$$

where q is the number of parameters fitted (five in the illustrative example), $\mathscr{S}^0_\Omega/\sigma^2$ is distributed as χ^2 with $N-q$ degrees of freedom. It should be emphasized that the foregoing refers to the case where the 'errors' are assumed to be $N(0, \sigma^2)$.

The direct calculation of $\mathscr{S}^0_\Omega$

Although it is useful to display the residuals $\hat{e}_{ij} \equiv x_{ij} - \hat{x}_{ij}$ – and most computer programs provide for this† – it is not necessary to square these items individually to arrive at $\mathscr{S}^0_\Omega$, the residual sum of squares.

In order to demonstrate this we will review our vector notation. It has been seen that $\mathbf{a}'\mathbf{a}$ means the sum of the squares of the components of the vector $\mathbf{a}$. But what does $(\mathbf{a}+\mathbf{b})'(\mathbf{a}+\mathbf{b})$ mean? Let us consider the case of two three-component vectors

$$\mathbf{a} = \begin{bmatrix} a_1 \\ a_2 \\ a_3 \end{bmatrix} \qquad \mathbf{b} = \begin{bmatrix} b_1 \\ b_2 \\ b_3 \end{bmatrix}$$

It is reasonable to propose that

$$\mathbf{a}+\mathbf{b} = \begin{bmatrix} a_1+b_1 \\ a_2+b_2 \\ a_3+b_3 \end{bmatrix}$$

with the result that

$$(\mathbf{a}+\mathbf{b})'(\mathbf{a}+\mathbf{b}) = (a_1+b_1)^2+(a_2+b_2)^2+(a_3+b_3)^2$$

and it is easily shown that the definition

$$(\mathbf{a}+\mathbf{b})' = \mathbf{a}'+\mathbf{b}'$$

which leads to

$$(\mathbf{a}+\mathbf{b})'(\mathbf{a}+\mathbf{b}) = \mathbf{a}'(\mathbf{a}+\mathbf{b})+\mathbf{b}'(\mathbf{a}+\mathbf{b})$$

produces exactly the same result.

In the foregoing we have used the 'obvious' rule that, if β is a constant,

$$\mathbf{a}\beta = \begin{bmatrix} a_1 \\ a_2 \\ a_3 \end{bmatrix} \beta = \begin{bmatrix} a_1\beta \\ a_2\beta \\ a_3\beta \end{bmatrix}$$

Similarly for $\mathbf{a}'\beta$.

□□□ Returning, now, to $\mathscr{S}^0_\Omega$ we note that it is the sum of squares of 10 values of $\hat{e}_{ij}$. These 10 residuals can be written succinctly as the 10-component vector

$$\hat{\mathbf{e}} \equiv \mathbf{x} - \mathbf{z}_0\hat{\beta}_0 - \mathbf{z}_1\hat{\beta}_1 - \mathbf{z}_2\hat{\beta}_2 - \mathbf{z}_3\hat{\beta}_3 - \mathbf{z}_4\hat{\beta}_4$$

† A check on the constancy of σ is obtained by graphing each residual against its corresponding x-value.

For example, if we look at the fifth component the corresponding equivalence is (from p. 7)

$$\hat{e}_{31} = x_{31} - \hat{\beta}_0 - \hat{\beta}_1 - 4\hat{\beta}_2 + \hat{\beta}_3 + \hat{\beta}_4$$

The sum of squares of the 10 components of $\hat{\mathbf{e}}$ is

$$\begin{aligned}
\mathscr{S}^0_\Omega &\equiv \hat{\mathbf{e}}'\hat{\mathbf{e}} \\
&= (\mathbf{x} - \mathbf{z}_0\hat{\beta}_0 - \mathbf{z}_1\hat{\beta}_1 - \mathbf{z}_2\hat{\beta}_2 - \mathbf{z}_3\hat{\beta}_3 - \mathbf{z}_4\hat{\beta}_4)' \\
&\qquad \times (\mathbf{x} - \mathbf{z}_0\hat{\beta}_0 - \mathbf{z}_1\hat{\beta}_1 - \mathbf{z}_2\hat{\beta}_2 - \mathbf{z}_3\hat{\beta}_3 - \mathbf{z}_4\hat{\beta}_4) \\
&= (\mathbf{x}' - \mathbf{z}_0'\hat{\beta}_0 - \mathbf{z}_1'\hat{\beta}_1 - \mathbf{z}_2'\hat{\beta}_2 - \mathbf{z}_3'\hat{\beta}_3 - \mathbf{z}_4'\hat{\beta}_4) \\
&\qquad \times (\mathbf{x} - \mathbf{z}_0\hat{\beta}_0 - \mathbf{z}_1\hat{\beta}_1 - \mathbf{z}_2\hat{\beta}_2 - \mathbf{z}_3\hat{\beta}_3 - \mathbf{z}_4\hat{\beta}_4) \\
&= \mathbf{x}'(\mathbf{x} - \mathbf{z}_0\hat{\beta}_0 - \mathbf{z}_1\hat{\beta}_1 - \mathbf{z}_2\hat{\beta}_2 - \mathbf{z}_3\hat{\beta}_3 - \mathbf{z}_4\hat{\beta}_4) \\
&\qquad -\hat{\beta}_0\mathbf{z}_0'(\mathbf{x} - \mathbf{z}_0\hat{\beta}_0 - \mathbf{z}_1\hat{\beta}_1 - \mathbf{z}_2\hat{\beta}_2 - \mathbf{z}_3\hat{\beta}_3 - \mathbf{z}_4\hat{\beta}_4) \\
&\qquad -\hat{\beta}_1\mathbf{z}_1'(\mathbf{x} - \mathbf{z}_0\hat{\beta}_0 - \mathbf{z}_1\hat{\beta}_1 - \mathbf{z}_2\hat{\beta}_2 - \mathbf{z}_3\hat{\beta}_3 - \mathbf{z}_4\hat{\beta}_4) \\
&\qquad - \ldots \text{etc.} \\
&= \mathbf{x}'\mathbf{x} - \mathbf{x}'\mathbf{z}_0\hat{\beta}_0 - \mathbf{x}'\mathbf{z}_1\hat{\beta}_1 - \mathbf{x}'\mathbf{z}_2\hat{\beta}_2 - \mathbf{x}'\mathbf{z}_3\hat{\beta}_3 - \mathbf{x}'\mathbf{z}_4\hat{\beta}_4 \\
&\qquad -\hat{\beta}_0(\mathbf{z}_0'\mathbf{x} - \mathbf{z}_0'\mathbf{z}_0\hat{\beta}_0 - \mathbf{z}_0'\mathbf{z}_1\hat{\beta}_1 - \mathbf{z}_0'\mathbf{z}_2\hat{\beta}_2 - \mathbf{z}_0'\mathbf{z}_3\hat{\beta}_3 - \mathbf{z}_0'\mathbf{z}_4\hat{\beta}_4) \\
&\qquad -\hat{\beta}_1(\mathbf{z}_1'\mathbf{x} - \mathbf{z}_1'\mathbf{z}_0\hat{\beta}_0 - \mathbf{z}_1'\mathbf{z}_1\hat{\beta}_1 - \mathbf{z}_1'\mathbf{z}_2\hat{\beta}_2 - \mathbf{z}_1'\mathbf{z}_{3\,3} - \mathbf{z}\hat{\beta}_1'\mathbf{z}_4\hat{\beta}_4) \\
&\qquad - \ldots \text{etc.}
\end{aligned}$$

Reference to the five normal equations on pp. 9–10 shows that the expressions multiplying $\hat{\beta}_0$, $\hat{\beta}_1$, ... in the second, third, ... lines of the expression last written *are all zero.*

We thus have the simple result

$$\begin{aligned}
\mathscr{S}^0_\Omega &= \mathbf{x}'\mathbf{x} - \mathbf{x}'\mathbf{z}_0\hat{\beta}_0 - \mathbf{x}'\mathbf{z}_1\hat{\beta}_1 - \mathbf{x}'\mathbf{z}_2\hat{\beta}_2 - \mathbf{x}'\mathbf{z}_3\hat{\beta}_3 - \mathbf{x}'\mathbf{z}_4\hat{\beta}_4 \\
&= \mathbf{x}'\mathbf{x} - \mathbf{z}_0'\mathbf{x}\hat{\beta}_0 - \mathbf{z}_1'\mathbf{x}\hat{\beta}_1 - \mathbf{z}_2'\mathbf{x}\hat{\beta}_2 - \mathbf{z}_3'\mathbf{x}\hat{\beta}_3 - \mathbf{z}_4'\mathbf{x}\hat{\beta}_4
\end{aligned}$$

This is an important formula which will be used again and again in what follows. We notice, in particular, that $\mathbf{x}'\mathbf{x}$ is the sum of the squares of the original observations, and that all the $\mathbf{z}'\mathbf{x}$ and $\hat{\beta}$ terms have already been calculated.

In our numerical example $\mathbf{x}'\mathbf{x} = 44{\cdot}5574$ and

$$\begin{aligned}
\mathscr{S}^0_\Omega &= 44{\cdot}5574 - 12{\cdot}12 \times 1{\cdot}212 - (-7{\cdot}62)(-0{\cdot}762) - (-12{\cdot}72)(-0{\cdot}0525) \\
&\qquad - 19{\cdot}58 \times 0{\cdot}5935 - 13{\cdot}33 \times 0{\cdot}4685 \\
&= 5{\cdot}527885 \text{ exactly,}
\end{aligned}$$

showing that we have a fifth-place error in our previous approximation. The variate $\mathscr{S}^0_\Omega/\sigma^2$ is a randomly-drawn value from the χ^2 distribution with $10-5=5$ degrees of freedom. The difficulty that this statement involves the unknown σ^2 will be neatly bypassed in what follows.

As a final comment we note that

$$\mathbf{x}'\mathbf{x}-\mathbf{z}_0'\mathbf{x}\hat{\beta}_0 = \mathbf{x}'\mathbf{x}-\left(\sum_{i,j} x_{ij}\right)\bar{x} = \sum_{i,j} x_{ij}^2-\frac{\left(\sum_{i,j} x_{ij}\right)^2}{10}$$

since $\mathbf{z}_0$ is a vector of units and $\hat{\beta}_0$ is the mean. The first two terms of $\mathscr{S}_\Omega^0$ thus coalesce into the sum of squares of the observations about the mean $\bar{x}$.

The 'restricted' model

We have now proposed a model Ω to 'interpret' the experimental results and have estimated all its parameters μ (or β_0), β_1, β_2, β_3, β_4 and σ^2. Can we achieve more within this framework?

A glance at the $\hat{\beta}$-values on pp. 10–11 leads us to think that the calculation of $\hat{\beta}_2$ was unnecessary. Its negative sign implies that sheep on the poor diet grew faster than the controls – which presumably does not make sense. On the other hand it is numerically so small that it could surely be replaced by zero.

However, if we pursue this line of thought a little further we may be led to wonder whether $\hat{\beta}_4$ is 'worthwhile' in comparison with $\hat{\beta}_1$ – although we should reflect that, when $i=5$, $\hat{\beta}_4$ is multiplied by 4 while none of the multipliers of $\hat{\beta}_1$ is other than ± 1. In short, we would like to have some criterion for deciding whether some or all of the β-values could be zero without making the observations look unreasonable.

Note the way this is expressed. The 'best' estimates of all the β's have already been calculated and none of them is zero. But could we set some β's equal to zero and still obtain as good results as we have already produced for Ω?

It is here that we have an *embarras de choix*. Which, and how many, β's should be set equal to zero? We hope that it is obvious to the reader that we should not choose the small $\hat{\beta}$'s and make them equal to zero in turn or together. Such a progressive procedure, dictated by the behaviour of the observations under the numerous alternatives that may suggest themselves, does not permit valid probabilistic conclusions to be drawn. This is because each new hypothesis is conditioned by the conclusions drawn about all previous hypotheses. It is clear that, sooner or later, we could find a hypothesis to fit the data.

Thus, since we do not know the *a priori* probabilities of the various hypotheses about the β's, we must proceed from assumptions made *before the data became available*. If we then find that certain pre-selected groups of β's do *not* vanish as a whole we may continue with various subhypotheses suggested by the data. Scheffé (1959) shows how this can be done without changing the probability level at which we have rejected the hypothesis of zero β's in a given group.

In Ryder's nutritional experiment we are not really interested in testing whether $\beta_1 = 0$. We 'know' that (unmatched) sheep vary and we are happy to have 'extracted' this mean level of variation from the observational results. On the other hand the whole experiment rested on the notion that β_2 and β_3, and possibly β_4, differed from zero, although the unforeseen lack of response after two weeks at the lowered nutritional plane came as a surprise. We will therefore try to ascertain whether a model ignoring the dietary changes represents the observations as well as our previous more complex model. In fact our new 'restricted' model is

$$\omega: \quad x_{ij} = \mu + \beta_1 z_{1ij} + e_{ij}$$

where the β_2, β_3 and β_4 of Ω have been suppressed.

We now proceed to 'fit' this model to our 10 observations by Least Squares. The normal equations to determine β_0 (or μ) and β_1 are

$$\mathbf{z}_0'\mathbf{z}_0\hat{\hat{\beta}}_0 + \mathbf{z}_0'\mathbf{z}_1\hat{\hat{\beta}}_1 = \mathbf{z}_0'\mathbf{x}$$
$$\mathbf{z}_1'\mathbf{z}_0\hat{\hat{\beta}}_0 + \mathbf{z}_1'\mathbf{z}_1\hat{\hat{\beta}}_1 = \mathbf{z}_1'\mathbf{x}$$

Notice the 'double hat' on our 'best' estimates of the model's β's. Although in this case – for reasons we consider more fully in Chapter II – $\hat{\hat{\beta}} = \hat{\beta}$, *in general this is not true.*

Numerically we have (from p. 10)

$$10\hat{\hat{\beta}}_0 = 12{\cdot}12 \quad \text{and} \quad 10\hat{\hat{\beta}}_1 = -7{\cdot}62$$

resulting in

$$\hat{\hat{\beta}}_0 = \bar{x} = 1{\cdot}212 = \hat{\beta}_0$$

and

$$\hat{\hat{\beta}}_1 = -0{\cdot}762 = \hat{\beta}_1$$

Furthermore,

$$\begin{aligned}\mathcal{S}^0_\omega &= \mathbf{x}'\mathbf{x} - \mathbf{z}_0'\mathbf{x}\hat{\hat{\beta}}_0 - \mathbf{z}_1'\mathbf{x}\hat{\hat{\beta}}_1 \\ &= 44{\cdot}5574 - 12{\cdot}12 \times 1{\cdot}212 - (-7{\cdot}62)(-0{\cdot}762) \\ &= 24{\cdot}06152\end{aligned}$$

and $\mathcal{S}^0_\omega/\sigma^2$ is distributed as χ^2 with $10-2 = 8$ degrees of freedom.

Comparison of ω with Ω

Our objective is now to compare the adequacy of the model ω in comparison with the more general Ω – which the experimenter hopes is correct! We note that (under Ω) $\hat{\sigma}^2_\Omega = 5{\cdot}52787/5 = 1{\cdot}10557$ while

$\hat{\sigma}_{\omega}^2 = 24{\cdot}06152/8 = 3{\cdot}00769$. The mean square residual under Ω is substantially less than under ω, but this comparison is not so striking when we compare standard deviations (the square root of the variance), namely 1·0515 and 1·7343. What we need is an objective test whether the residual variance under Ω is 'really' smaller than under ω (i.e., Ω is 'really' a better 'fit').

A theorem in mathematical statistics states that the distribution of the quotient of two *independent* values of χ^2 with degrees of freedom ν_1 (in the numerator) and ν_2 (in the denominator) is that of $(\nu_1/\nu_2)F_{\nu_1,\nu_2}$, where F_{ν_1,ν_2} is a random variable that has been comprehensively tabulated. In our case it can be proved that, although $\mathscr{S}_{\Omega}^0$ and $\mathscr{S}_{\omega}^0$ are *not* independent, the variates $\mathscr{S}_{\omega}^0 - \mathscr{S}_{\Omega}^0$ and $\mathscr{S}_{\Omega}^0$ are. But, if we only fitted s parameters in the 'restricted' model:

$$\begin{array}{ll} \mathscr{S}_{\omega}^0/\sigma^2 & \text{is distributed as } \chi^2 \text{ with } N-s \text{ d.f.} \\ \mathscr{S}_{\Omega}^0/\sigma^2 & \text{is distributed as } \chi^2 \text{ with } N-q \text{ d.f.} \\ \hline (\mathscr{S}_{\omega}^0 - \mathscr{S}_{\Omega}^0)/\sigma^2 & \text{is distributed as } \chi^2 \text{ with } q-s \text{ d.f.} \end{array}$$

Thus

$$\frac{\mathscr{S}_{\omega}^0 - \mathscr{S}_{\Omega}^0}{\mathscr{S}_{\Omega}^0} \text{ is distributed as } \frac{\chi_{q-s}^2}{\chi_{N-q}^2} \quad \text{or} \quad \frac{q-s}{N-q} F_{q-s,\,N-q}$$

It is more convenient to sum this up by saying that

$$\frac{(\mathscr{S}_{\omega}^0 - \mathscr{S}_{\Omega}^0) \div (q-s)}{\mathscr{S}_{\Omega}^0 \div (N-q)} \text{ is distributed as } F_{q-s,\,N-q}$$

The foregoing may be expressed by saying that if we can compare by division: (i) the average of that part of the residual sum of squares from ω that is due to the $(q-s)$ parameters 'lost' in the transition from Ω to ω, with (ii) the average residual sum of squares derived from the model Ω, we have a variate from an F-distribution with $q-s$ and $N-q$ degrees of freedom. In terms of our numerical illustration

$$\frac{(24{\cdot}06152 - 5{\cdot}52788) \div (5-2)}{5{\cdot}52788 \div (10-5)} = \frac{6{\cdot}17788}{1{\cdot}10558} = 5{\cdot}588$$

is distributed as $F_{3,5}$. But the F-tables show that 5% of randomly-sampled F-values are larger than 5·410 which is less than our observed value of 5·588. We conclude from this that ω is significantly different from Ω. Or, in other words, if Ω were the 'true' model underlying the observations an experimenter postulating ω has found a set of discrepancies from ω that would occur on less than 5% of all occasions in which Ω is the truth.

Note particularly that this judgement is relative to Ω. We have no means of determining whether Ω is the 'real truth' and it is up to the experimenter to include in Ω as many parameters as he considers reasonably plausible *a priori*. If he has 'too many' parameters they may then be discarded by testing an appropriate ω-model.

We mention that the danger of accounting for too few parameters (β's) in Ω is minimized by 'randomizing' the experimental animals or plants that are considered indistinguishable by the model (except for their supposedly different e's). Thus, for example, if the offspring of a single female cannot be ascribed to their various male parents a random allotment of treatments among them will, in some cases, ensure that the interpretations remain valid in the long run (Scheffé, *loc. cit.*, Chapter 9).

Scheffé's S-method of judging contrasts

We are satisfied about the reality of the nutritional effects comprised in the three parameters β_2, β_3 and β_4. But we would like to summarize the experiment by more specific statements about these effects and, in particular, would like to select a few telling comparisons by inspection of the data. Notice that the above three β's were based on an *a priori* concept of the experiment but that we now intend to combine these parameters (which, as a whole, are significantly different from zero) into a number of statements based on the 'run' of the data themselves. This can be achieved, without change in probability level (5% in this case), by means of a method due to Scheffé (*loc. cit.*, Chapter 3).

A *contrast* is defined to be a linear expression in a group of significant β's (other than β_0), e.g.,

$$c_2\beta_2+c_3\beta_3+c_4\beta_4 \equiv \psi \text{ (say)}$$

where the coefficients c_2, c_3 and c_4 are completely arbitrary. Any one of them can be positive, zero or negative but, in applying the following formulation, it must be remembered that the components of the $\mathbf{z}$ attached to any β must add to zero.

Having chosen any number of sets of c's to suit the experimental results we may then state, with a confidence of $1-\alpha$, where α is the probability level at which we found the set of β's to be significant ($\alpha = 0{\cdot}05$ and thus $1-\alpha = 0{\cdot}95$ in the illustrative example), that the values of all the resulting ψ's lie between the various pairs of limits defined by

$$\hat{\psi}-(\nu_1 F_{\alpha;\nu_1,\nu_2})^{1/2}\hat{\sigma}_{\hat{\psi}} \leqslant \psi \leqslant \hat{\psi}+(\nu_1 F_{\alpha;\nu_1,\nu_2})^{1/2}\hat{\sigma}_{\hat{\psi}}$$

[Scheffé writes the factor involving F as S; hence the name of this technique.]

Here

$$\hat{\psi} = c_2\hat{\beta}_2+c_3\hat{\beta}_3+c_4\hat{\beta}_4$$

is the estimated value of ψ, $F_{\alpha;\nu_1,\nu_2}$ is the 100α% point in the F-table with ν_1 and ν_2 degrees of freedom, and $\hat{\sigma}_{\hat{\psi}}$ is the estimated standard deviation of the estimate $\hat{\psi}$. Note that ν_1 is the number of β's equated to zero in the formulation of ω, while ν_2 is N minus the number of β's in Ω.

For example, in the illustrative case, $\nu_1 = q-s = 5-2 = 3$, $\nu_2 = N-q = 10-5 = 5$, and $F_{0\cdot 05;3,5} = 5\cdot 410$ (see p. 18). The $\hat{\beta}$'s were calculated on p. 11 and $\hat{\sigma}^2 = 1\cdot 01557$ (p. 13). All we need, therefore, is an expression for $\sigma^2_{\hat{\psi}}$ (which will involve σ^2 itself) and we can proceed with our selection of suitable sets of c's.

Estimating the variance of $\hat{\psi}$

In order to obtain this variance, which we may write alternatively as $\mathscr{V}(\hat{\psi})$, we need a simple theorem from mathematical statistics.

DEFINITION 1

The *variance* of a random variable x of mean μ is the expected value (i.e., the mean over an infinite number of random samples) of the square of $(x-\mu)$. Algebraically, writing $\mathscr{E}$ for the expected-value operator,

$$\mathscr{E}(x) = \mu$$

$$\mathscr{V}(x) = \mathscr{E}(x-\mu)^2$$

DEFINITION 2

The *covariance* of two random variables x and y of means μ and ν, respectively, is the expected value of the product $(x-\mu)(y-\nu)$, i.e.,

$$\mathscr{C}(x,y) = \mathscr{E}\{(x-\mu)(y-\nu)\}$$

THEOREM

The variance of a linear combination $ax+by+cz+\ldots$ of a number of random variables $x, y, z, \ldots$, where a, b and c are arbitrary constants, is given by

$$\begin{aligned}\mathscr{V}(ax+by+cz+\ldots) = {} & a^2\mathscr{V}(x)+b^2\mathscr{V}(y)+c^2\mathscr{V}(z)+\ldots \\ & +2ab\mathscr{C}(x,y)+2bc\mathscr{C}(y,z) \\ & +2ca\mathscr{C}(x,z)+\ldots\end{aligned}$$

□□□ This is easily proved for two random variables since

$$\mathscr{E}(ax+by) = a\mathscr{E}(x)+b\mathscr{E}(y) = a\mu+b\nu$$

so that

$$\begin{aligned}\mathscr{V}(ax+by) &= \mathscr{E}\{a(x-\mu)+b(y-\nu)\}^2 \\ &= \mathscr{E}\{a^2(x-\mu)^2+b^2(y-\nu)^2+2ab(x-\mu)(y-\nu)\} \\ &= a^2\mathscr{E}(x-\mu)^2+b^2\mathscr{E}(y-\nu)^2+2ab\mathscr{E}\{(x-\mu)(y-\nu)\} \\ &= a^2\mathscr{V}(x)+b^2\mathscr{V}(y)+2ab\mathscr{C}(x,y)\end{aligned}$$

Applying this theorem to

$$\hat{\psi} = c_2\hat{\beta}_2 + c_3\hat{\beta}_3 + c_4\hat{\beta}_4$$

we obtain

$$\mathscr{V}(\hat{\psi}) = c_2^2\mathscr{V}(\hat{\beta}_2) + c_3^2\mathscr{V}(\hat{\beta}_3) + c_4^2\mathscr{V}(\hat{\beta}_4) + 2c_2c_3\mathscr{C}(\hat{\beta}_2, \hat{\beta}_3)$$
$$+ 2c_2c_4\mathscr{C}(\hat{\beta}_2, \hat{\beta}_4) + 2c_3c_4\mathscr{C}(\hat{\beta}_3, \hat{\beta}_4)$$

The covariance of two $\hat{\beta}$'s

Our next step is thus to find the value of $\mathscr{C}(\hat{\beta}_2, \hat{\beta}_3)$ since this will extend to the other two covariances by interchanging the suffices. We should note also that

$$\mathscr{C}(x, x) \equiv \mathscr{V}(x)$$

□□□ From p. 12 we see that

$$\hat{\beta}_2 = \begin{vmatrix} \mathbf{z}_2'\mathbf{x} & -10 & -10 \\ \mathbf{z}_3'\mathbf{x} & 40 & -10 \\ \mathbf{z}_4'\mathbf{x} & -10 & 40 \end{vmatrix} \div \Delta \qquad \hat{\beta}_3 = \begin{vmatrix} 40 & \mathbf{z}_2'\mathbf{x} & -10 \\ -10 & \mathbf{z}_3'\mathbf{x} & -10 \\ -10 & \mathbf{z}_4'\mathbf{x} & 40 \end{vmatrix} \div \Delta$$

where

$$\Delta = \begin{vmatrix} 40 & -10 & -10 \\ -10 & 40 & -10 \\ -10 & -10 & 40 \end{vmatrix} = 50{,}000$$

Let us remember that we may interchange two *adjacent* columns (or rows) of a determinant if we multiply the result by (-1). Thus

$$\hat{\beta}_3 = (-1)\begin{vmatrix} \mathbf{z}_2'\mathbf{x} & 40 & -10 \\ \mathbf{z}_3'\mathbf{x} & -10 & -10 \\ \mathbf{z}_4'\mathbf{x} & -10 & 40 \end{vmatrix} \div \Delta$$

Denoting by M_{ij} the minor (determinant) obtained by deleting the ith row and jth column of Δ we have

$$\hat{\beta}_2 = (\mathbf{z}_2'\mathbf{x}M_{11} - \mathbf{z}_3'\mathbf{x}M_{21} + \mathbf{z}_4'\mathbf{x}M_{31})/\Delta$$

and

$$\hat{\beta}_3 = (-\mathbf{z}_2'\mathbf{x}M_{21} + \mathbf{z}_3'\mathbf{x}M_{22} - \mathbf{z}_4'\mathbf{x}M_{32})/\Delta$$
$$= (-\mathbf{x}'\mathbf{z}_2M_{21} + \mathbf{x}'\mathbf{z}_3M_{22} - \mathbf{x}'\mathbf{z}_4M_{32})/\Delta$$

Now

$$\Delta = \begin{vmatrix} \mathbf{z}_2'\mathbf{z}_2 & \mathbf{z}_2'\mathbf{z}_3 & \mathbf{z}_2'\mathbf{z}_4 \\ \mathbf{z}_3'\mathbf{z}_2 & \mathbf{z}_3'\mathbf{z}_3 & \mathbf{z}_3'\mathbf{z}_4 \\ \mathbf{z}_4'\mathbf{z}_2 & \mathbf{z}_4'\mathbf{z}_3 & \mathbf{z}_4'\mathbf{z}_4 \end{vmatrix} = \mathbf{z}_2'\mathbf{z}_2M_{11} - \mathbf{z}_3'\mathbf{z}_2M_{21} + \mathbf{z}_4'\mathbf{z}_2M_{31}$$

while

$$\mathbf{z}_2'\mathbf{z}_3M_{11} - \mathbf{z}_3'\mathbf{z}_3M_{21} + \mathbf{z}_4'\mathbf{z}_3M_{31} = \begin{vmatrix} \mathbf{z}_2'\mathbf{z}_3 & \mathbf{z}_2'\mathbf{z}_3 & \mathbf{z}_2'\mathbf{z}_4 \\ \mathbf{z}_3'\mathbf{z}_3 & \mathbf{z}_3'\mathbf{z}_3 & \mathbf{z}_3'\mathbf{z}_4 \\ \mathbf{z}_4'\mathbf{z}_3 & \mathbf{z}_4'\mathbf{z}_3 & \mathbf{z}_4'\mathbf{z}_4 \end{vmatrix}$$

But it is easily verified that any determinant in which one column (row) is a multiple of another column (row) is identically zero. Hence the latter expression in M's is zero and this is true also of the similar expressions involving $\mathbf{z}_4$, $\mathbf{z}_1$ or $\mathbf{z}_0$ as multipliers in place of $\mathbf{z}_3$. These properties make it possible to find, e.g., $\mathscr{E}(\hat{\beta}_2)$ and $\mathscr{C}(\hat{\beta}_2,\hat{\beta}_3)$ quite easily.

Consider first $\mathscr{E}(\hat{\beta}_2)$ which consists of three terms of the form $\mathscr{E}(\mathbf{z}'\mathbf{x})$ multiplied by constants of the type M/Δ. Each component of the vector product $\mathbf{z}'\mathbf{x}$ will consist of a (constant) z-value multiplied by a variate value x. But $\mathscr{E}(x) = z_0\beta_0 + z_1\beta_1 + z_2\beta_2 + \ldots$ and this, with the appropriate z-values component by component, replaces the x-values in $\mathbf{z}'\mathbf{x}$. We thus obtain, e.g.,

$$\begin{aligned}\mathscr{E}(\mathbf{z}_2'\mathbf{x}) &= \mathbf{z}_2'(\mathbf{z}_0\beta_0 + \mathbf{z}_1\beta_1 + \mathbf{z}_2\beta_2 + \mathbf{z}_3\beta_3 + \mathbf{z}_4\beta_4)\\ &= \mathbf{z}_2'\mathbf{z}_0\beta_0 + \mathbf{z}_2'\mathbf{z}_1\beta_1 + \mathbf{z}_2'\mathbf{z}_2\beta_2 + \mathbf{z}_2'\mathbf{z}_3\beta_3 + \mathbf{z}_2'\mathbf{z}_4\beta_4\end{aligned}$$

with similar expressions for $\mathscr{E}(\mathbf{z}_3'\mathbf{x})$ and $\mathscr{E}(\mathbf{z}_4'\mathbf{x})$. When these are inserted into the expression for $\mathscr{E}(\hat{\beta}_2)$, namely

$$\mathscr{E}(\hat{\beta}_2) = \{M_{11}\mathscr{E}(\mathbf{z}_2'\mathbf{x}) - M_{21}\mathscr{E}(\mathbf{z}_3'\mathbf{x}) + M_{31}\mathscr{E}(\mathbf{z}_4'\mathbf{x})\}/\Delta$$

we notice that the eventual coefficients of β_0, β_1, β_3 and β_4 are all zero while the coefficient of β_2 is Δ. Hence

$$\mathscr{E}(\hat{\beta}_2) = \Delta\beta_2/\Delta = \beta_2$$

This means that if we were able to repeat our sheep experiment indefinitely – and if the model is really applicable! – the average of all the calculated values of $\hat{\beta}_2$ would be the unknown β_2. Since we do not even contemplate such a repetition of experiments this result is only conceptual. It is, however, reassuring.

Turning now to $\mathscr{C}(\hat{\beta}_2,\hat{\beta}_3)$ let us consider a typical term from $\hat{\beta}_3$ multiplied by all three terms of $\hat{\beta}_2$. For example

$$(\mathbf{x}'\mathbf{z}_3 M_{22})(\mathbf{z}_2'\mathbf{x}M_{11} - \mathbf{z}_3'\mathbf{x}M_{21} + \mathbf{z}_4'\mathbf{x}M_{31})/\Delta^2$$

Any particular product like $(\mathbf{x}'\mathbf{z}_3)(\mathbf{z}_4'\mathbf{x})$ is a product of two linear expressions each involving all N x-values. We are to find the expected value of such a product with the proviso that each x-value is reduced by its appropriate expectation (see Definition 2 of p. 20). But the covariance of two different sample x's is zero (sample values are independent) while the expectation of the square of a sample x-value (taken about its mean) is always σ^2. Hence $\mathscr{E}\{(\mathbf{x}'\mathbf{z}_3)(\mathbf{z}_4'\mathbf{x})\}$ degenerates into σ^2 times the product of the terms in $(\mathbf{x}'\mathbf{z}_3)$ and in $(\mathbf{z}_4'\mathbf{x})$ that have the same x-values. Thus

$$\mathscr{E}\{(\mathbf{x}'\mathbf{z}_3)(\mathbf{z}_4'\mathbf{x})\} = \mathbf{z}_3\mathbf{z}_4'\sigma^2 = \mathbf{z}_3'\mathbf{z}_4\sigma^2$$

so that, on multiplying the various terms of $\hat{\beta}_3$ by *all* terms of $\hat{\beta}_2$ and replacing x-products by σ^2,

$$\begin{aligned}\mathscr{C}(\hat{\beta}_2, \hat{\beta}_3) &= (-\mathbf{z}_2'\mathbf{z}_2 M_{11} + \mathbf{z}_3'\mathbf{z}_2 M_{21} - \mathbf{z}_4'\mathbf{z}_2 M_{31}) M_{21}\sigma^2/\Delta^2 \\ &\quad + (\mathbf{z}_2'\mathbf{z}_3 M_{11} - \mathbf{z}_3'\mathbf{z}_3 M_{21} + \mathbf{z}_4'\mathbf{z}_3 M_{31}) M_{22}\sigma^2/\Delta^2 \\ &\quad + (-\mathbf{z}_2'\mathbf{z}_4 M_{11} + \mathbf{z}_3'\mathbf{z}_4 M_{21} - \mathbf{z}_4'\mathbf{z}_4 M_{31}) M_{32}\sigma^2/\Delta^2 \\ &= -\Delta\frac{M_{21}}{\Delta^2}\sigma^2 \quad \text{the other terms vanishing} \\ &= -\frac{M_{12}}{\Delta}\sigma^2\end{aligned}$$

Similarly it may be shown that

$$\mathscr{V}(\hat{\beta}_2) = \frac{M_{11}}{\Delta}\sigma^2 \quad \text{and that} \quad \mathscr{C}(\hat{\beta}_2, \hat{\beta}_4) = \frac{M_{13}}{\Delta}\sigma^2$$

etc., where the negative sign appears on the right when the sum of the suffices of M is *odd*. Notice that the suffices of M refer to the rows and columns of Δ and that row (column) 1 is associated with the *first* $\hat{\beta}$ (which is $\hat{\beta}_2$), row (column) 2 is associated with the *second* $\hat{\beta}$ (which is $\hat{\beta}_3$), etc.

Numerical illustration

The numerical values of the minors M_{ij} are found to be

$$\begin{array}{lll} M_{11} = 1500 & M_{12} = -500 & M_{13} = 500 \\ M_{21} = -500 & M_{22} = 1500 & M_{23} = -500 \\ M_{31} = 500 & M_{32} = -500 & M_{33} = 1500 \end{array}$$

so that

$$\mathscr{V}(\hat{\beta}_2) = 0{\cdot}03\sigma^2 = \mathscr{V}(\hat{\beta}_3) = \mathscr{V}(\hat{\beta}_4)$$

$$\mathscr{C}(\hat{\beta}_2, \hat{\beta}_3) = 0{\cdot}01\sigma^2 \qquad \mathscr{C}(\hat{\beta}_2, \hat{\beta}_4) = 0{\cdot}01\sigma^2 \qquad \mathscr{C}(\hat{\beta}_3, \hat{\beta}_4) = 0{\cdot}01\sigma^2$$

[Note the way the negative signs vanish in this case.]

Finally

$$\mathscr{V}(\hat{\psi}) = \{0{\cdot}03(c_2^2 + c_3^2 + c_4^2) + 0{\cdot}02(c_2c_3 + c_2c_4 + c_3c_4)\}\sigma^2$$

and to estimate this variance for given c-values we insert $\hat{\sigma}^2 = 1{\cdot}10558$ for σ^2.

The contrasts of Ryder's experiment

We now return to the summary of experimental results on p. 4. We have shown that the lowering of the nutritional plane has a real effect on the size of the tattooed areas of skin. Ryder writes *loc. cit.*:

'... there is evidence for the onset of a diet effect between sampling times 3 and 4, i.e. reduction in skin area only appeared towards the end of the experiment. ... The skin area differences between the experimental sheep and their controls at sampling times 4 and 5 differ ... from the [earlier] values ... suggesting a delay in recovery of the skin areas after the experiment.'

Let us examine these statements by means of Scheffé's S-method.

The two contrasts mentioned by Ryder can be written algebraically, by reference to the table on p. 6, as:

$$\begin{aligned}\psi_a &= \tfrac{1}{2}(2\mu-2\beta_2+8\beta_3-2\beta_4)-\tfrac{1}{2}(2\mu+8\beta_2-2\beta_3-2\beta_4)\\ &= 5(\beta_3-\beta_2)\end{aligned}$$

which means that the c_2, c_3 and c_4 of p. 19 are -5, 5 and 0, respectively; and

$$\begin{aligned}\psi_b &= \tfrac{1}{4}(4\mu-4\beta_2+6\beta_3+6\beta_4)-\tfrac{1}{6}(6\mu+4\beta_2-6\beta_3-6\beta_4)\\ &=\tfrac{5}{6}(-2\beta_2+3\beta_3+3\beta_4)\end{aligned}$$

It will be observed that each ψ is a difference between two means and that μ and β_1 are not involved.

On inserting the estimated β's, namely

$$\hat{\beta}_2 = -0{\cdot}0525 \qquad \hat{\beta}_3 = 0{\cdot}5935 \qquad \hat{\beta}_4 = 0{\cdot}4685$$

into these expressions we obtain

$$\hat{\psi}_a = 3{\cdot}2300 \qquad \hat{\psi}_b = 2{\cdot}7425$$

while the formula for $\mathscr{V}(\hat{\psi})$ on p. 23 gives

$$\mathscr{V}(\hat{\psi}_a) = \sigma^2 \qquad \mathscr{V}(\hat{\psi}_b) = 0{\cdot}41\dot{6}\sigma^2$$

and, on inserting the estimate of σ^2, these become

1·10558 and 0·46066, respectively.

The two estimates $\hat{\sigma}_{\hat{\psi}}$ are thus (on taking the square roots):

1·05147 and 0·67872, respectively.

The multiplier of these estimated standard errors (deviations) is the square root of $3F_{0{\cdot}05;3,5} = 16{\cdot}230$ (see p. 18) or 4·0286, whence we finally obtain the two required 95% confidence intervals, namely

$$\begin{aligned}-1{\cdot}006 \leqslant \psi_a \leqslant 7{\cdot}466\\ 0{\cdot}008 \leqslant \psi_b \leqslant 5{\cdot}477\end{aligned}$$

where, for example, the two limits for ψ_a are calculated from $3{\cdot}2300 \pm 4{\cdot}0286 \times 1{\cdot}05147$.

Now the first of these intervals overlaps zero. This means that a zero value of ψ_a is one of those of which we are 95% confident and we are unable to say (confidently) that the apparent change between the measurements at the third and fourth time-points is real.

On the other hand we are 95% confident that ψ_b is positive and less than $5\frac{1}{2}$ cm^2.

In conclusion, we mention that, in order to develop the general S-method and the concomitant calculation of $\mathscr{V}(\hat{\psi})$, we have complicated the computations required *in this particular case*. Thus a glance at the table on p. 7 shows that:

$$\hat{\psi}_a = \text{(mean of two observations at time-point 4)} - \text{(mean of two observations at time-point 3)}$$

Since these four x-values are independent (so that their covariances are zero) the Theorem of p. 20 immediately provides

$$\mathscr{V}(\hat{\psi}_a) = (\tfrac{1}{2})^2\sigma^2 + (\tfrac{1}{2})^2\sigma^2 + (-\tfrac{1}{2})^2\sigma^2 + (-\tfrac{1}{2})^2\sigma^2 = \sigma^2 \quad \text{as before}$$

It may be observed that the foregoing simplified procedure is always available when ψ can be easily expressed as a linear combination of the original observations x. In particular it may be used in problems 3 and 5 that follow.

Problems 1

1. In the nutritional experiment used throughout this chapter, test whether β_1, the 'pair effect', can be taken as zero. Interpret your answer from the viewpoint of the design of the experiment.

2. In reporting Ryder's (*loc. cit.*) results on p. 4 the first pair of measurements, made four weeks after the commencement of the experiment but only three days after the diet of concentrates was strictly controlled, was deleted. These measurements were:

Time point	*First pair*	*Second pair*
0	2·38	−3·13

Recalculate the five parameters of model Ω and the two of model ω using all 12 observations, and test whether ω is a valid substitute for Ω.

(*Answer:* $\mathscr{S}^0_\Omega = 26{\cdot}5880$; $\mathscr{S}^0_\omega = 48{\cdot}8746$)

3. Using these 12 observations, obtain the contrast that corresponds to ψ_a of p. 24 and find its 90% confidence interval.

(*Answer:* $-2{\cdot}688 \leqslant \psi \leqslant 9{\cdot}148$)

4. Each of the following 12 results is the weight of seed obtained by harvesting plots of one square yard in size during the months indicated. Write down the general model appropriate to this situation, and also the restricted model designed to test the hypothesis that the month of cutting does not affect the yield. Carry out this test by computing $\mathscr{S}^0_\Omega$ and $\mathscr{S}^0_\omega$ and using the appropriate F-statistic.

(*Answer*: $F = 17{\cdot}2$)

	Plot no. 1	2	3	4
April	16	13	15	9
May	30	22	29	23
June	24	20	18	24

5. Use the S-method to obtain a 95% confidence interval for the difference between April and June yields in the above example, and a similar 95% interval for the difference between the May mean yield and the average of the April and June yields. Each of these contrasts applies a coefficient to each of the 12 results shown above [a given coefficient can be zero]. Use these coefficients as two new vectors replacing the two that represented 'months' in Ω of Problem 4. Recalculate $\mathscr{S}^0_\Omega$ with these new vectors; it should have exactly the same value as before.

References in Chapter One and the Introduction

RAO, C. R. (1952) *Advanced Statistical Methods in Biometric Research*. New York.

RYDER, M. L. (1956) 'Observations of nutritional and seasonal changes in the fleeces of some Masham sheep.' *J. Agric. Sci.* **47**, 129–144.

SCHEFFÉ, H. (1959) *The Analysis of Variance*. New York.

CHAPTER TWO

Orthogonal Vectors and the Analysis of Variance

While the methods developed in Chapter One may be applied very generally in the analysis of experimental data, nevertheless a suitably 'balanced' experimental design can materially simplify the subsequent analysis. It is the purpose of this chapter to describe how these computational simplifications occur, and to enable the biologist to use desk machines in the reduction of his symmetrically arranged experiments. Once again we will illustrate the discussion by means of an example.

The observational data

In an experiment to determine, *inter alia*, the trend of seasonal variation in percentage protein content of pasture grass, two random samples of grass, each $2\frac{1}{2}$ yards square, were harvested on three occasions, in duplicate, from each of two plots differentiated by their manurial treatment. Plot 1 had a long history of treatment with basic slag every third year, and was further treated with phosphoric acid throughout the experiment. On the other hand Plot 2 had remained untreated for over thirty years and was left untreated throughout the experiment.†

Date of cutting	Plot 1	Plot 2	Totals
July 7	12·0	8·5	40·2
	11·2	8·5	
Aug. 20	12·5	7·5	42·4
	14·2	8·2	
Sept. 30	13·9	6·8	41·5
	13·1	7·7	
Totals	76·9	47·2	124·1

The model Ω

The experimental layout suggests that the experimenters had in mind:

(a) A basic differential effect between the manured plot and the control; and

(b) A seasonal effect which might be different for each of the two plots.

† The data were 'selected' from a much larger set contained in Thomas, B. *et al.* (1932).

Let us write $2\beta_1$ for the difference in (real) protein content between Plot 1 and Plot 2. Specifically we will allot $-\beta_1$ to every measurement on Plot 2 and $+\beta_1$ to every measurement on Plot 1. Since there are six observations on each plot the total 'plot' effect is thus $6\beta_1 - 6\beta_1 = 0$.

As for the seasonal effect we will set up the following table which would apply to each set of three observations, one made at each time-point:

Date	'Effect'	'Effect' minus mean effect	Three times preceding column
July 7	0	$-\beta/3$	$-\beta_2-\beta_3$
Aug. 20	β_2	$\beta_2-\beta/3$	$2\beta_2-\beta_3$
Sept. 30	β_3	$\beta_3-\beta/3$	$-\beta_2+2\beta_3$
Totals	β	0	0

Note that initially we inserted a zero entry for the 'effect' of July 7. This is to conform with the notion that there are only two differential effects in comparison with the 'base line' of July 7.

But we also wish to allow for the possibility of a different complex of seasonal effects in each of the two plots. This effect is known as the 'interaction' between 'date' and 'plot' effects.

A two-way table of the six aggregate effects we have introduced so far will be a helpful starting point. Note that it refers to a set of six individual measurements, one made at each date-plot point.

Date	Plot 1	Plot 2	Total
July 7	$\beta_1-\beta_2-\beta_3$	$-\beta_1-\beta_2-\beta_3$	$-2\beta_2-2\beta_3$
Aug. 20	$\beta_1+2\beta_2-\beta_3$	$-\beta_1+2\beta_2-\beta_3$	$4\beta_2-2\beta_3$
Sept. 30	$\beta_1-\beta_2+2\beta_3$	$-\beta_1-\beta_2+2\beta_3$	$-2\beta_2+4\beta_3$
Totals	$3\beta_1$	$-3\beta_1$	0

So far as β_1 is concerned, every one of the three Plot 1 individuals is undifferentiated. Similarly, at any given date, both observed individuals have the same β_2, β_3 values. Our objective is to differentiate between Plot 1 and Plot 2 with respect to seasonal effects. However, we must not change the two bottom and three side marginal totals, since we have already chosen them to signify overall 'plot' and 'date' effects, respectively.

Suppose we were to introduce two new 'interaction' parameters β_4 and β_5 in the first two cells of Plot 1. Because these new effects must not affect the marginal totals our super-posed two-way table of 'interaction' effects must be as follows:

Date	Plot 1	Plot 2	Total
July 7	β_4	$-\beta_4$	0
Aug. 20	β_5	$-\beta_5$	0
Sept. 30	$-\beta_4-\beta_5$	$\beta_4+\beta_5$	0
Totals	0	0	0

It may be confirmed by trial that if a further parameter β_6 had been introduced it would have proved redundant. On the other hand less than two 'interaction' parameters would not have sufficed to measure the seasonal variation.

We mention, by the way, that we could have immediately introduced *four* parameters to measure the two separate sets of seasonal differences in Plot 1 and Plot 2, respectively. Nevertheless the advantage of our present procedure is that, if β_4 and β_5 prove unnecessary (i.e., are not significantly different from zero), we are left with β_2 and β_3 as the overall seasonal effects.

We should here note a danger to which the model builder is exposed. Having three β's available to express seasonal and plot differences and having introduced β_4 to represent an interaction between these effects there is a possibility that a further chosen $\mathbf{z}_5$, say, is a linear compound of the four preceding vectors, namely

$$\mathbf{z}_5 = a\mathbf{z}_1+b\mathbf{z}_2+c\mathbf{z}_3+d\mathbf{z}_4$$

where a, b, c and d are arbitrary numbers and any (but not all) of them could be zero. It requires little mathematical insight to realize that none of the vectors comprising the Ω-model must be capable of representation as a linear compound of *some* or *all* the remaining vectors. Our procedure this far has satisfied this requirement.

We can now write out the whole model Ω in vector form overleaf.

An important reservation must be made about the mathematical adequacy of this model. An essential requirement for the theoretical optimality of the Least Squares technique is that e_{ijk} should be $N(0, \sigma^2)$. Note particularly the 'constancy' of σ^2 from observation to observation.

Now the illustrative observational data are *proportions* expressed as percentages. In general, the distribution of a proportion (e.g., the proportion of forty-year-old males dying in a year, the proportion of experimental animals exhibiting a specified characteristic, etc.) is Binomial with a mean of the 'true' proportion, π say, and a variance of $\pi(1-\pi)/n$ where n is the number of 'observations' in the denominator of the proportion.

In this case we may suppose that n is more or less constant in each

$2\frac{1}{2}$ square yard sample of pasture grass. However, the constancy of π is the very thing we have developed our model in five parameters to test. In other words, π is only constant throughout the experiment if $\beta_1 = \beta_2 = \beta_3 = \beta_4 = \beta_5 = 0$.

One way out of this dilemma is to use a transformation of x which introduces constancy of the variance. The appropriate transformation

Plot i	Date j	Repl. k	$x_{ijk} = \mu +$	$\beta_1 \times +$	$\beta_2 \times +$	$\beta_3 \times +$	$\beta_4 \times +$	$\beta_5 \times + e_{ijk}$
1	1	1	12·0	1	−1	−1	1	0
		2	11·2	1	−1	−1	1	0
	2	1	12·5	1	+2	−1	0	1
		2	14·2	1	+2	−1	0	1
	3	1	13·9	1	−1	+2	−1	−1
		2	13·1	1	−1	+2	−1	−1
2	1	1	8·5	−1	−1	−1	−1	0
		2	8·5	−1	−1	−1	−1	0
	2	1	7·5	−1	+2	−1	0	−1
		2	8·2	−1	+2	−1	0	−1
	3	1	6·8	−1	−1	+2	+1	+1
		2	7·7	−1	−1	+2	+1	+1
	Total		124·1					

for proportions is provided in most statistical textbooks. The other approach is to note that the range of variability in the underlying π-values is likely to be less than 6·8% to 14·2%, the observed range of percentage protein content. But:

if $\quad \pi = 0{\cdot}068 \quad \pi(1-\pi) = 0{\cdot}063$

if $\quad \pi = 0{\cdot}142 \quad \pi(1-\pi) = 0{\cdot}122$

and, by assuming constancy of σ^2, we will be working with a value of $\pi(1-\pi)$ equal to about 0·09. We are prepared to accept this degree of insensitivity. Others may prefer to use the appropriate transform.†

Proceeding to form the vector sums and products for Ω we may write the coefficients of the $\hat{\beta}$'s in the normal equations in the form of a square 'matrix' in which we may ignore entries below the diagonal since they repeat those already appearing above the diagonal. Excluding the

† See, e.g., Sec. 5e. 3 of Rao (1952) cited in Chapter One.

equation for $\hat{\mu}$, which, *because we have arranged that the components of all other* **z**'s *sum to zero*, is always $N\hat{\mu} = \sum_{i,j,k} x_{ijk}$, we obtain

$$\begin{bmatrix} 12 & 0 & 0 & 0 & 0 \\ & 24 & -12 & 0 & 0 \\ & & 24 & 0 & 0 \\ & & & 8 & 4 \\ & & & & 8 \end{bmatrix} \qquad \begin{bmatrix} 29{\cdot}7 \\ 3{\cdot}1 \\ 0{\cdot}4 \\ -6{\cdot}3 \\ -1{\cdot}5 \end{bmatrix}$$

where the 5×1 'matrix' of the 'constants' on the right of the normal equations is the 'vector' shown above on the right of the 5×5 matrix.

It will be noticed that when we attach the $\hat{\beta}$'s to the coefficients of the 5×5 matrix above, $\hat{\beta}_1$ is immediately obtainable while two separate pairs of simultaneous equations in two unknowns must be used to obtain $\hat{\beta}_2$, $\hat{\beta}_3$ and $\hat{\beta}_4$, $\hat{\beta}_5$, respectively. This is a considerable simplification in comparison with the solution of five simultaneous equations in five unknowns. It is our purpose to discover how this simplification came about and to ask if it could not be extended a little further so that, for example, each of the parameters could be determined from one equation in which it appeared alone. But, first, let us complete the Least Squares solution and formulate suitable ω-models.

We obtain, without difficulty,

$$\hat{\beta}_1 = 2{\cdot}475 \quad \hat{\beta}_2 = 0{\cdot}18\dot{3} \quad \hat{\beta}_3 = 0{\cdot}108\dot{3} \quad \hat{\beta}_4 = -0{\cdot}925 \quad \hat{\beta}_5 = 0{\cdot}275$$

(where, e.g., $0{\cdot}0\dot{3} = 0{\cdot}0333 \ldots$) while $\hat{\mu} = 124{\cdot}1/12 = 10{\cdot}341\dot{6}$. Hence, from the formula of p. 15,

$$\begin{aligned} \mathscr{S}^0_\Omega &= 1365{\cdot}67 - 124{\cdot}1 \times 10{\cdot}341\dot{6} - 29{\cdot}7 \times 2{\cdot}475 - 3{\cdot}1 \times 0{\cdot}18\dot{3} \\ &\quad - 0{\cdot}4 \times 0{\cdot}108\dot{3} - (-6{\cdot}3) \times (-0{\cdot}925) - (-1{\cdot}5) \times (0{\cdot}275) \\ &= 2{\cdot}735 \end{aligned}$$

where 1365·67 is the sum of the squares of the 12 original observations. The variate $\mathscr{S}^0_\Omega/\sigma^2$ is distributed as χ^2 with $12-6 = 6$ degrees of freedom.

The first ω-model

The first question we ask about this Ω- model is whether the 'plot effect' β_1 is real. That is to say we write (in vector notation):

$$\omega_1: \quad \mathbf{x} = \mathbf{l}\mu + \mathbf{z}_2\beta_2 + \mathbf{z}_3\beta_3 + \mathbf{z}_4\beta_4 + \mathbf{z}_5\beta_5 + \mathbf{e}$$

where **l** is a 12-component vector of units.

On writing down the normal equations for this model we see that, except for the disappearance of the equation for $\hat{\beta}_1$, they are the same as those of Ω. Our estimates of μ, β_2, … β_5 are thus unchanged and, what is very important, the value of $\mathscr{S}^0_{\omega_1}$ only differs from that of $\mathscr{S}^0_{\Omega}$ by the omission of the subtractive term $\mathbf{z}_1'\mathbf{x}\hat{\beta}_1 = 29{\cdot}7 \times 2{\cdot}475$. Thus

$$\mathscr{S}^0_{\omega_1} - \mathscr{S}^0_{\Omega} = 29{\cdot}7 \times 2{\cdot}475 = 73{\cdot}5075$$

and, after division by σ^2, this is distributed as χ^2 with one degree of freedom. Our F-test of ω_1 is thus (see p. 18)

$$F = \frac{73{\cdot}5075 \div 1}{2{\cdot}735 \div 6} = 161{\cdot}260$$

which is very significant (values larger than 13·7 only appear by chance once on every hundred occasions the $F_{1,6}$ distribution is sampled).

The second and third ω-models

The next question we ask about Ω is whether the *two* 'seasonal' parameters β_2 and β_3 could be zero. We are now assuming that:

$$\omega_2: \quad \mathbf{x} = \mathbf{l}\mu + \mathbf{z}_1\beta_1 + \mathbf{z}_4\beta_4 + \mathbf{z}_5\beta_5 + \mathbf{e}$$

As in the preceding case the original normal equations still apply, once we have deleted the two equations that contain *only* β_2 and β_3. It should be clear that if some of the other equations involved β_2 and β_3 – and the only reason they do not is because of the zeros in the matrix of p. 31 – deletion of the *terms* in β_2, β_3 would result in completely new estimates for β_1, β_4 and β_5.

In a similar way then

$$\mathscr{S}^0_{\omega_2} - \mathscr{S}^0_{\Omega} = \mathbf{z}_2'\mathbf{x}\hat{\beta}_2 + \mathbf{z}_3'\mathbf{x}\hat{\beta}_3 = 3{\cdot}1 \times 0{\cdot}18\dot{3} + 0{\cdot}4 \times 0{\cdot}108\dot{3}$$
$$= 0{\cdot}611\dot{6}$$

and the F-test of the hypothesis ω_2 is obtained by computing

$$\frac{0{\cdot}611\dot{6} \div 2}{2{\cdot}735 \div 6} = 0{\cdot}671$$

which is not significant.

Finally, the ω-model that eliminates (only) the two 'interaction' parameters β_4 and β_5 leads to

$$\mathscr{S}^0_{\omega_3} - \mathscr{S}^0_{\Omega} = (-6{\cdot}3) \times (-0{\cdot}925) + (-1{\cdot}5) \times (0{\cdot}275) = 5{\cdot}415$$

and an F-value of

$$\frac{5{\cdot}415 \div 2}{2{\cdot}735 \div 6} = 5{\cdot}940 \quad (F_{0{\cdot}05;2,6} = 5{\cdot}14)$$

Because of this successive splitting-off of the various components of $\mathscr{S}^0_{\Omega}$ the foregoing three ω-models and their comparison with Ω may be shown in the form of a so-called 'analysis of variance' (ANOVA for short) as follows:

Hypothesis:	Variability on account of	Degrees of freedom	Sum of squares	Mean square
$\beta_1 = 0$	Plot differences	1	73·5075	73·5075
$\beta_2 = 0 = \beta_3$	Date differences	2	0·6117	0·3058
$\beta_4 = 0 = \beta_5$	Interaction between plots and dates	2	5·4150	2·7075
	Residual	6	2·7350	0·4558
	Totals	11	82·2692	

The 'total' sum of squares 82·2692 is actually the sum of squares about the mean $\bar{x}$, and consists of the first two terms of $\mathscr{S}^0_\Omega$, the 'residual sum of squares', or 2·7350.

We conclude from the foregoing that there are real plot differences but that, in the aggregate, the date of harvesting makes no difference to the protein content of the pasture grass. However, the significance of the interaction effect shows that differential seasonal differences between the two plots have masked the importance of harvest dates. We would need to use the S-method to obtain more detailed information about the two non-zero parameters β_4 and β_5.

Orthogonality of vectors

If **a** and **b** are two vectors each with the same number of components and if $\mathbf{a}'\mathbf{b} = 0 = \mathbf{b}'\mathbf{a}$, the vectors are said to be orthogonal (perpendicular) to one another.

It was the presence of orthogonality between the various **z**'s that caused the 'collapse' of the five normal equations into three separate sets. This orthogonality was a feature of the experimental design. It is not our purpose to discuss this subject at length but the reader will have noticed that the symmetry of the pasture grass experiment led to a clear conceptual model as well as to simple numerical analysis. While the non-orthogonal experiment can nowadays be analysed very quickly on electronic computers its parameters are not easily visualized. This is why the balanced experiment is still of importance.

Having noted the computational simplification of having a vector orthogonal to every other vector attached to the β's of the model Ω, and remembering that close investigation of a *group* of significant β's can be undertaken by using the S-method, we ask what happens when we change the vectors attached to the β's of a specified group. To answer this let us take as our 'group' of vectors all those attached to $\beta_1, \beta_2, \ldots \beta_5$ in the foregoing illustration. We will first produce a set of vectors the members of which are mutually orthogonal and we will then apply these to our numerical example.

A further model Ω

Consider the following five six-component vectors which are an orthogonal set.

1	2	3	4	5
1	1	1	1	1
−1	1	1	1	1
0	−2	1	1	1
0	0	−3	1	1
0	0	0	−4	1
0	0	0	0	−5

Let us use these vectors (suitably duplicated for the duplicate observations) in lieu of the **z**'s of p. 30 although the five resulting β's (which we will call $\beta_1', \beta_2', \ldots \beta_5'$) will be nonsense parameters.

The matrix of coefficients and the vector of 'constants' in the normal equations are found to be:

$$\begin{bmatrix} 4 & 0 & 0 & 0 & 0 \\ & 12 & 0 & 0 & 0 \\ & & 24 & 0 & 0 \\ & & & 40 & 0 \\ & & & & 60 \end{bmatrix} \qquad \begin{bmatrix} -3{\cdot}5 \\ -4{\cdot}1 \\ 25{\cdot}9 \\ 31{\cdot}1 \\ 37{\cdot}1 \end{bmatrix}$$

and these lead at once to:

$$\hat{\beta}_1' = -0{\cdot}875 \qquad \hat{\beta}_2' = -0{\cdot}341\dot{6} \qquad \hat{\beta}_3' = 1{\cdot}0791\dot{6}$$

$$\hat{\beta}_4' = 0{\cdot}7775 \qquad \hat{\beta}_5' = 0{\cdot}618\dot{3}$$

and

$$\mathscr{S}_\Omega^0 = 82{\cdot}2692 - 3{\cdot}0625 - 1{\cdot}4008 - 27{\cdot}9504 - 24{\cdot}1803 - 22{\cdot}9402$$

$$= 82{\cdot}2692 - 79{\cdot}5342 = 2{\cdot}7350 \quad \text{with } 12 - 6 = 6 \text{ d.f.}$$

What is interesting about this is that these five 'nonsense' vectors and parameters have extracted the same quantity from $\sum\limits_{i,j,k} (x_{ijk} - \bar{x}\ldots)^2$ as the original meaningful parameters.

On the other hand none of the subtractive items $\mathbf{z}'\mathbf{x}\,\hat{\beta}'$ is equal to $\mathbf{z}_1'\mathbf{x}\,\hat{\beta}_1$ of p. 31 (namely 73·5075), nor do any two of them add to either of the two two-degree-of-freedom items of the analysis of variance of p. 33. While *each* of the foregoing items $\mathbf{z}'\mathbf{x}\hat{\beta}'$ is a proper value of $\mathscr{S}^0_\omega - \mathscr{S}^0_\Omega$ to test the hypothesis that the corresponding (nonsense) β' is zero, it is only when taken all together that they equal the 79·5342 of the experimental model Ω.

Now, in calculating the subtractive terms in $\mathscr{S}^0_\Omega$, whether for the experimental or the 'nonsense' Ω, every pair of duplicate observations was (in effect) added together before applying the vector component. In other words, for the purpose of these subtractive terms there were only six observations – and six $\hat{\beta}$'s (including $\hat{\mu}$ as a $\hat{\beta}$) were calculated. This begins to look like a general theorem, but before enunciating it let us attempt yet another model for the illustrative experiment.

The third model Ω

In order not to confuse this model with those already discussed, let us introduce five parameters $\gamma_1, \ldots \gamma_5$ instead of the previous β's. The mean μ is to remain unchanged.

Once again we will measure σ^2 by the variability between duplicate observations, which is all that is left once we have 'extracted' the variability contributed by the six parameters of the model. This alternative mode of expression suggests that $\mathscr{S}^0_\Omega$ is the aggregate sum of squares *within* the six cells of the experimental layout. For example, it would seem that the contribution of the first cell is

$$(12{\cdot}0)^2+(11{\cdot}2)^2-\frac{(12{\cdot}0+11{\cdot}2)^2}{2} = 0{\cdot}32$$

[or, alternatively, $(12{\cdot}0-11{\cdot}6)^2+(11{\cdot}2-11{\cdot}6)^2$ or, rather surprisingly, $(12{\cdot}0-11{\cdot}2)^2/2$, which is a general result for observational pairs]. Adding together all six contributions we obtain $\mathscr{S}^0_\Omega = 2{\cdot}7350$ (as before) with six degrees of freedom.

In the new Ω-model which 'explains' the whole variability of the six cell-totals let us first concentrate on each plot separately. Consider, for example, the three cell totals of Plot 1, namely 23·2, 26·7 and 27·0. If these were plotted on a graph they would appear as shown overleaf. If the three points lay on a straight line (which they obviously do not) the subtraction of twice the middle value from the sum of the first and last values would produce zero or – since we are working with observations containing 'errors' – near zero. When we ask how near zero, the answer is that we must set up an ω-model to be tested against the broader non-linear model which the foregoing observations suggest. Our problem is to express these ideas in the form of a vector attached to γ_1 (say) so that we may then test the restricted model ω: $\gamma_1 = 0$.

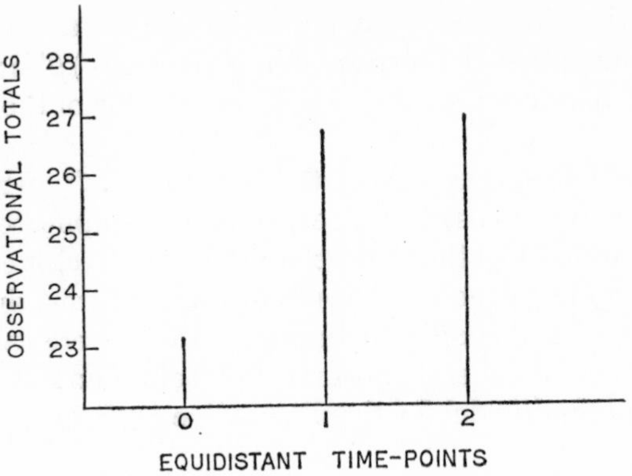

Now if all five vectors attached to the γ's are mutually orthogonal each normal equation for a $\hat{\gamma}$ will be of the form:

$$\mathbf{z}_l'\mathbf{z}_l\hat{\gamma}_l = \mathbf{z}_l'\mathbf{x} \qquad (l = 1, 2, 3, 4, 5)$$

The coefficient of $\hat{\gamma}_l$ (and thus its eventual denominator) is the sum of the squares of the components of $\mathbf{z}_l$ and must always be non-zero and positive. If, therefore, $\hat{\gamma}_l$ is to be near enough to zero to tempt us to formulate the hypothesis that $\gamma_l = 0$, the right-hand side of the equation, namely the numerator of $\hat{\gamma}_l$, must be near zero. But $\mathbf{z}_l'\mathbf{x}$ is the chosen vector $\mathbf{z}_l$ multiplied by the vector of observations. Thus, if we chose $\mathbf{z}_1' = \{1 \;\; -2 \;\; 1\}$ the computation of $\mathbf{z}_1'\mathbf{x}$ would be the same as the subtraction discussed in the previous paragraph as a suitable criterion to decide whether the three observational points 23·2, 26·7 and 27·0 lay on a straight line.

We conclude that a suitable vector to attach to γ_1 will be

$$\mathbf{z}_1 = \begin{bmatrix} 1 \\ -2 \\ 1 \end{bmatrix}$$

A test of the hypothesis $\gamma_1 = 0$ will then be a test whether the protein content of Plot 1 lies on a straight line (if $\gamma_1 = 0$) or a curve (if $\gamma_1 \neq 0$).

Now if we concluded that $\gamma_1 = 0$ we would say that the three observational points lay on a straight line. This line could slope upward, downward or not at all. Why shouldn't we make γ_2 a measure of the slope of the straight line supposedly joining the three points and if it turns out to be zero we will know that there is no slope, i.e., that the three observations are equal within the limits set by sampling errors? But here we have the difficulty of deciding whether to subtract the first observation from the second, the second from the third or the first observation from the third (and halve the result). Only the last of these produces a vector orthogonal to $\mathbf{z}_1$. For if

$$\mathbf{z}_2 = \begin{bmatrix} -1 \\ 0 \\ 1 \end{bmatrix}$$

then $\mathbf{z}_1'\mathbf{z}_2 = 0$.

We have now developed the vectors to attach to γ_1 and γ_2 and, since they were deemed to apply to Plot 1, we complete them to a six-component size by inserting zero components throughout Plot 2. Similar considerations hold for Plot 2 so that the vectors attached to γ_3 and γ_4 will have zero components in Plot 1.

None of these four vectors, which are mutually orthogonal, make any comparison of the behaviour of Plot 1 with that of Plot 2. This is achieved by a fifth vector which is the same as the vector attached to β_1 on p. 30. This vector is orthogonal to the four preceding vectors.

The matrix of five γ-vectors is thus:

$$\begin{bmatrix} 1 & -1 & 0 & 0 & 1 \\ -2 & 0 & 0 & 0 & 1 \\ 1 & 1 & 0 & 0 & 1 \\ 0 & 0 & 1 & -1 & -1 \\ 0 & 0 & -2 & 0 & -1 \\ 0 & 0 & 1 & 1 & -1 \end{bmatrix}$$

There is no difficulty about obtaining the corresponding normal equations and calculating $\mathscr{S}_\Omega^0$ and the various $\mathscr{S}_\omega^0$. We are already prepared for the fact that $\mathscr{S}_\Omega^0$ will equal 2·7350 although the only parametric equivalences between the β- and the γ-models are that $\hat{\beta}_1 = \hat{\gamma}_5$. This means that the single degree of freedom represented by $\mathbf{z}_1'\mathbf{x}\hat{\beta}_1$ in the first case, and by $\mathbf{z}_5'\mathbf{x}\hat{\gamma}_5$ in our present model, makes a unique contribution.

A fourth model Ω

Let us examine the above matrix. The first two (column) vectors refer exclusively to Plot 1 effects, and the second two to Plot 2 effects. Might it not be better to ask a different set of questions, namely:

(i) When Plots 1 and 2 are taken together (i.e., aggregated or averaged) do the three 'date' observations show:

- (a) A linear or curved trend; and
- (b) A non-zero slope?

(ii) Do Plots 1 and 2 show different:

- (a) Curvatures; and
- (b) Slopes?

(iii) Do the overall levels of Plots 1 and 2 differ?

4

The reader should verify for himself that the first two (column) vectors of the following matrix will serve to answer question (i), and that the next two will answer question (ii) (by offsetting the curvatures and slopes of the two plots one against the other). The final vector still answers the same question as it did before.

$$\begin{bmatrix} 1 & -1 & 1 & -1 & 1 \\ -2 & 0 & -2 & 0 & 1 \\ 1 & 1 & 1 & 1 & 1 \\ 1 & -1 & -1 & 1 & -1 \\ -2 & 0 & 2 & 0 & -1 \\ 1 & 1 & -1 & -1 & -1 \end{bmatrix}$$

Proceeding to the normal equations the matrices of coefficients (remembering that each vector component shown above is applied *twice* in its corresponding cell) are:

$$\begin{bmatrix} 24 & 0 & 0 & 0 & 0 \\ & 8 & 0 & 0 & 0 \\ & & 24 & 0 & 0 \\ & & & 8 & 0 \\ & & & & 12 \end{bmatrix} \qquad \begin{bmatrix} -3\cdot1 \\ 1\cdot3 \\ -3\cdot3 \\ 6\cdot3 \\ 29\cdot7 \end{bmatrix}$$

resulting in

$$\hat{\gamma}_1' = -0\cdot1291\dot{6} \qquad \hat{\gamma}_2' = 0\cdot1625 \qquad \hat{\gamma}_3' = -0\cdot1375$$
$$\hat{\gamma}_4' = 0\cdot7875 \qquad \hat{\gamma}_5' = 2\cdot475$$

Noting that the 'sum of squares' corresponding to each *single* degree of freedom in an ANOVA is of the form

$$\mathbf{z}_l'\mathbf{x}\hat{\gamma}_l' = \mathbf{z}_l'\mathbf{x}(\mathbf{z}_l'\mathbf{x}/\mathbf{z}_l'\mathbf{z}_l) = (\mathbf{z}_l'\mathbf{x})^2/\mathbf{z}_l'\mathbf{z}_l$$

we quickly obtain

Hypothesis:	d.f.	s.s.	m.s.
$\gamma_1' = 0$	1	0·4004	
$\gamma_2' = 0$	1	0·2113	
$\gamma_3' = 0$	1	0·4538	
$\gamma_4' = 0$	1	4·9612	
$\gamma_5' = 0$	1	73·5075	
Residual	6	2·7350	0·4558
Total	11	82·2692	

where, for example, the 's.s.' for γ_1' is $(-3\cdot1)^2/24$. Reference to a table of $F_{1,6}$ shows that γ_4' and γ_5' are significantly different from zero.

Our interpretation of this analysis, apart from the large difference between Plots 1 and 2 as a whole ($\gamma_5' \neq 0$), is that there is no discernible curvature in either plot ($\gamma_1' = 0 = \gamma_3'$), that the overall slope of the line joining 'date' results is zero ($\gamma_2' = 0$), but that the slopes of Plots 1 and 2 are different ($\gamma_4' \neq 0$). The reasonable explanation here is that Plots 1 and 2 have slopes going in opposite directions which cancel one another in the aggregate ($\gamma_2' = 0$).

Is there a 'proper' model Ω?

By now the reader must be surfeited with models and must be wondering if there is any way for the experimenter to decide upon the 'proper' one. Before we indicate our views let us state a theorem that is implicit in the foregoing analyses.

Suppose we have N observations x_i ($i = 1, 2, \ldots N$) and we construct a model linear in a fixed number, q, of parameters β to 'explain' them. The vectors $\mathbf{z}$ attached to these β's may be arbitrary subject to: (i) $\mathbf{z}_0$ is a vector of units, (ii) the components of all the other $\mathbf{z}$-vectors sum to zero, and (iii) no vector $\mathbf{z}$ can be written as a linear expression in some or all the remainder. Under these circumstances $\mathscr{S}^0_\Omega$ with $N-q$ degrees of freedom does not depend on the actual components of the $\mathbf{z}$'s which may be mutually, or partially, or not at all, orthogonal to one another. Furthermore, as q approaches nearer to N the 'residual' $\mathscr{S}^0_\Omega$ gets smaller and, eventually, when $q = N$ we have $\mathscr{S}^0_\Omega = 0$, and the model has fully explained the observations!

Since this theorem applies to *any* set of x-values it obviously applies to any set of y's (say) which have been formed from an original set of x's by aggregating them in an appropriate manner. This is best illustrated numerically.

When we developed our first model for the pasture grass experiment β_2 and β_3 were 'date' effects that applied equally in Plot 1 and Plot 2. A glance at the vectorial model of p. 30 confirms that the vectors $\mathbf{z}_2$ and $\mathbf{z}_3$ apply the same coefficients to each of the corresponding observations in each plot. So far as these vectors (and β's) are concerned the duplicate observations at each 'date' in the two plots could be aggregated (four observations per cell) *provided* it is remembered that the $\mathbf{z}_2'\mathbf{z}_2$ and $\mathbf{z}_3'\mathbf{z}_3$ of the denominator of $\hat{\beta}_2$ and $\hat{\beta}_3$ – and thus of the 'date' component of the total 'sum of squares', namely $\mathbf{z}_2'\mathbf{x}\hat{\beta}_2 + \mathbf{z}_3'\mathbf{x}\hat{\beta}_3$ – are to be extended over 12 (and not three aggregate) observations.

Thus the 'date' totals obtained from p. 30 are

Date j		Aggregate of x's
1		40·2
2		42·4
3		41·5
	Total	124·1

and their sum of squares about their mean is

$$40{\cdot}2^2 + 42{\cdot}4^2 + 41{\cdot}5^2 - \frac{(124{\cdot}1)^2}{3}$$

or $2{\cdot}44\dot{6}$. The theorem enunciated above states that this total will be reproduced by using any two three-component vectors **z** (the third vector $\mathbf{z}_0$ has extracted the mean $124{\cdot}1/3$) to calculate the corresponding

$$\mathbf{z}_2'\mathbf{x}\hat{\beta}_2 + \mathbf{z}_3'\mathbf{x}\hat{\beta}_3$$

But the vectors $\mathbf{z}_2$ and $\mathbf{z}_3$ of p. 30 are such vectors (except that they are repeated four times), and the only way the expression just written differs from the corresponding terms of $\mathcal{S}^0_{\omega_2} - \mathcal{S}^0_{\Omega}$ on p. 32 is that there the denominators of the $\hat{\beta}$'s are four times as large.

We conclude, therefore, that the contribution of $\hat{\beta}_2$ and $\hat{\beta}_3$ to the total sum of squares of the analysis of variance of p. 33 is one-fourth of $2{\cdot}44\dot{6}$ or $0{\cdot}611\dot{6}$. In general this is the manner in which the elementary textbooks obtain the sum of squares 'due to' a group of β's orthogonal to the rest.

Returning now to the question of a 'proper' model let us review the four models for the pasture grass experiment. The experimental layout suggested that the experimenters were prepared for differences between the three cutting dates. With three dates three differences are possible but the third can always be obtained by combining the other two appropriately. We recognized this by allowing two β's for cutting-date differences.

But the presence of two plots in the experiment suggested that the foregoing cutting-date differences could be different in each plot. There were thus two sets of (two) β's for cutting-date differences. These four β's did not allow for different *levels* of protein content in the two plots and a further (fifth) β was necessary to take care of this possibility.

We then discovered that the single β for the plot difference had a unique value and always contributed the same quantity to $\mathcal{S}^0_{\Omega}$ and to any $\mathcal{S}^0_{\omega}$ in which it appeared. This was because the symmetry of the experiment caused the z-vector attached to this β to be orthogonal to every vector expressing the cutting-date differences. We could, however, 'overlook' the existence of this 'plot' β and obtain (as we did in the second model) the same $\mathcal{S}^0_{\Omega}$ for all *five* β's. If there are six (n) observations that sum to zero (by previously subtracting their mean from each) any arbitrary five ($n-1$) zero-sum vectors, none of which can be derived as a linear combination of the remaining four, will always result in the same $\mathcal{S}^0_{\Omega}$ value, namely zero.

There were, however, several 'sensible' ways of allowing for cutting-date differences. All of these involved four β's. Thus:

(i) The first model allowed for two 'overall' date differences and two 'interactions';

(ii) The third model recognized the two different (plot) pairs of cutting-date differences; and

(iii) The fourth model was a modification of the first in that it recognized two specifically interesting 'overall' cutting-date comparisons and their differential effects in the two plots.

Since any six observations will lead to the same (zero) $\mathscr{S}_\Omega^0$ when five β's (and the mean) are allowed for, and since the single orthogonal component for the overall plot difference is unique, the three contributions to $\mathscr{S}_\Omega^0$ derived from the three different sets of four β's just mentioned will all have the same value, namely $0{\cdot}6117+5{\cdot}4150 = 6{\cdot}0267$ (see p. 33).

Nevertheless it is clearly improper to invent new sets of four z-vectors to 'explain' this 6·0267. In fact we have already mentioned that this is the purpose of Scheffé's S-method. We may therefore conclude with the following recommendations to the biologist.

If a given experiment was devised to isolate a single comparison between a treatment (say) and a control, the single β-estimate and its zero-sum vector $\mathbf{z}$ will be unique in that the product $\mathbf{z}'\mathbf{x}\hat{\beta}$ will always be the same, and there will result a unique $\mathscr{S}_\omega^0 - \mathscr{S}_\Omega^0$ value with one degree of freedom. On the other hand if there is a set of comparisons which can be conceived of in various ways – summed-up in the pasture grass experiment by the phrase 'cutting-date differences and their interactions with plots' – then the simplest procedure is to use a 'nonsense' set of orthogonal vectors and, if the corresponding β's are significant as a group, use Scheffé's S-method on as many comparisons as desired.

Let us illustrate the latter suggestion by rewriting the matrix of vectors for the pasture grass experiment as:

$$\begin{bmatrix} 1 & 1 & 0 & 0 & 1 \\ -1 & 1 & 0 & 0 & 1 \\ 0 & -2 & 0 & 0 & 1 \\ 0 & 0 & 1 & 1 & -1 \\ 0 & 0 & -1 & 1 & -1 \\ 0 & 0 & 0 & -2 & -1 \end{bmatrix}$$

Here the last vector compares the two plots on an overall basis while we have used two pairs of 'nonsense' vectors (supplemented by zeros) to express the four degrees of freedom that remain in the analysis of the six observational totals.

The resulting normal equations are summarized in the two matrices:

$$\begin{bmatrix} 4 & 0 & 0 & 0 & 0 \\ & 12 & 0 & 0 & 0 \\ & & 4 & 0 & 0 \\ & & & 12 & 0 \\ & & & & 12 \end{bmatrix} \qquad \begin{bmatrix} -3{\cdot}5 \\ -4{\cdot}1 \\ 1{\cdot}3 \\ 3{\cdot}7 \\ 29{\cdot}7 \end{bmatrix}$$

The four 'nonsense' $\hat{\beta}$'s are then:

$$\hat{\beta}_1 = -0{\cdot}875 \qquad \hat{\beta}_2 = -0{\cdot}341\dot{6} \qquad \hat{\beta}_3 = 0{\cdot}325 \qquad \hat{\beta}_4 = 0{\cdot}308\dot{3}$$

and it is easily verified that their contribution to $\mathscr{S}^0_\Omega$ is $6{\cdot}02\dot{6}$. The hypothesis that these four β's are all zero leads to an $F_{4,6}$ of 3·306 which is only 'significant' at the 10% level. Let us, therefore, consider some contrasts ψ and their 90% confidence intervals. Note that, if any vector $\mathbf{z}_i$ is orthogonal to *every* other vector in the model, the corresponding

$$\hat{\beta}_i = \frac{\mathbf{z}_i'\mathbf{x}}{\mathbf{z}_i'\mathbf{z}_i}$$

Since $\mathbf{z}_i'\mathbf{z}_i$ is the sum of the squares of the components of $\mathbf{z}_i$ the denominator is a number which can be used to 'normalize' the components of $\mathbf{z}_i'$ in the numerator. The result shows that $\hat{\beta}_i$ is a *linear compound of the N observations x*. A trial with a small value of N and an arbitrary vector $\mathbf{z}_i$ will convince the reader that the Theorem of p. 20 then implies

$$\mathscr{V}(\hat{\beta}_i) = \frac{\sigma^2}{\mathbf{z}_i'\mathbf{z}_i}$$

where σ^2 is to be estimated by $\mathscr{S}^0_\Omega/(N-q)$.

Suppose that we are interested in comparing the cutting-date gradients in the treated and untreated plots. Since these gradients are independent of the protein levels in the two plots it is reasonable to assume that the slope differential is included in the four degrees of freedom 'absorbed' by the 'nonsense' β's. In a balanced layout of the type under consideration this slope contrast can be obtained directly from the observations and then expressed in terms of the 'nonsense' β's. It will then be found that the 'plot' β cancels out just as β_1 vanished from the contrasts of Ryder's experiment discussed in Chapter One. However, in the more general non-orthogonal design of experiment this method breaks down since we find that the 'contrast' of observational means involves β's outside the group supposedly accounting for the contrast. We will therefore illustrate the general procedure for obtaining the coefficients in ψ *based on the effects that the individual* β's *of the 'significant' group are supposed to measure*.†

† Equivalently, all other z's are given their mean values, zero.

If, then, we ignore β_0 and average over all z-values except those attached to β_1, β_2, β_3 and β_4 we have

$$\begin{aligned}
\hat{x}'_{11} &= \hat{\beta}_1 + \hat{\beta}_2 \\
\hat{x}'_{13} &= \quad -2\hat{\beta}_2 \\
\hat{x}'_{21} &= \qquad\qquad \hat{\beta}_3 + \hat{\beta}_4 \\
\hat{x}'_{23} &= \qquad\qquad\qquad -2\hat{\beta}_4
\end{aligned}$$

where, e.g., $\hat{x}'_{21}$ is the estimate for any observation in Plot 2 at date 1 when $\hat{\beta}$'s other than $\hat{\beta}_1$, $\hat{\beta}_2$, $\hat{\beta}_3$ and $\hat{\beta}_4$ are suppressed.

The slope differential in which we are interested is expressed by

$$\hat{\psi} = \tfrac{1}{2}(\hat{x}'_{13} - \hat{x}'_{11}) - \tfrac{1}{2}(\hat{x}'_{23} - \hat{x}'_{21})$$

namely, the slope in Plot 1 (the $\frac{1}{2}$ allowing for the two time intervals over which the difference occurs) minus the slope in Plot 2. Referring to the equations for $\hat{x}'$ in terms of the $\hat{\beta}$'s we see that

$$\begin{aligned}
\hat{\psi} &= -\tfrac{1}{2}\hat{\beta}_1 - \tfrac{3}{2}\hat{\beta}_2 + \tfrac{1}{2}\hat{\beta}_3 + \tfrac{3}{2}\hat{\beta}_4 \\
&= 1{\cdot}575
\end{aligned}$$

and, using the result of p. 42,

$$\begin{aligned}
\mathscr{V}(\hat{\psi}) &= \{(\tfrac{1}{2})^2 \times \tfrac{1}{4} + (\tfrac{3}{2})^2 \times \tfrac{1}{12} + (\tfrac{1}{2})^2 \times \tfrac{1}{4} + (\tfrac{3}{2})^2 \times \tfrac{1}{12}\}\,\sigma^2 \\
&= \tfrac{1}{2}\sigma^2
\end{aligned}$$

This variance is estimated by $\frac{1}{2} \times 0{\cdot}4558 = (0{\cdot}47739)^2$. Since $4F_{0\cdot1;\,4,\,6} = 12{\cdot}723 = (3{\cdot}567)^2$, we may thus write our 90% confidence interval for the mean slope differential between the two plots as

$$1{\cdot}575 - 3{\cdot}567 \times 0{\cdot}47739 < \psi < 1{\cdot}575 + 1{\cdot}703$$

i.e.,

$$-0{\cdot}128 < \psi < 3{\cdot}278$$

Our 'confidence' does not therefore extend to stating that this slope differential is non-zero. This directly contradicts the conclusion we drew about γ'_4 in the fourth model which 'selected' five parameters to test for significance.

This peculiarity draws attention to a feature of Ω-models with many

β's which can be tested separately. If the vectors for these β's are orthogonal each $\hat{\beta}$ is uncorrelated with the remainder (i.e., the covariances are all zero) and, since it is a linear combination of Normally distributed x-values, is itself Normally distributed. If all these $\hat{\beta}$'s were multiplied by the square-root of their corresponding $\mathbf{z}'\mathbf{z}$ values (to make their variances equal to σ^2) they would, if their universal equivalents (the β's of Ω) were zero, be a random sample from $N(0, \sigma^2)$. Clearly if there were 40 such $\hat{\beta}$'s we would 'expect' one of them to be in the upper 5% tail and one in the lower 5% tail. Even two or three such $\hat{\beta}$'s in the upper 5% tail would not be surprising *although the universal β's are all zero*. Here is an illustration of the danger of 'too many β's' tested individually for significance. The next numerical example may clarify it.

Factorial designs

As a further numerical illustration we will consider some data that can be regarded as an example of a so-called 2^3 factorial design.

In work preliminary to major experiment it may be questioned whether the animal being investigated is reacting 'normally' in a larger or a smaller cage, at a higher or a lower temperature, in a brighter or dimmer illumination, etc. In other words, the experimenter can think of half a dozen or more 'factors' (three in the foregoing illustration, namely, cage size, temperature, and illumination) for each of which he has *two* 'levels' at which to conduct his eventual experiment. An easily designed and analysed experiment is of the so-called $2 \times 2 \times 2 \times \ldots$ type where each '2' represents the number of 'levels' at which the corresponding 'factor' is being used.

If there are three 'factors' each at two 'levels' we will require $2^3 = 8$ observations if we are to note the animal's reaction under each of the possible factorial combinations. This would imply seven β's besides the mean (β_0) and, if every one of these was conceivably non-zero, there would be no 'residual sum of squares' $\mathscr{S}^0_\Omega$ with which to compare the model.

Suppose, however, that the eight animals used in this (first) experiment were all from the same litter. A replication of the experiment could then be made with a further litter of eight animals. Let us assume that three litters of eight animals were used in this replication design, sometimes written $2^3(3)$.

There are now 24 experimental animals and we can introduce two β's for litter differences which we assume do not 'interact' with the 'factors' of the experiment. That is to say, we assume, for example, that the difference in reaction caused by differential illumination is characteristic of the animal generally and is not restricted to certain litters. Under this hypothesis our ANOVA will appear in the form:

Hypothesis:	d.f.
Two 'litter' β's $= 0$	2
Three 'factor' β's $= 0$	3
Four 'factor interaction' β's $= 0$	4
Residual	14
Total	23

We will illustrate the detailed analysis of the seven degrees of freedom for 'factors' and their 'interactions' on a set of data that do not appear, at first sight, to be of factorial type.

The following are the frequencies with which the specified sequences of sexes occurred among births in 815 families of three children (exactly) of certain Swedish ministers of religion (Edwards, A. W. F. and Fraccaro, M., 1960).

♀	♀	♀	89
♂	♀	♀	100
♀	♂	♀	97
♂	♂	♀	108
♀	♀	♂	101
♂	♀	♂	87
♀	♂	♂	106
♂	♂	♂	127
		Total	815

We at once recognize that these figures differ from the x's we have considered so far in that they are 'counts' of families, and that the total of all the cells must equal the number of families counted, namely 815. However, we will ignore this distinction for the time being and will proceed as if the recorded frequencies were x-values in our previous notation.

We will consider the following three 'factors':

(i) The 'maleness' of the first child, F;
(ii) The 'maleness' of the second child, S;
(iii) The 'maleness' of the third child, T.

On seeking to measure any of these factors we will use a small letter to denote its presence, and absence of that letter to denote absence of that factor. For example, s means that we are observing non-maleness at the first and third births, and maleness at the second birth. This is standard notation and the absence of all factors is written, not 0 but, (1).

We may thus rewrite the foregoing 'experimental' results and append eight vectors of coefficients to 'explain' them. Since every factor is either present or absent we may write a $+\beta$ for its effect when present and a $-\beta$ for the lack of its effect. This means, as we have seen, that 2β is the difference between presence and absence.

The vector of coefficients for β_0 (or μ) is a series of units (as usual) but we have suppressed the 1's and have written them as +'s. β_1 is supposed to be the 'effect' of maleness at the first birth; a $+1$ therefore appears whenever f is present in the left-hand column and a -1 whenever f is

			I	*F*	*S*	*FS*	*T*	*FT*	*ST*	*FST*
	x	=	β_0 ×	+ β_1 ×	+ β_2 ×	+ β_3 ×	+ β_4 ×	+ β_5 ×	+ β_6 ×	+ β_7 ×
(1)	89		+	−	−	+	−	+	+	−
f	100		+	+	−	−	−	−	+	+
s	97		+	−	+	−	−	+	−	+
fs	108		+	+	+	+	−	−	−	−
t	101		+	−	−	+	+	−	−	+
ft	87		+	+	−	−	+	+	−	−
st	106		+	−	+	−	+	−	+	−
fst	127		+	+	+	+	+	+	+	+
Total	815									

absent. Once again we have omitted the units, but it will be observed that the vector's components add to zero.

β_2 is, then, the effect of maleness at the second birth. What should be the vector attached to β_3 if the latter is to represent the 'interaction' effect of F and S? The answer can easily be seen when we set up a two-way table in which we have supposed the two t and non-t halves of the experiment to be amalgamated into four results shown in the body of the following table:

	(1)	*f*	
(1)	$-\beta_1-\beta_2+\beta_3$	$\beta_1-\beta_2-\beta_3$	$-2\beta_2$
s	$-\beta_1+\beta_2-\beta_3$	$\beta_1+\beta_2+\beta_3$	$2\beta_2$
	$-2\beta_1$	$2\beta_1$	0

This enables us to fill in the vector attached to β_3. What is noteworthy about this vector which will account for the interaction, $F \times S$, between F and S is that each of its components is the product of the corresponding components of the vectors of F (i.e., of β_1) and S (i.e., of β_2). Although we have not tested for orthogonality it is easily verified that the three vectors attached to β_1, β_2 and β_3 are mutually orthogonal.

Proceeding in this way we may complete the model Ω. We note that the vector attached to β_7, and representing the second-order interaction between the three factors (written $F \times S \times T$ or FST), is the product of those of: (i) β_1, β_2 and β_4, (ii) β_3 and β_4, (iii) β_2 and β_5, or (iv) β_1 and β_6. All seven vectors (in fact, all eight) are mutually orthogonal.

The matrices of coefficients for the normal equations are thus:

$$\begin{bmatrix} 8 & 0 & 0 & 0 & 0 & 0 & 0 \\ & 8 & 0 & 0 & 0 & 0 & 0 \\ & & 8 & 0 & 0 & 0 & 0 \\ & & & 8 & 0 & 0 & 0 \\ & & & & 8 & 0 & 0 \\ & & & & & 8 & 0 \\ & & & & & & 8 \end{bmatrix} \quad \text{and} \quad \begin{bmatrix} 29 \\ 61 \\ 35 \\ 27 \\ -15 \\ 29 \\ 35 \end{bmatrix}$$

with $\hat{\beta}_0 = \hat{\mu} = 815/8 = 101{\cdot}875$.

The ANOVA is then directly obtainable as follows:

Effect	d.f.	s.s.	s.s. ÷ 101·875
F	1	105·125 = $(29)^2/8$	1·032
S	1	465·125 = $(61)^2/8$	4·566
FS	1	153·125 etc.	1·503
T	1	91·125	0·894
FT	1	28·125	0·276
ST	1	105·125	1·032
FST	1	153·125	1·503
Totals	7	1100·875 = $84{,}129 - \dfrac{(815)^2}{8}$	10·806

If this had been a non-replicated 2^3 experiment we would now have to decide (without looking at the values in the 's.s.' column) which of the 'effects' were really 'error' (e.g., the second-order interaction and some or all of the first-order interactions) and measure the (possibly) real effects against the presumed 'residual'.

However, because we have been dealing with frequencies, the situation is much simpler. If all seven 'effects' were zero each of the eight original cells would have an expectation of $815/8 = 101{\cdot}875$, and the values in the 's.s.' column would be the squared deviations of observed frequencies from this expectation. Even if some of the 'effects' were non-zero the application of the orthogonal z-vectors to the frequencies would allow the foregoing statement to be true of the others. But a squared deviation of a frequency from its expectation divided by said expectation is approximately distributed as χ^2 with one degree of freedom. This is the explanation of the last column of the table, namely s.s. ÷ 101·875.

Now, the probability of a single χ_1^2 in excess of 4·566 is 0·0326. On the other hand the probability of obtaining *at least one* variate value larger than 4·566 in sampling seven variates from χ_1^2 is $1-(0{\cdot}9674)^7$, namely certainty minus the probability that *none* of the seven variates exceed 4·566. This probability is 0·2071, so that we might expect a single 'large' χ_1^2 once in every five times we took a sample of seven.

Our apparent conclusion that the second child of three is prone to be male is thus indicated to be one of the vagaries of random sampling.

The reader will find further discussion of the so-called analysis of contingency table frequencies by partition of χ^2 in Lancaster (1951).†

Another illustration

Because of the freedom of choice among the possible sets of **z**'s for a given experimental layout it often happens that it is easier to *test* a specified ω than it is to *estimate* the β's it equates to zero (if they turn out to be significantly different from zero).

Consider the following 16 pairs of observations made in the comparison of eight thermometers (Youden and Connor, 1954). The thermometers were immersed in a bath of water the temperature of which rose slightly as the experiment progressed. The readings are shown in the order in which they were obtained, the times between pairs being of longer duration than those within pairs.

Pair	Therm. no.	°C	Pair	Therm. no.	°C
1	1	40·00	9	2	40·23
	7	39·99		6	40·22
2	5	40·08	10	8	40·24
	3	40·13		4	40·15
3	8	40·15	11	7	40·12
	2	40·17		3	40·20
4	6	40·13	12	5	40·23
	4	40·05		1	40·16
5	3	40·18	13	6	40·26
	8	40·18		3	40·28
6	7	40·07	14	7	40·15
	2	40·19		4	40·20
7	1	40·10	15	5	40·27
	6	40·18		2	40·30
8	5	40·17	16	1	40·21
	4	40·13		8	40·31

† Recent work suggests that this χ^2 approximation may not be too good.

The model Ω that suggests itself comprises:

(i) The usual vector of units for the mean;
(ii) 15 zero-sum vectors representing differences between the experimental pairs; and
(iii) 7 zero-sum vectors for differences between the thermometers.

The natural ω to hypothesize is that the seven β's attached to the vectors of (iii) are all zero.

Now ω will lead to a value of $\mathscr{S}^0_\omega$ that can be obtained from:

		d.f.	s.s.
Differences between pairs		15	0·1465219
Residual		16	0·0325500 $= \mathscr{S}^0_\omega$
	Total	31	0·1790719

where, for example (measuring all temperatures from 40° C),
$0{\cdot}1465219 = (\tfrac{1}{2})\{(-0{\cdot}01)^2+(0{\cdot}21)^2+(0{\cdot}32)^2+\ldots+(0{\cdot}52)^2\}-(\tfrac{1}{32})(5{\cdot}47)^2$.
The residual sum of squares can either be obtained as a subtractive item or as *half* the sum of the squares of the 16 within-pair differences. [The 16 vectors $\mathbf{z}$ each consist of two non-zero elements, the first being -1 and the second, occurring in the same pair, $+1$. The 16 values of $\mathbf{z}'\mathbf{z}$ are thus each $(-1)^2+(+1)^2$.]

This latter consideration reminds us that the seven degrees of freedom for thermometer differences are part of the 16 degrees for the 'residual' of ω. However, a direct comparison of the thermometers does *not* produce a set of vectors $\mathbf{z}$ each of which is orthogonal to every one of the 15 'pair' vectors. Nevertheless a device can be used to identify three groups of $\mathbf{z}$'s the members of which are orthogonal to each of the 15 'pair' vectors *and* to the vectors of the two other groups.

Let us subtract each of the thermometers numbered 5–8 from each of those numbered 1–4. The 16 differences then appear as:

Therm. no.	Thermometer no. 5	6	7	8	Totals
1	−0·07	−0·08	0·01	−0·10	−0·24
2	0·03	0·01	0·12	0·02	0·18
3	0·05	0·02	0·08	0·00	0·15
4	−0·04	−0·08	0·05	−0·09	−0·16
Totals	−0·03	−0·13	0·26	−0·17	−0·07

Any 16-component vector we apply to the 16 elements of the foregoing table will necessarily be orthogonal to the 15 vectors of (ii) – since each of the 16 components has to be repeated twice within each pair of experimental results – and will also be orthogonal to the mean vector (i) *if* the 16 components sum to zero.

Let us therefore choose three vectors that apply the same components to all the elements of any one column of the above 4×4 table. These three vectors could be made spuriously orthogonal to one another if desired. Since there are four different sets of equal components in each vector we could pretend that we had to deal with a 2×2 factorial experiment. For example, we could write:

Thermometer	Hypothetical variate	A $\mathbf{z}_1$	B $\mathbf{z}_2$	AB $\mathbf{z}_3$
5	(1)	−1	−1	+1
6	*a*	+1	−1	−1
7	*b*	−1	+1	−1
8	*ab*	+1	+1	+1

Similarly we could choose three vectors to distinguish the rows of the table. Whether or not the first set of three vectors was chosen so that they were orthogonal among themselves every one of the second set of vectors will be found to be orthogonal to each vector of the first set.

Having chosen three vectors to represent column differences and three more to represent row differences a single vector of 32 units can be used to compare thermometers 1–4 with thermometers 5–8. This vector is orthogonal to all six of the vectors introduced above.

The result of the foregoing computations is to 'extract' from the earlier value of $\mathscr{S}^0_\omega$ three mutually orthogonal terms with an aggregate of seven degrees of freedom, namely

	d.f.	*s.s.*
Differences between columns	3	0·0141344
Differences between rows	3	0·0171094
Thermometers 1–4 *vs.* 5–8	1	0·0001531
Totals	7	0·0313969

We thus obtain

$$\mathscr{S}^0_\Omega = \mathscr{S}^0_\omega - 0{\cdot}0313969 = 0{\cdot}0325500 - 0{\cdot}0313969$$
$$= 0{\cdot}0011531 \quad \text{with 9 d.f.}$$

Hence

$$F = \frac{0{\cdot}0313969 \div 7}{0{\cdot}0011531 \div 9} = \frac{0{\cdot}0044853}{0{\cdot}0001281} = 35{\cdot}01$$

which is highly significant.

When we now try to estimate some of the 'interesting' contrasts, for example the linear combination of the seven β's for thermometer differences which compares thermometer No. 1 with the mean of thermometers 5, 6, and 8, we realize that we have not solved the normal equations and do not know the estimates of the individual β's nor their variances and covariances.

Actually this illustration is an example of an incomplete block design, the computations for which can be reduced to relatively simple form. The estimation of the treatment differences is detailed in Appendix II, which will only be understood after Chapter Four has been thoroughly assimilated.

Problems 2

1. Complete the ANOVA implied by the matrix of five γ-vectors of p. 37. These five γ's are not all equal to zero so we may use the S-method on the contrasts they comprise. One such is the slope differential measured by γ_4' of the fourth model Ω. Obtain an expression for this differential as a linear combination of the original observations and use the Theorem of p. 20 to derive a 95% confidence interval for it.

2. In the vectorial model of p. 30 introduce six more vectors $\mathbf{z}$ attached to new parameters $\beta_6, \beta_7, \ldots \beta_{11}$. The first of these vectors has its first two components -1 and $+1$, respectively, and the remainder zero. The second vector has its third and fourth components -1 and $+1$, respectively, and the remainder zero. And so on. Show that *each* of these six vectors is orthogonal with the five shown on p. 30 and calculate the corresponding six values of $(\mathbf{z}'\mathbf{x})^2/\mathbf{z}'\mathbf{z}$ for entry in the 's.s.' column of the ANOVA of p. 33. Why is there no longer a 'residual sum of squares'?

3. Pugsley (1946) gives the following increases (length + height in mm) of combs of capons injected with testosterone propionate.

Standard preparation			Test preparation		
20 μg	40 μg	80 μg	20 μg	40 μg	80 μg
6	12	19	6	12	16
6	11	14	6	11	18
5	12	14	6	12	19
6	10	15	7	12	16
7	7	14	4	10	15

Discuss the relevance of the application of the (fourth) model of p. 37 *et seq.* to these results. Analyse the resulting five degrees of freedom separately and interpret your conclusions.

(*Answer:* 4·80, 510·05, 4·05, 0·01$\dot{6}$, 0·15)

4. Suppose we are to conduct a 2^4 experiment on the leaves of a certain type of plant. The intra-plant variability of the individual leaf measurements is Normal with $\sigma \approx 1$. There will be 15 degrees of freedom for the 'effects' and it is proposed to test for their significance as a whole, using $F_{0\cdot05;15,15(b-1)}$ where b is the number of plants (replicates, blocks) from each of which 16 leaves have been sampled. If the result is significant it is intended to use the S-method with a 95% confidence level to estimate the larger 'effects' β's of the type indicated in the vector layout of p. 46. It is desired that if such an effect is $(\frac{1}{2})\sigma$ or more it should lead to a confidence interval that does not overlap zero. Find, by trial and error, how large b should be to achieve this. Discuss the consequences of this from the viewpoint of experimental design. (*Answer:* $b = 7$)

References in Chapter Two

EDWARDS, A. W. F. and FRACCARO, M. (1960) 'Distribution and sequences of sexes in a selected sample of Swedish families.' *Ann. Hum. Genet., Lond.* **24**, 245–252.

LANCASTER, H. O. (1951) 'Complex contingency tables treated by the partition of χ^2.' *J. R. Statist. Soc.* B, **13**, 242–249.

PUGSLEY, L. L. (1946) 'The application of the principles of statistical analysis to the biological assay of hormones.' *Endocrin.* **39**, 161–176.

THOMAS, B. and ELLIOTT, F. J. (1932) 'On the yields and composition of pasture grass from the Tree Field plots at Cockle Park.' *J. Agric. Sci.* **22**, 736–754.

YOUDEN, W. J. and CONNOR, W. S. (1954) 'New experimental designs for paired observations.' *J. Res., Nat. Bur. Stand.* **53**, 191–196.

CHAPTER THREE

The Analysis of Covariance

Suppose that we have a typical set of vectors $\mathbf{z}$ that are deemed appropriate to a specified experimental design. In general, the balanced nature of such an experiment will lead to vectors that are orthogonal to one another, individually or in groups. However, let us suppose that *one* of the vectors consists of observations made on the experimental animal or plant before the experimental treatments were applied. Such observations might be the animal's weight prior to the experiment, or the yield of a given plant in the year prior to the experiment.

Notice carefully that the observational vector under discussion is regarded as an explanatory variable. If it were observed *along with* x at the end of the experiment we would have two 'dependent variables' and, in general, we would prefer to use the techniques developed in Part B.

Our purpose is to investigate what happens to the Least Square computations when a single $\mathbf{z}$ cannot be made orthogonal to any of the rest except the mean vector $\mathbf{z}_0$. Orthogonality with the latter can always be achieved by measuring the observational z-values about their mean.†

The model Ω

In order to illustrate the procedure let us consider some (partial) results of an experiment designed to discover the effect of thyroxine on the utilization of vitamin A by a rat's liver (Heimer, Maslow and Sobel, 1949). The values in the vector $\mathbf{x}$ are the μg storage in the liver of the rat whose weight just prior to the experiment is shown in $\mathbf{z}_5$ after the mean weight of all eight rats (66·625) has been deducted. Four litters of rats were used (all females except for the second rat in the first litter), and 'treatment 1' is thyroxine while 'treatment 2' is the control.

Considering the model Ω displayed below, the vector $\mathbf{z}_0 = \mathbf{1}$, as usual. The three vectors $\mathbf{z}_1$, $\mathbf{z}_2$ and $\mathbf{z}_3$ are intended to represent the three comparisons we can make between the four litter totals (or means). As a convenient computational device we here utilize the three vectors comparing two factors A and B in a 2^4 experiment. That is to say we

† A rough test whether a quadratic model would be an improvement over a fitted linear model would be to square each estimate $\hat{x}_i - \bar{x}$ and treat it as a further (non-zero-sum) z-vector the β of which would be estimated and tested for significance by the covariance procedure here described.

Litter	Treatment	x =	β_0 + ×	β_1 + ×	β_2 + ×	β_3 + ×	β_4 + ×	β_5 + e ×
1	1	43	1	−1	−1	1	1	5·375
	2	49	1	−1	−1	1	−1	−33·625
2	1	$40\frac{1}{2}$	1	1	−1	−1	1	−27·625
	2	18	1	1	−1	−1	−1	− 6·625
3	1	30	1	−1	1	−1	1	15·375
	2	21	1	−1	1	−1	−1	19·375
4	1	36	1	1	1	1	1	17·375
	2	24	1	1	1	1	−1	10·375

have supposed the four litter totals to represent (1), a, b and ab, respectively, and β_1, β_2 and β_3 to be proportional to A, B and AB, respectively.

The vector $\mathbf{z}_4$ determines the contrast we are interested in, namely whether the thyroxine has any effect on vitamin A utilization.

Notice that β_5 is assumed *not* to vary with litter or treatment. We are assuming that the 'effect' of initial weight on the final vitamin intake is a 'straight line' upward or downward (depending on the sign of β_5 which measures the slope of the line) as the initial weight increases. Although the effects of litter or treatment differences may shift this line up or down, all such shifts leave the resulting line (vitamin intake plotted against initial weight) parallel to the 'average' line for all litters and treatments.

Another point is that we do *not* regard the z_5-values as a random sample. Instead, we consider them a *fixed* set which is typical of the universe of rats. Alternatively, we can suppose that the observed x's are to be interpreted conditionally on the observed randomly chosen z_5's. Whatever interpretation we use it is essential that the variance of the e's is a constant, σ^2, independent of the z_5-values.

The matrices of coefficients for the normal equations are thus:

$$\begin{bmatrix} 8 & 0 & 0 & 0 & -13{\cdot}0 \\ 0 & 8 & 0 & 0 & 125{\cdot}0 \\ 0 & 0 & 8 & 0 & -1{\cdot}0 \\ 0 & 0 & 0 & 8 & 21{\cdot}0 \\ -13 & 125 & -1 & 21 & 2987{\cdot}875 \end{bmatrix} \qquad \begin{bmatrix} -24{\cdot}5 \\ -39{\cdot}5 \\ 42{\cdot}5 \\ 37{\cdot}5 \\ -911{\cdot}9375 \end{bmatrix}$$

while $\hat{\beta}_0 = \bar{x} = 261{\cdot}5/8 = 32{\cdot}6875$. The sum of the squares of the x's is $9427{\cdot}25$.

These five equations in five unknowns are relatively easy to solve directly and will lead to the required value of $\mathscr{S}^0_\Omega$. However, the corresponding set of equations in four (or less) unknowns must be solved independently for *each* β (or set of β's) that is equated to zero in a particular ω-model. In this case our real interest lies in the ω that repeats Ω but with $\beta_4 = 0$. Hence we would only have one other set of normal equations to solve to obtain $\mathscr{S}^0_\omega$.

For those who have ready access to an electronic computer the solution of different sets of simultaneous equations presents no difficulty. Those with only an occasional need for covariance analysis as it is called (z_5 being the covariable) may prefer not to learn the following computational technique since it is only a neat way of solving the various possible sets of equations for the case where one vector $\mathbf{z}_5$ is non-orthogonal to the rest.

Solution of the normal equations

Reverting to the matrices of normal equations we note that, in general notation, on transferring the $\hat{\beta}_5$ term to the right-hand side, the first four equations may be written:

$$\begin{aligned}
\mathbf{z}_1'\mathbf{z}_1\hat{\beta}_1 &= \mathbf{z}_1'\mathbf{x}-\mathbf{z}_1'\mathbf{z}_5\hat{\beta}_5\\
\mathbf{z}_2'\mathbf{z}_2\hat{\beta}_2 &= \mathbf{z}_2'\mathbf{x}-\mathbf{z}_2'\mathbf{z}_5\hat{\beta}_5\\
\mathbf{z}_3'\mathbf{z}_3\hat{\beta}_3 &= \mathbf{z}_3'\mathbf{x}-\mathbf{z}_3'\mathbf{z}_5\hat{\beta}_5\\
\mathbf{z}_4'\mathbf{z}_4\hat{\beta}_4 &= \mathbf{z}_4'\mathbf{x}-\mathbf{z}_4'\mathbf{z}_5\hat{\beta}_5
\end{aligned}$$

Thus the 'other' $\hat{\beta}$'s are all determined once $\hat{\beta}_5$ has been calculated.

Let us look at the last (fifth) of the normal equations with a view to obtaining $\hat{\beta}_5$. In general none of the coefficients of the 'other' $\hat{\beta}$'s in this equation is zero but they can each be eliminated by taking a multiple of the corresponding normal equation in which this $\hat{\beta}$ appears alone with $\hat{\beta}_5$ and subtracting the result from the last of the normal equations.

Thus, for example, in the numerical illustration if we multiply the first equation by $-13/8$ the coefficient of $\hat{\beta}_1$ becomes -13, which is the same as the coefficient of $\hat{\beta}_1$ in the fifth of the normal equations. The multiplier of the second equation is correspondingly $125/8$; and so on. If the aggregate of these multiplied equations (four of them) is subtracted from the fifth equation the result is to eliminate $\hat{\beta}_1$, $\hat{\beta}_2$, $\hat{\beta}_3$ and $\hat{\beta}_4$ leaving $\hat{\beta}_5$ and 'constant' terms.

□ □ □ Using the general notation, the algebraic manipulations of the preceding paragraph imply multiplying the first of the normal equations by $\mathbf{z}_5'\mathbf{z}_1/\mathbf{z}_1'\mathbf{z}_1$, the second by $\mathbf{z}_5'\mathbf{z}_2/\mathbf{z}_2'\mathbf{z}_2$, and so on. On subtracting these four results from the fifth of the normal equations the first four terms vanish and we are left only with the term involving $\hat{\beta}_5$ on the left and with the 'constant' on the right. It may be verified that the algebraic expression thus obtained is

$$\left\{\mathbf{z}_5'\mathbf{z}_5 - \frac{(\mathbf{z}_5'\mathbf{z}_1)^2}{\mathbf{z}_1'\mathbf{z}_1} - \frac{(\mathbf{z}_5'\mathbf{z}_2)^2}{\mathbf{z}_2'\mathbf{z}_2} - \frac{(\mathbf{z}_5'\mathbf{z}_3)^2}{\mathbf{z}_3'\mathbf{z}_3} - \frac{(\mathbf{z}_5'\mathbf{z}_4)^2}{\mathbf{z}_4'\mathbf{z}_4}\right\}\hat{\beta}_5$$

$$= \mathbf{z}_5'\mathbf{x} - \frac{(\mathbf{z}_5'\mathbf{z}_1)(\mathbf{z}_1'\mathbf{x})}{\mathbf{z}_1'\mathbf{z}_1} - \frac{(\mathbf{z}_5'\mathbf{z}_2)(\mathbf{z}_2'\mathbf{x})}{\mathbf{z}_2'\mathbf{z}_2} - \dots - \frac{(\mathbf{z}_5'\mathbf{z}_4)(\mathbf{z}_4'\mathbf{x})}{\mathbf{z}_4'\mathbf{z}_4}$$

Although this relation for $\hat{\beta}_5$ may look complicated it is composed of the products and quotients of quantities that have already been calculated. Let us write this equation

$$D\hat{\beta}_5 = M$$

so that

$$\hat{\beta}_5 = \frac{M}{D}$$

where the (nu)M(erator) and D(enominator) are obtained from the equation derived above.

Inserting the appropriate numerical values from the matrices of p. 54 we find

$$M = -911{\cdot}9375 - 39{\cdot}8125 + 617{\cdot}1875 + 5{\cdot}3125 - 98{\cdot}4375$$

$$D = 2987{\cdot}875 - 21{\cdot}125 - 1953{\cdot}125 - 0{\cdot}125 - 55{\cdot}125$$

and

$$\hat{\beta}_5 = \frac{-427{\cdot}6875}{958{\cdot}375} = -0{\cdot}44626$$

Once $\hat{\beta}_5$ is determined $\hat{\beta}_1, \dots \hat{\beta}_4$ may be obtained at once from the four equations of p. 55. However, before computing these values and the subsequent $\mathscr{S}^0_{\Omega}$, it is desirable to consider our first model ω.

The model ω_1

It is usual to test the hypothesis that $\beta_5 = 0$ before proceeding to the 'interesting' model that eliminates other β's.

Now the matrices of equations for the model ω_1 eliminating β_5 are the same as those of p. 54 with the fifth equation, and all the coefficients of $\hat{\beta}_5$, removed. The result is a set of four equations of the 'orthogonal' type. Keeping to the general notation we can thus write at once:

$$\mathscr{S}^0_{\omega_1} = \mathbf{x}'\mathbf{x} - \frac{(\mathbf{z}_0'\mathbf{x})^2}{\mathbf{z}_0'\mathbf{z}_0} - \frac{(\mathbf{z}_1'\mathbf{x})^2}{\mathbf{z}_1'\mathbf{z}_1} - \dots - \frac{(\mathbf{z}_4'\mathbf{x})^2}{\mathbf{z}_4'\mathbf{z}_4} \quad \text{with } N-5 \text{ d.f.}$$

and we need not calculate the actual $\hat{\hat{\beta}}$'s that produce this value. Numerically

$$\mathscr{S}^0_{\omega_1} = 9427{\cdot}25 - 8547{\cdot}78125 - 75{\cdot}03125 - 195{\cdot}03125 - 225{\cdot}78125 - 175{\cdot}78125$$

$$= 207{\cdot}84375 \quad \text{with 3 d.f.}$$

□ □ □ Utilizing the four equations of p. 55 which provide $\hat{\beta}_1, \dots \hat{\beta}_4$, the general expression (cf. p. 15)

$$\mathscr{S}^0_{\Omega} = \mathbf{x}'\mathbf{x} - \frac{(\mathbf{z}_0'\mathbf{x})^2}{\mathbf{z}_0'\mathbf{z}_0} - \mathbf{z}_1'\mathbf{x}\hat{\beta}_1 - \mathbf{z}_2'\mathbf{x}\hat{\beta}_2 - \dots - \mathbf{z}_5'\mathbf{x}\hat{\beta}_5 \quad \text{with } N-6 \text{ d.f.}$$

can be written as

$$\mathscr{S}^0_{\Omega} = \mathbf{x}'\mathbf{x} - \frac{(\mathbf{z}_0'\mathbf{x})^2}{\mathbf{z}_0'\mathbf{z}_0} - \mathbf{z}_1'\mathbf{x}\frac{\mathbf{z}_1'\mathbf{x} - \mathbf{z}_1'\mathbf{z}_5\hat{\beta}_5}{\mathbf{z}_1'\mathbf{z}_1} - \dots - \mathbf{z}_4'\mathbf{x}\frac{\mathbf{z}_4'\mathbf{x} - \mathbf{z}_4'\mathbf{z}_5\hat{\beta}_5}{\mathbf{z}_4'\mathbf{z}_4} - \mathbf{z}_5'\mathbf{x}\hat{\beta}_5$$

$$= \mathbf{x}'\mathbf{x} - \frac{(\mathbf{z}_0'\mathbf{x})^2}{\mathbf{z}_0'\mathbf{z}_0} - \frac{(\mathbf{z}_1'\mathbf{x})^2}{\mathbf{z}_1'\mathbf{z}_1} - \dots - \frac{(\mathbf{z}_4'\mathbf{x})^2}{\mathbf{z}_4'\mathbf{z}_4} + \left\{\frac{(\mathbf{z}_1'\mathbf{x})(\mathbf{z}_1'\mathbf{z}_5)}{\mathbf{z}_1'\mathbf{z}_1} + \dots + \frac{(\mathbf{z}_4'\mathbf{x})(\mathbf{z}_4'\mathbf{z}_5)}{\mathbf{z}_4'\mathbf{z}_4} - \mathbf{z}_5'\mathbf{x}\right\}\hat{\beta}_5$$

$$= \mathscr{S}^0_{\omega_1} - M\hat{\beta}_5$$

since the expression in curled brackets is minus the M-value introduced on p. 56.

But since $\hat{\beta}_5 = M/D$ we have thus shown that

$$\mathscr{S}^0_{\Omega} = \mathscr{S}^0_{\omega_1} - M^2/D$$

or

$$\mathscr{S}^0_{\omega_1} - \mathscr{S}^0_{\Omega} = M^2/D \quad \text{with } (N-5)-(N-6) = 1 \text{ d.f.}$$

Our F-test of the model ω_1 (namely, of the hypothesis that $\beta_5 = 0$) is

$$\frac{\mathscr{S}^0_{\omega_1} - \mathscr{S}^0_{\Omega}}{\mathscr{S}^0_{\Omega} \div (N-6)} = \frac{M^2/D}{(\mathscr{S}^0_{\omega_1} - M^2/D) \div (N-6)} \quad \text{with 1 and } N-6 \text{ d.f.}$$

$$= \frac{(-427{\cdot}6875)^2/958{\cdot}375}{(207{\cdot}84375 - 190{\cdot}86119) \div 2} = \frac{190{\cdot}86119}{8{\cdot}49128}$$

$$= 22{\cdot}477 \quad \text{with 1 and 2 d.f.}$$

This is significant at the 5% level, thus confirming the experimenter's 'hunch' that initial weight was of importance in discriminating between vitamin A intake.

There is, unfortunately, no way round making these calculations if we wish to test whether $\beta_5 = 0$. However, we shall now see how we can arrange our work so that we can utilize most of the terms that were involved in M and D in testing our next ω model.

The model ω_2

In this model we suppress β_4 (the treatment effect) from Ω and consider how we are to calculate $\mathscr{S}^0_{\omega_2}$.

To do this let us turn back to the matrices of normal equations on p. 54 and review the calculations for Ω remembering that we are now omitting the *fourth* equation and the (fourth) column of coefficients of $\hat{\beta}_4$.

The relation for $\hat{\beta}_5$ on p. 56 becomes modified to (say)

$$D'\hat{\hat{\beta}}_5 = M'$$

where

$$D' = D + \frac{(\mathbf{z}_5'\mathbf{z}_4)^2}{\mathbf{z}_4'\mathbf{z}_4}$$

and

$$M' = M + \frac{(\mathbf{z}_5'\mathbf{z}_4)(\mathbf{z}_4'\mathbf{x})}{\mathbf{z}_4'\mathbf{z}_4}$$

because, in calculating D' and M', we no longer need to subtract the terms arising on account of $\hat{\beta}_4$.

The 'correction' $(\mathbf{z}_5'\mathbf{z}_4)^2/\mathbf{z}_4'\mathbf{z}_4$ is similar to the term $(\mathbf{z}_4'\mathbf{x})^2/\mathbf{z}_4'\mathbf{z}_4$ subtracted for $\hat{\beta}_4$ in $\mathscr{S}^0_{\omega_1}$ of p. 56. In the analysis of variance which we could have calculated for this experiment *if we had used the initial weight in lieu of x*, this corrective item would be the 's.s. for treatments' with one degree of freedom.

On the other hand the 'correction' for M', namely $(\mathbf{z}_5'\mathbf{z}_4)(\mathbf{z}_4'\mathbf{x})/\mathbf{z}_4'\mathbf{z}_4$, differs from the previous 'correction' in that *one* of the two identical factors of the numerator has been changed in such a way that $\mathbf{x}$ has been substituted for the covariate vector $\mathbf{z}_5$.

This similarity in the 'corrections' is even more extensive than may appear from this particular case. In order to see this let us examine the three expressions:

$$\mathscr{S}^0_{\omega_1} = \mathbf{x}'\mathbf{x} - \frac{(\mathbf{z}_0'\mathbf{x})^2}{\mathbf{z}_0'\mathbf{z}_0} - \frac{(\mathbf{z}_1'\mathbf{x})^2}{\mathbf{z}_1'\mathbf{z}_1} - \ldots - \frac{(\mathbf{z}_4'\mathbf{x})^2}{\mathbf{z}_4'\mathbf{z}_4}$$

$$M = \mathbf{z}_5'\mathbf{x} - \frac{(\mathbf{z}_0'\mathbf{z}_5)(\mathbf{z}_0'\mathbf{x})}{\mathbf{z}_0'\mathbf{z}_0} - \frac{(\mathbf{z}_1'\mathbf{z}_5)(\mathbf{z}_1'\mathbf{x})}{\mathbf{z}_1'\mathbf{z}_1} - \ldots - \frac{(\mathbf{z}_4'\mathbf{z}_5)(\mathbf{z}_4'\mathbf{x})}{\mathbf{z}_4'\mathbf{z}_4}$$

$$D = \mathbf{z}_5'\mathbf{z}_5 - \frac{(\mathbf{z}_0'\mathbf{z}_5)^2}{\mathbf{z}_0'\mathbf{z}_0} - \frac{(\mathbf{z}_1'\mathbf{z}_5)^2}{\mathbf{z}_1'\mathbf{z}_1} - \ldots - \frac{(\mathbf{z}_4'\mathbf{z}_5)^2}{\mathbf{z}_4'\mathbf{z}_4}$$

It will be noticed that we have introduced a couple of zero items (since $\mathbf{z}_0'\mathbf{z}_5 = 0$) and have interchanged the order of multiplication of certain vector pairs. This was to emphasize the remarkable algebraic, and thus computational, symmetry of the three expressions.

Let us, therefore, interpret the calculation of M and D in the light of the now familiar term-by-term calculation of $\mathscr{S}^0_{\omega_1}$ in an analysis of variance layout. It will be seen that each term of D is an exact analogue of the corresponding term of $\mathscr{S}^0_{\omega_1}$ except that the vectors $\mathbf{z}_0, \mathbf{z}_1, \ldots \mathbf{z}_4$ are applied to the components of $\mathbf{z}_5$ instead of to the components of $\mathbf{x}$. The 'residual' D is thus the last line of an 'analysis of variance' of the covariate values.

Turning now to M we see that whereas we have *squared* certain items in the numerators of terms in $\mathscr{S}^0_{\omega_1}$ and in D we must now take the *products of the same quantities*, one from $\mathscr{S}^0_{\omega_1}$ and one from D. Since the operations to obtain $\mathscr{S}^0_{\omega_1}$ and D are identical except that the former uses x's and the latter z_5's we can sum up by saying that M is calculated by replacing *every* x^2-type term in $\mathscr{S}^0_{\omega_1}$ by the product of that x-item (individual value or group aggregate) and the corresponding z_5-item.

Finally, we note from the 'correction' terms of p. 58 that the preceding argument is valid throughout the whole of the analysis of variance table. We must, in fact, replace the original column of sums of squares of x by *three* columns, one of sums of squares of x, another of sums of squares of z_5, and the third of sums of products of x and z_5. A convenient form of computation is shown overleaf.

The portion of the table to the left of the vertical line is completed in the usual manner, but with one or more extra lines below the 'Total'. As described on pp. 39 *et seq.* the group of degrees of freedom for 'litters' is obtained as (cf. p. 54):

$$\frac{(43+49)^2+(40\tfrac{1}{2}+18)^2+\ldots}{2}-\frac{(261\tfrac{1}{2})^2}{8} \quad \text{for } x$$

$$\frac{(5{\cdot}375+\overline{-33{\cdot}625})^2+(\overline{-27{\cdot}625}+\overline{-6{\cdot}625})^2+\ldots}{2}-\frac{0^2}{8} \quad \text{for } z_5$$

and, because of the algebraic analogy discussed above,

$$\frac{(43+49)(5{\cdot}375-33{\cdot}625)+(40\tfrac{1}{2}+18)(-27{\cdot}625-6{\cdot}625)+\ldots}{2}$$

$$-\frac{(261\tfrac{1}{2})(0)}{8} \quad \text{for } x, z_5$$

The right-hand side of the table is filled in line by line in the order indicated by the parenthetical numbers on the extreme right. The first M^2/D value is obtained as described on p. 57; it is the square of the 'residual'

Hypothesis:	d.f.	s.s. x	s.p. x, z_5	s.s. z_5	M^2/D	Adjusted s.s. x	Adjusted d.f.	
(1) $\beta_1=\beta_2=\beta_3=0$ (litters)	3	495·844	−582·688	1974·375				
(2) $\beta_4=0$ (treatments)	1	175·781	98·438	55·125		259·680	1	(3)
Residual	3	207·844	−427·688	958·375	190·861	16·983 $=\mathscr{S}^0_\Omega$	2	(1)
Total	7	879·469	−911·938	2987·875				
Residual *plus* treatments	4	383·625	−329·250	1013·500	106·962	276·663 $=\mathscr{S}^0_{\omega_2}$	3	(2)

s.p. divided by the 'residual' for z_5, namely $(-427{\cdot}688)^2/958{\cdot}375$. Then (see p. 57) $\mathscr{S}^0_\Omega = 207{\cdot}844 - 190{\cdot}861 = 16{\cdot}983$. The test of the hypothesis, ω_1, that $\beta_5 = 0$ is made by computing $190{\cdot}861/(16{\cdot}983 \div 2)$ as an F with one and two degrees of freedom (see p. 57).

In line (2) we first calculate $(M')^2/D'$ in the same way as we obtained M^2/D *except* that we now use the old M and D *increased* by their respective 'treatment' items (cf. pp. 58 *et seq.*). This results in a new M^2/D equal to $(-329{\cdot}250)^2/1013{\cdot}500$, and subtraction of this from the *increased* sum of squares for x (namely, from 383·625) provides the required value of $\mathscr{S}^0_{\omega_2}$ to use in testing whether $\beta_4 = 0$.

It is convenient to effect the subtraction $\mathscr{S}^0_{\omega_2} - \mathscr{S}^0_\Omega$ in line (3). We thus finally obtain

$$F = \frac{259{\cdot}680}{16{\cdot}983 \div 2} = 30{\cdot}581 \quad \text{with 1 and 2 d.f.}$$

This is significant at the 5% level thus confirming the reality of β_4, the effect of thyroxine on vitamin A intake.

Statement of results

The foregoing analysis has shown that both β_4 and β_5 are real effects and our general knowledge tells us that β_1, β_2 and β_3 are 'real' even though a statistical test might indicate that *in this particular sample* they could be regarded as zero. We now want to summarize our information about the β_4 and β_5 effects.

In the first place let us calculate their point-estimates $\hat{\beta}_4$ and $\hat{\beta}_5$. From p. 56

$$\hat{\beta}_5 = -0{\cdot}44626$$

and, from the equations on p. 55, this means that

$$8\hat{\beta}_4 = 37{\cdot}5 - 21\hat{\beta}_5 = 46{\cdot}87146$$

or

$$\hat{\beta}_4 = 5{\cdot}8589$$

Although it is possible to calculate the variances of $\hat{\beta}_4$ and $\hat{\beta}_5$ without using the general method described on pp. 21 *et seq.*, it is convenient to illustrate the use of this method once again. The determinant of the coefficients of the $\hat{\beta}$'s in the normal equations is here (cf. p. 54)

$$\Delta = \begin{vmatrix} 8 & 0 & 0 & 0 & -13 \\ 0 & 8 & 0 & 0 & 125 \\ 0 & 0 & 8 & 0 & -1 \\ 0 & 0 & 0 & 8 & 21 \\ -13 & 125 & -1 & 21 & 2987{\cdot}875 \end{vmatrix}$$

Expanding this determinant in terms of its first column (cf. pp. 11 *et seq.* we obtain

$$\Delta = 8M_{11} + (-13)\,M_{51}$$

This expression, requiring the calculation of only two minors of Δ in order to obtain Δ, applies generally where there is a single covariate. These minors can, in turn, be expanded in terms of their first columns. We thus obtain

$$M_{11} = 8\begin{vmatrix} 8 & 0 & -1 \\ 0 & 8 & 21 \\ -1 & 21 & 2987{\cdot}875 \end{vmatrix} - 125\begin{vmatrix} 0 & 0 & 125 \\ 8 & 0 & -1 \\ 0 & 8 & 21 \end{vmatrix}$$

$$= 8\left\{8\begin{vmatrix} 8 & 21 \\ 21 & 2987{\cdot}875 \end{vmatrix} - 1\begin{vmatrix} 0 & -1 \\ 8 & -21 \end{vmatrix}\right\} + 125\times 8\begin{vmatrix} 0 & 125 \\ 8 & 21 \end{vmatrix}$$

$$= 8(8\times 23{,}462 - 8) - 125\times 8\times 1000 = 501{,}504$$

and, similarly but more easily,

$$M_{51} = 6{,}656$$

resulting in

$$\Delta = 3{,}925{,}504$$

We saw in Chapter One that

$$\mathscr{V}(\hat{\beta}_4) = \frac{M_{44}}{\Delta}\sigma^2 \quad \text{and} \quad \mathscr{V}(\hat{\beta}_5) = \frac{M_{55}}{\Delta}\sigma^2$$

where, in this case,

$$M_{44} = 518{,}912 \qquad M_{55} = 8^4 = 4{,}096$$

Hence

$$\mathscr{V}(\hat{\beta}_4) = 0{\cdot}13219\,\sigma^2 \quad \text{and} \quad \mathscr{V}(\hat{\beta}_5) = 0{\cdot}0010434\,\sigma^2$$

where σ^2 is to be estimated from

$$\hat{\sigma}^2 = \mathscr{S}^0_\Omega/(N-6) = 16{\cdot}983/2 = 8{\cdot}4915 = (2{\cdot}9140)^2$$

Having produced these results the 'hard way' we mention that it can be shown generally that

$$\mathscr{V}(\hat{\beta}_5) = \frac{M_{55}}{\Delta}\sigma^2 = \frac{\sigma^2}{D} = \frac{\sigma^2}{958{\cdot}375}$$

and that $\hat{\beta}_5$ is uncorrelated with any of the vector products $\mathbf{z}_i\mathbf{x}$ ($i = 1, 2, 3, 4$). As to the former statement the equality $\Delta = DM_{55}$ can be verified numerically, and with regard to the latter expansion of M shows that the required covariance is made up of terms like

$$\begin{aligned}\mathscr{C}(\mathbf{z}_i'\mathbf{x}, \mathbf{z}_j'\mathbf{x}) &= (\mathbf{z}_i'\mathbf{z}_j)\,\sigma^2 \qquad i \neq j \\ &= 0\end{aligned}$$

and two non-zero values of $\mathscr{C}(\mathbf{z}_i'\mathbf{x}, \mathbf{z}_5'\mathbf{x})$ with opposite signs. Using the Theorem of p. 20 on the relation

$$8\hat{\beta}_4 = 37{\cdot}5 - 21\hat{\beta}_5 = \mathbf{z}_4'\mathbf{x} - 21\hat{\beta}_5$$

we thus obtain

$$\begin{aligned}\mathscr{V}(\hat{\beta}_4) &= \frac{1}{8^2}\mathbf{z}_4'\mathbf{z}_4\,\sigma^2 + \frac{21^2}{8^2}\mathscr{V}(\hat{\beta}_5) \\ &= \frac{1}{8^2}\left(\mathbf{z}_4'\mathbf{z}_4 + \frac{21^2}{D}\right)\sigma^2 \\ &= \frac{1}{64}\left(8 + \frac{441}{958{\cdot}375}\right)\sigma^2 \\ &= 0{\cdot}13219\,\sigma^2 \quad \text{as before.}\end{aligned}$$

Finally, putting $\nu_1 = 1$ in the general expression for the confidence statement about ψ on p. 19, we have, with 90% confidence,

$$\hat{\beta}_4 - (F_{0\cdot1;1,2})^{1/2}\hat{\sigma}_{\hat{\beta}_4} < \beta_4 < \hat{\beta}_4 + (F_{0\cdot1;1,2})^{1/2}\hat{\sigma}_{\hat{\beta}_4}$$

i.e., $\quad 2{\cdot}77 < \beta_4 < 5{\cdot}859 + 2{\cdot}920 \times 0{\cdot}36358 \times 2{\cdot}914 = 8{\cdot}95$

Similarly

$$-0{\cdot}72 < \beta_5 < -0{\cdot}446 + 2{\cdot}920 \times 0{\cdot}03230 \times 2{\cdot}914 = -0{\cdot}17$$

These absurdly wide limits are all that can be obtained from eight observations!

Extension to several 'slopes'

It was mentioned on page 54 that the straight-line relationship between initial weight and eventual vitamin intake was assumed slope-invariate for the various litters and for both treatments. We now consider a case where the possible change in slope is an important feature of the investigation. As usual, we proceed by means of an illustration. The biological relevance of the models we develop may be confirmed by referring to Olson and Miller (1951) and Lundelius (1957).

Olson and Miller (1958) provide 18 measurements made on each of a number of specimens of *Knightia*, an Eocene teleost fish. These specimens were collected from four different localities and, although lateral compression had altered the dimensions from life-conditions, a comparison of the four samples was thought reasonable.

Here we limit ourselves to consideration of the length of the base of the dorsal fin in relation to the overall length of the skeleton,† and, to save space, we (1) omit Sample No. 3 in its entirety, and (2) discard the last four specimens from each of the remaining three samples. These samples will be called, respectively, Green River, Mid-Eocene, and Paleocene, corresponding to the formation or horizon in which the fossils were found.

Model Ω has been written out at length on the next page and β_0 is, as usual, the mean dorsal fin length of all 26 specimens. The vectors $\mathbf{z}_1$ and $\mathbf{z}_2$ attached to β_1 and β_2, respectively, represent the differences between the sample means. While β_1 is proportional to the difference between the means of G and M, β_2 is a linear combination of the means of the three samples. It was obtained by writing the three 'sample' components of $\mathbf{z}_2$ as 1, a, and b and by 'solving' for a and b so that $\mathbf{z}_1'\mathbf{z}_2 = 0$.

The components of the vector $\mathbf{z}_3$ are the overall skeleton lengths of the specimens in sample G *measured about their mean length* 40·727 (in order to make the aggregate of the vector's components add to zero). The vectors $\mathbf{z}_4$ and $\mathbf{z}_5$ refer to samples M and P where the mean skeletal lengths were, respectively, 78·125 and 57·571. Note that in Ω we are allowing for the possibilities that:

(i) The dorsal fin lengths of the three samples differ from one another; and

(ii) The 'slopes' (the β's) of the linear relation between overall length and dorsal fin length may be different in the three samples.

† The distance from the anterior tip of the mandible to the posterior end of the vertebral column, measured parallel to the longitudinal axis.

Sample i	Specimen j	$\mathbf{x}$	$=\beta_0 \times$	$+\ \beta_1 \times$	$+\ \beta_2 \times$	$+\ \beta_3 \times$	$+\ \beta_4 \times$	$+\ \beta_5 \times$	$+\ \mathbf{e}$
G	1	6·0	1	−8	7	5·273	—	—	
	2	5·7	1	−8	7	0·273	—	—	
	3	7·1	1	−8	7	6·273	—	—	
	4	5·0	1	−8	7	−2·727	—	—	
	5	5·5	1	−8	7	−1·727	—	—	
	6	4·0	1	−8	7	−8·727	—	—	
	7	4·9	1	−8	7	−7·727	—	—	
	8	4·0	1	−8	7	−3·727	—	—	
	9	6·8	1	−8	7	8·273	—	—	
	10	5·6	1	−8	7	6·273	—	—	
	11	4·9	1	−8	7	−1·727	—	—	
M	1	14·2	1	11	7	—	11·875	—	
	2	12·8	1	11	7	—	1·875	—	
	3	8·9	1	11	7	—	−8·125	—	
	4	9·0	1	11	7	—	−7·125	—	
	5	11·2	1	11	7	—	3·875	—	
	6	12·0	1	11	7	—	1·875	—	
	7	12·9	1	11	7	—	0·875	—	
	8	11·8	1	11	7	—	−5·125	—	
P	1	4·6	1	—	−19	—	—	2·429	
	2	6·7	1	—	−19	—	—	11·429	
	3	8·3	1	—	−19	—	—	−2·571	
	4	9·1	1	—	−19	—	—	−4·571	
	5	5·9	1	—	−19	—	—	−5·571	
	6	9·4	1	—	−19	—	—	−1·571	
	7	8·4	1	—	−19	—	—	0·429	

When we proceed to the normal equations we notice the convenient orthogonality of the vectors $\mathbf{z}$ since we obtain:

$$\begin{bmatrix} 1{,}672 & 0 & 0 & 0 & 0 \\ & 3{,}458 & 0 & 0 & 0 \\ & & 338\cdot1818 & 0 & 0 \\ & & & 306\cdot875 & 0 \\ & & & & 197\cdot7143 \end{bmatrix} \qquad \begin{bmatrix} 544\cdot8 \\ 70\cdot5 \\ 49\cdot8435 \\ 72\cdot9 \\ -19\cdot2204 \end{bmatrix}$$

together with $\hat{\beta}_0 = 204\cdot7/26 = 7\cdot8731$ and $\mathbf{x}'\mathbf{x} = 1844\cdot03$. Thus, from pp. 15 and 38,

$$\begin{aligned} \mathscr{S}^0_\Omega &= 1844\cdot03 - \frac{(204\cdot7)^2}{26} - \frac{(544\cdot8)^2}{1{,}672} - \frac{(70\cdot5)^2}{3{,}458} - \ldots \text{ etc.} \\ &= 1844\cdot03 - 1611\cdot6188 - 177\cdot5162 - 1\cdot4373 - 7\cdot3463 \\ &\qquad - 17\cdot3178 - 1\cdot8685 \\ &= 26\cdot9251 \quad \text{with } 26 - 6 = 20 \text{ d.f.} \end{aligned}$$

Because of the mutual orthogonality of all the vectors $\mathbf{z}$ in model Ω we know that we may test whether a particular β (or group of β's) is significantly different from zero by dividing the (mean of the) corresponding subtractive term (or terms) of $\mathscr{S}^0_\Omega$ by $\mathscr{S}^0_\Omega \div 20$.

For example we may test whether the three samples differ in their mean dorsal fin lengths by calculating

$$F = \frac{(177\cdot5162 + 1\cdot4373) \div 2}{26\cdot9251 \div 20} = 66\cdot463 \quad \text{with 2 and 20 d.f.}$$

This is highly significant.

We may also test whether any one, or all, of the 'slope' β's, namely β_3, β_4 and β_5, is equal to zero. Remember, however, that tests of single β's based on 'how they look' is properly effected through the Scheffé S-method based on the significance of the whole group of β's under consideration.

Now the foregoing differential in the mean dorsal fin lengths from universe to universe is not surprising. In fact we expected it because the overall sizes of the *Knightia* differ in the different horizons. What is more interesting is the possibility that, given the differences in mean fin lengths, the 'slope' of the relationship connecting fin length and overall length remains the same in the three samples. In other words, has there been a change of 'shape' of the fish associated with the known change in general 'size'?

The model ω_1 that expresses this concept may be written:

$$\omega_1: \quad \mathbf{x} = \mathbf{z}_0\beta_0 + \mathbf{z}_1\beta_1 + \mathbf{z}_2\beta_2 + \mathbf{z}_6\beta_6$$

where the vectors $\mathbf{z}_0$, $\mathbf{z}_1$ and $\mathbf{z}_2$ are as in Ω, while the (i,j) component (i = sample number, j = specimen number) of $\mathbf{z}_6$ is $z_{ij} - z_{i.}$, where z_{ij} is the skeletal length of the (i,j) specimen and $z_{i.}$ is the average value of all specimens in sample number i. Note that the components of $\mathbf{z}_6$ add to zero in *each* of the three samples. We are, in fact, making the hypothesis that $\beta_3 = \beta_4 = \beta_5$ in Ω without modifying the non-zero components in the vectors attached to these parameters.

The normal equations are now obtained from the matrices:

$$\begin{bmatrix} 1{,}672 & 0 & 0 \\ & 3{,}458 & 0 \\ & & 842\cdot7711 \end{bmatrix} \qquad \begin{bmatrix} 554\cdot8 \\ 70\cdot5 \\ 103\cdot5231 \end{bmatrix}$$

which are immediately available from the original pair on p. 64 by amalgamating the last three (diagonal) entries into one.

We thus obtain

$$\begin{aligned} \mathscr{S}^0_{\omega_1} &= 1844\cdot03 - 1611\cdot6188 - 177\cdot5162 - 1\cdot4373 - 13\cdot8895 \\ &= 39\cdot5682 \quad \text{with } 26-4 = 22 \text{ d.f.} \end{aligned}$$

In fact, the last three subtractive terms of $\mathscr{S}^0_\Omega$ have been replaced by $(103{\cdot}5231)^2/842{\cdot}7711$.

Our test of the adequacy of the model ω_1 thus depends on the size of:

$$F = \frac{(\mathscr{S}^0_{\omega_1} - \mathscr{S}^0_\Omega) \div 2}{\mathscr{S}^0_\Omega \div 20} = \frac{6{\cdot}3216}{1{\cdot}3463} = 4{\cdot}696 \quad \text{with 2 and 20 d.f.}$$

This value lies beyond the 2·5% value of $F_{2,20}$, namely 4·46. We conclude that the 'slope' of the relationship between skeletal length and fin length is different in the three horizons.

The various possible ω-models and their tests in this type of problem are often collected together in the form of an ANOVA. We think the reader will prefer to utilize the foregoing approach where the models are carefully specified and the z's shown to be orthogonal.

Problems 3

1. An experiment (Yates, 1934) was carried out to test the performance of newly-weaned pigs when fed on dry or wet meal, with or without the addition of green food. The effect of varying the numbers in a pen was also tested, equal floor space being assigned to each pig.

Six pigs (3 hogs and 3 gilts) from each of four litters, i.e., 24 pigs in all, were kept for six weeks in seven pens. One pen contained 8 pigs, two pens contained 4 pigs each, and four pens contained 2 pigs each. The arrangement is shown below, the numbers indicating whether the pig was in a 2-pen, a 4-pen or an 8-pen.

Litter no.:	1		2		3		4	
Sex:	H	G	H	G	H	G	H	G
Dry and Green	8	2	2	8		4	4	
Wet and Green		4	4		2	8	8	2
Dry	4			4	2	8	8	2
Wet	8	2	2	8	4			4

The initial and final weights at the beginning and end of the experiment, respectively, were recorded to the nearest pound and are shown below, the initial weight being given to the left of the final weight of each pig.

It will be seen that this is a balanced experiment in four factors, the total number of combinations of levels being 2 (wet or dry) × 2 (green or no-green) × 2 (sex) × 3 (amount of 'company') = 24. There is, in fact, a single replication of all possible combinations.

Litter no.:	1		2		3		4	
Sex:	H	G	H	G	H	G	H	G
Dry and Green	21, 31	24, 46	37, 75	25, 45	—	45, 80	40, 76	—
Wet and Green	—	28, 58	29, 60	—	47, 116	50, 103	30, 82	37, 93
Dry	26, 52	—	—	30, 55	60, 98	39, 65	38, 84	29, 39
Wet	24, 35	30, 54	25, 46	27, 54	61, 116	—	—	37, 83

(a) Write out the 24 components of each of the five mutually orthogonal vectors designed to test the 24 observations for the existence of:

(1) The two-level factors S (for 'sex'), W (for 'wet') and G (for 'green'); and

(2) A slope and a curvature effect of 'company', L and Q, say.

(b) We must now recognize litter differences which we will find are orthogonal to the foregoing five vectors. Instead of producing three mutually non-orthogonal vectors, comparing the first of the litters with the second, third and fourth, respectively, let us work with three orthogonal vectors. This may be achieved by labelling the four litter totals as (1), a, b and ab, respectively, and by constructing the vectors that enable us to test the (hypothetical) factor effects A, B and AB.

(c) Check that the whole set of eight vectors constructed in (a) and (b) is a mutually orthogonal set.

(d) By regarding initial weight as a covariate make an analysis of covariance to determine the significance of the factorial effects. The final (adjusted) residual should involve 14 degrees of freedom.

(e) Estimate and interpret the non-zero parameters of Ω by means of 90% confidence intervals.

(f) We have not considered the possibility of factor interactions. Suppose that the interaction between the factors W and G, for example, is to be measured by a vector each of whose components is obtained by multiplying together the corresponding components of the W and G vectors. Construct three further vectors to test the interactions WG, WL and WGS, respectively. Discard the vector (or vectors) that is (or are) not orthogonal to all of those already used in Ω and, utilizing the remainder, 'extract' the appropriate quantities from the three 'residuals' in the analysis of covariance. Finally, test the significance of the new effects thus introduced.

2. An experiment (DeLury, 1948) was carried out to determine the effect of different drugs as inhibitors of the atrophy of denervated muscles. The four drugs chosen were A, a large dose of atropine sulphate; B, a moderate dose of quinidine sulphate; C, a moderate dose of atropine sulphate; and D, a saline solution (control). Forty-eight rats were used in the experiment, 12 (chosen at random) being given drug A throughout, 12 drug B, 12 drug C and 12 drug D. The weight of each of the rats was recorded at the outset and one of its hind legs was then chosen randomly and deprived of its nerve supply by severing the appropriate nerves.

At the end of four days 16 randomly chosen rats were killed (four of them having had drug A, four having had drug B, etc.) and the weights of their denervated muscles were recorded. A similar procedure was carried out after eight days, and the remaining 16 rats were sacrificed at the end of 12 days (the conclusion of the experiment). The logarithms of the pairs of observations for each of the 48 rats are given below; x is 1000 times the logarithm of the denervated muscle weight, and z is 1000 times the mantissa of the logarithm of the initial weight of the rat.

	A		B		C		D	
Days	z	x	z	x	z	x	z	x
4	336	−37	297	76	422	86	258	−4
	391	64	394	61	301	−46	425	179
	408	100	255	−66	322	0	438	190
	301	−71	338	83	283	0	255	−9
8	423	−41	270	−60	250	−174	288	−13
	394	−137	342	17	274	−143	438	29
	377	−284	299	−56	398	33	346	64
	255	−187	380	−17	290	−125	438	17
12	297	−469	367	−387	310	−244	270	−92
	243	−367	398	−60	369	−97	456	4
	299	−387	461	−41	324	−161	389	−13
	350	−319	407	−60	330	−76	332	−60

(a) Write out a general linear model Ω which will associate:

(i) Two parameters with a time trend and a time curvature, the same for all four drugs;

(ii) Three parameters with differential levels of general drug effectiveness;

(iii) Six parameters with differential slopes and curvatures of the time curves of the four drugs; and

(iv) One parameter with the (log of the) initial overall weight of the rat.

The nine vectors attached to the parameters of (ii) and (iii) may be made (spuriously) orthogonal by assigning 'treatments' (1), p, q and pq to the four drugs. The three 'time' components within each drug will then be multiplied by a (+1) or a (−1) in accordance with the familiar 2^2 factorial pattern. In the subsequent analysis, however, the parameters of (ii) and (iii) should be grouped in threes for significance testing.

(b) Test the appropriate individual β's or groups of β's for significance by solving the normal equations or by means of an analysis of covariance. Calculate a 90% confidence interval for the parameter connecting the (log of the) final muscle observation with the (log of the) initial weight.

(c) The three β's for the individual drug gradients (slopes) are actually multiples of the differences between the mean gradients of two pairs of drugs. Examine the corresponding estimated $\hat{\beta}$'s, singly and in pairs (sums and differences), and use the *S*-method to provide 90% confidence intervals for ψ's that you consider summarize the results of the experiment with respect to differential drug gradients.

3. In comparisons between the sizes (x) of the maxillae of three genera of anteaters in relation to the corresponding cranial lengths (z) E. C. R. Reeve (1940) provides the following statistics (using the notation of this chapter):

	23 *Myrmecophaga*	78 *Tamandua*	35 *Cyclopes*
$\mathbf{x}'\mathbf{x}$	120·70592	229·65738	48·46790
$\mathbf{z}'\mathbf{x}$	110·39749	240·45143	61·62618
$\mathbf{z}'\mathbf{z}$	101·01348	251·89690	78·39105
Sum x	52·6429	133·6980	41·1586
Sum z	48·1862	140·1121	52·3690

Discuss these results from the viewpoint of relative growth of maxillae in the three genera.

References in Chapter Three

DELURY, D. B. (1948) 'The analysis of covariance.' *Biometrics* **4**, 153–170.

HEIMER, C. B., MASLOW, H. L. and SOBEL, A. E. (1949) 'Influence of thyroid on utilization of vitamin A.' *J. Nutr.* **38**, 345–351.

LUNDELIUS, E. (1957) 'Skeletal adaptations in two species of *Sceloporus*.' *Evolution* **11**, 65–83.

OLSON, E. C. and MILLER, R. L. (1951) 'Relative growth in paleontological studies.' *J. Paleontol.* **25**, 212–223.

OLSON, E. C. and MILLER, R. L. (1958) *Morphological Integration.* Chicago, Ill.

REEVE, E. C. R. (1940) 'Relative growth in the snout of anteaters. A study in the application of quantitative methods to systematics.' *Proc. Zool. Soc. Lond.* **A110**, 47–80.

YATES, F. (1934) 'A complex pig-feeding experiment.' *J. Agric. Sci.* **24**, 511–531.

CHAPTER FOUR

Multiple Regression

We will now return to the general model of Chapter One where the z-vectors are no longer instrumental variables but are actually measurements. In effect, the single covariate of Chapter Three has now been extended to many covariates. However, we do not exclude the case of several instrumental variables and several covariates.

In general, then, it is proposed to 'explain' a measurement x in terms of q others, namely $z_0, z_1, z_2, \ldots z_{q-1}$. Following our notational convention we assume that all the z's except z_0 are measured about their means. If we also subtract the observed mean $\bar{x}$ from each of the N x-values we can omit the parameter β_0 (estimated as $\bar{x}$) from our model.

We are now familiar with the Least Squares procedure for fitting such a model, namely

$$\Omega: \quad \mathbf{x} = \mathbf{z}_1\beta_1 + \mathbf{z}_2\beta_2 + \ldots + \mathbf{z}_{q-1}\beta_{q-1} + \mathbf{e}$$

The estimates of the β's are determined from the normal equations

$$\begin{array}{rcl} \mathbf{z}_1'\mathbf{z}_1\hat{\beta}_1 + \mathbf{z}_1'\mathbf{z}_2\hat{\beta}_2 + \ldots + \mathbf{z}_1'\mathbf{z}_{q-1}\hat{\beta}_{q-1} & = & \mathbf{z}_1'\mathbf{x} \\ \mathbf{z}_2'\mathbf{z}_1\hat{\beta}_1 + \mathbf{z}_2'\mathbf{z}_2\hat{\beta}_2 + \ldots + \mathbf{z}_2'\mathbf{z}_{q-1}\hat{\beta}_{q-1} & = & \mathbf{z}_2'\mathbf{x} \\ \ldots \quad \ldots \quad \ldots \quad \ldots & & \ldots \\ \mathbf{z}_{q-1}'\mathbf{z}_1\hat{\beta}_1 + \mathbf{z}_{q-1}'\mathbf{z}_2\hat{\beta}_2 + \ldots + \mathbf{z}_{q-1}'\mathbf{z}_{q-1}\hat{\beta}_{q-1} & = & \mathbf{z}_{q-1}'\mathbf{x} \end{array} \qquad (N)$$

and have the properties

$$\mathscr{E}(\hat{\beta}_i) = \beta_i \quad \text{and} \quad \mathscr{C}(\hat{\beta}_i, \hat{\beta}_j) = (-1)^{i+j}\frac{M_{ij}}{\Delta}\sigma^2$$

where Δ is the determinant of coefficients on the left-hand side of the normal equations, and M_{ij} is the minor (determinant) obtained from Δ by deleting its ith row and jth column.

Under these circumstances the residual sum of squares obtained by deducting the estimated model values from the original observations, squaring the N results and adding, is equal to

$$\mathscr{S}_{\Omega}^{0} = \mathbf{x}'\mathbf{x} - \mathbf{z}_1'\mathbf{x}\hat{\beta}_1 - \mathbf{z}_2'\mathbf{x}\hat{\beta}_2 - \ldots - \mathbf{z}_{q-1}'\mathbf{x}\hat{\beta}_{q-1}$$

and is an estimate of $(N-q)\sigma^2$, where σ^2 is the invariant variance of the 'errors' contained in the vector $\mathbf{e}$. When every e is $N(0, \sigma^2)$, $\mathscr{S}_{\Omega}^{0}/\sigma^2$ is distributed as χ^2 with $N-q$ degrees of freedom.

The practical difficulty with this general model has been the labour involved in solving $q-1$ simultaneous equations in the unknown $\hat{\beta}$'s –

particularly where q exceeds five or six. Although computational devices exist to simplify the solution of such equations it is only the advent of the electronic computer that has made this solution 'child's play'. The effort that the biologist would otherwise have expended in acquiring the technique of 'equation solving' can thus be employed in learning the mathematical terminology and 'rules' for matrices.

Matrix notation

In order to fix our ideas we will reconsider the 10 observations of Ryder's experiment in Chapter One but we will first deduct the general mean 1·212 from each of them.† This implies:

$$\mathbf{x} = \begin{bmatrix} -0\cdot842 \\ -1\cdot942 \\ -1\cdot712 \\ 0\cdot458 \\ -1\cdot912 \\ -0\cdot632 \\ 0\cdot558 \\ 3\cdot358 \\ 0\cdot098 \\ 2\cdot568 \end{bmatrix}$$

The right-hand sides of the four normal equations of p. 10 (since we have eliminated $\hat{\beta}_0$) consist of four vector products of the form $\mathbf{z}'\mathbf{x}$ where $\mathbf{z}'$ differs from equation to equation while $\mathbf{x}$ is the vector shown above. In our numerical illustrations we have already written these four vector products in the form of a four-component vector, namely

$$\begin{bmatrix} \mathbf{z}_1'\mathbf{x} \\ \mathbf{z}_2'\mathbf{x} \\ \mathbf{z}_3'\mathbf{x} \\ \mathbf{z}_4'\mathbf{x} \end{bmatrix} = \begin{bmatrix} -7\cdot62 \\ -12\cdot72 \\ 19\cdot58 \\ 13\cdot33 \end{bmatrix} \qquad \text{(See p. 10)}$$

Now each $\mathbf{z}'$ is a row vector and when all four of them are written out at length, one below the other, their components constitute a 4×10 matrix (more generally, a $\overline{q-1} \times N$ matrix) of numbers, namely

$$\begin{bmatrix} z_{11} & z_{12} & z_{13} & \cdots & z_{1,10} \\ z_{21} & z_{22} & z_{23} & \cdots & z_{2,10} \\ z_{31} & z_{32} & z_{33} & \cdots & z_{3,10} \\ z_{41} & z_{42} & z_{43} & \cdots & z_{4,10} \end{bmatrix} \equiv \mathbf{Z} \text{ (say)}$$

† In practice it is not necessary to make these subtractions. With zero-sum z-vectors the right-hand side of (N) remains the same whether or not we reduce the x's by $\bar{x}$. However in the latter case the subtractive term $\mathbf{z}_0'\mathbf{x}\hat{\beta}_0$ must appear in $\mathscr{S}^0_\Omega$.

It is thus tempting to define the product **Zx** as

$$\begin{bmatrix} z_{11} & z_{12} & z_{13} & \dots & z_{1,10} \\ z_{21} & z_{22} & z_{23} & \dots & z_{2,10} \\ z_{31} & z_{32} & z_{33} & \dots & z_{3,10} \\ z_{41} & z_{42} & z_{43} & \dots & z_{4,10} \end{bmatrix} \times \begin{bmatrix} x_1 \\ x_2 \\ x_3 \\ x_4 \\ \vdots \\ x_{10} \end{bmatrix} = \begin{bmatrix} z_{11}x_1+z_{12}x_2+\dots+z_{1,10}x_{10} \\ z_{21}x_1+z_{22}x_2+\dots+z_{2,10}x_{10} \\ z_{31}x_1+z_{32}x_2+\dots+z_{3,10}x_{10} \\ z_{41}x_1+z_{42}x_2+\dots+z_{4,10}x_{10} \end{bmatrix}$$

which is only extending our definition of a row vector times a column vector *with the same number of components*. To emphasize the numbers of rows and columns in the three matrices above we may write

$$(4\times 10)\,(10\times 1) = (4\times 1)$$

Note how the number of observations gets 'lost' – as we must have noticed already when obtaining normal equations.

It is sometimes convenient to embellish a matrix product like **Zx** with the sizes of the matrices involved. The product could, for example, be written as

$$\underset{(4\times 10)}{\mathbf{Z}}\;\underset{(10\times 1)}{\mathbf{x}} \quad \text{or as} \quad \overset{(4\times 10)}{\mathbf{Z}}\;\overset{(10\times 1)}{\mathbf{x}}$$

An important and useful symmetric matrix is the (diagonal) matrix with units in the north-west, south-east diagonal, and zeros elsewhere, namely

$$\mathbf{I} = \begin{bmatrix} 1 & 0 & 0 & \dots & 0 \\ 0 & 1 & 0 & \dots & 0 \\ 0 & 0 & 1 & \dots & 0 \\ \cdot & \cdot & \cdot & \cdot & \cdot \\ 0 & 0 & 0 & \dots & 1 \end{bmatrix}$$

Sometimes the order of this matrix is shown by writing it as, e.g., $\mathbf{I}_q$.

Matrix multiplication

Now let us transpose **Z** so that rows become columns and columns, rows. We obtain the 10×4 matrix

$$\begin{bmatrix} z_{11} & z_{21} & z_{31} & z_{41} \\ z_{12} & z_{22} & z_{32} & z_{42} \\ z_{13} & z_{23} & z_{33} & z_{43} \\ \dots & \dots & \dots & \dots \\ z_{1,10} & z_{2,10} & z_{3,10} & z_{4,10} \end{bmatrix} = \mathbf{Z}' = \{\mathbf{z}_1 \quad \mathbf{z}_2 \quad \mathbf{z}_3 \quad \mathbf{z}_4\}$$

[Note: It is, perhaps, a poor notational choice to have **Z** as a matrix of four *row* vectors and **Z′** a matrix of four *column* vectors. But there is no sanctity in rows *vs.* columns where a matrix, rather than a vector, is concerned.]

Can we ascribe a meaning to $\mathbf{ZZ'}$? Let us examine the possibility of 'multiplying through' $\mathbf{Z'}$ by $\mathbf{Z}$:

$$\mathbf{ZZ'} = \mathbf{Z}[\mathbf{z}_1 \quad \mathbf{z}_2 \quad \mathbf{z}_3 \quad \mathbf{z}_4] = [\mathbf{Zz}_1 \quad \mathbf{Zz}_2 \quad \mathbf{Zz}_3 \quad \mathbf{Zz}_4]$$

The row vector last written has 'sensible' components since each of these is a $(4\times 10)(10\times 1)$ product, i.e., a column vector of four components.

But we might alternatively have written

$$\mathbf{ZZ'} = \begin{bmatrix} \mathbf{z}_1' \\ \mathbf{z}_2' \\ \mathbf{z}_3' \\ \mathbf{z}_4' \end{bmatrix} \mathbf{Z'} = \begin{bmatrix} \mathbf{z}_1'\mathbf{Z'} \\ \mathbf{z}_2'\mathbf{Z'} \\ \mathbf{z}_3'\mathbf{Z'} \\ \mathbf{z}_4'\mathbf{Z'} \end{bmatrix}$$

and still have 'made sense', since the result is a column vector each of whose components is a $(1 \times 10)(10 \times 4)$ product, i.e., a row vector of four components. Now, although we have decided how to multiply a matrix into a column vector (with the appropriate number of components) we have not yet defined a product like $\mathbf{z}_1'\mathbf{Z'}$. However, if we extend our 'along-and-down' rule we would write

$$\mathbf{z}_1'\mathbf{Z'} = \{z_{11} \quad z_{12} \quad z_{13} \quad \cdots \quad z_{1,10}\} \begin{bmatrix} z_{11} & z_{21} & z_{31} & z_{41} \\ z_{12} & z_{22} & z_{32} & z_{42} \\ z_{13} & z_{23} & z_{33} & z_{43} \\ \cdots & \cdots & \cdots & \cdots \\ z_{1,10} & z_{2,10} & z_{3,10} & z_{4,10} \end{bmatrix}$$

$$= \{\mathbf{z}_1'\mathbf{z}_1 \quad \mathbf{z}_1'\mathbf{z}_2 \quad \mathbf{z}_1'\mathbf{z}_3 \quad \mathbf{z}_1'\mathbf{z}_4\} \quad \text{i.e., a row vector}$$

With this understanding it may be seen that *both* modes of procedure result in

$$\mathbf{ZZ'} = \begin{bmatrix} \mathbf{z}_1'\mathbf{z}_1 & \mathbf{z}_1'\mathbf{z}_2 & \mathbf{z}_1'\mathbf{z}_3 & \mathbf{z}_1'\mathbf{z}_4 \\ \mathbf{z}_2'\mathbf{z}_1 & \mathbf{z}_2'\mathbf{z}_2 & \mathbf{z}_2'\mathbf{z}_3 & \mathbf{z}_2'\mathbf{z}_4 \\ \mathbf{z}_3'\mathbf{z}_1 & \mathbf{z}_3'\mathbf{z}_2 & \mathbf{z}_3'\mathbf{z}_3 & \mathbf{z}_3'\mathbf{z}_4 \\ \mathbf{z}_4'\mathbf{z}_1 & \mathbf{z}_4'\mathbf{z}_2 & \mathbf{z}_4'\mathbf{z}_3 & \mathbf{z}_4'\mathbf{z}_4 \end{bmatrix} = \begin{bmatrix} 10 & 0 & 0 & 0 \\ 0 & 40 & -10 & -10 \\ 0 & -10 & 40 & -10 \\ 0 & -10 & -10 & 40 \end{bmatrix}$$

Checking the component set-up we have thus found a $(4\times 10)(10\times 4)$ product to be a (4×4) matrix of numbers. If we had performed the multiplication $\mathbf{Z'Z}$, which is of the type $(10 \times 4)(4 \times 10)$ we would have reached a different result and, in fact, $\mathbf{Z'Z}$ is (10×10) while $\mathbf{ZZ'}$ is (4×4). Further, if, e.g., $\mathbf{A}$ is a (4×10) matrix and $\mathbf{B}$ is a (10×3) then, although the product $\mathbf{AB}$ is permissible, the product $\mathbf{BA}$ – which is $(10 \times 3)(4 \times 10)$ – is not defined. Hence, here again, $\mathbf{AB} \neq \mathbf{BA}$.

However, we have seen that sometimes the order of the matrices in a product may be changed without affecting the result. An immediate example concerns the identity matrix $\mathbf{I}_r$ when multiplied by a square $(r \times r)$ matrix **A**. We then have

$$\mathbf{IA} \equiv \mathbf{AI}$$

Another useful result is that if **A** is $(p \times q)$ and **B** is $(q \times r)$ then

$$\mathbf{AI}_q\mathbf{B} = \mathbf{AB}$$

Referring to the general normal equations (N) written out (for $\overline{q-1}$ instead of four $\hat{\beta}$'s) on p. 70, we see that the matrix of coefficients of the $\hat{\beta}$'s is what we have just written as $\mathbf{ZZ'}$, where $\mathbf{Z'}$ (*not* **Z**) is the set of four column vectors of z's which we introduced in Chapter One. But the four $\hat{\beta}$'s could themselves be written as a column vector $\hat{\boldsymbol{\beta}}$, say, and since $\mathbf{ZZ'}$ is a (4×4) matrix, we find that the set of four normal equations can be written succinctly as

$$(\mathbf{ZZ'})\hat{\boldsymbol{\beta}} = \mathbf{Zx} \qquad (N)$$

where **Z** is (4×10), $\hat{\boldsymbol{\beta}}$ is (4×1) and **x** is (10×1). More generally **Z** is $(\overline{q-1} \times N)$, $\hat{\boldsymbol{\beta}}$ is $(\overline{q-1} \times 1)$ and **x** is $(N \times 1)$.

It is essential that the reader now carries out for himself some examples of matrix multiplication. Two instructive examples will be found in numbers **1** and **2** of Problems 4.

The Ω-model in matrix notation

It is now possible to rewrite the model Ω in matrix form (Bartlett, 1934). We have hitherto written

$$\Omega: \quad \mathbf{x} = \mathbf{z}_1\beta_1 + \mathbf{z}_2\beta_2 + \ldots + \mathbf{z}_{q-1}\beta_{q-1} + \mathbf{e}$$

Remembering that

$$\mathbf{Z'} = [\mathbf{z}_1 \quad \mathbf{z}_2 \quad \mathbf{z}_3 \quad \ldots \quad \mathbf{z}_{q-1}]$$

and writing $\boldsymbol{\beta}$ for the column vector of $q-1$ β-values we may rewrite Ω as

$$\mathbf{x} = \mathbf{Z'}\boldsymbol{\beta} + \mathbf{e}$$

Pre-multiplying this equation by **Z** which is $(\overline{q-1} \times N)$ – and this shows why post-multiplication is not possible – replacing the β's by their $\hat{\beta}$ estimates, and dropping the 'errors', this becomes

$$\mathbf{Zx} = \mathbf{ZZ'}\hat{\boldsymbol{\beta}}$$

or, as we prefer to write it,

$$\mathbf{ZZ'}\hat{\boldsymbol{\beta}} = \mathbf{Zx} \qquad (N)$$

This is how the normal equations appear in matrix notation.

The inverse matrix

So far, this notation has been a mere 'shorthand' which allows us – after a little practice – to 'think' of whole arrays of vector products when we look at a short expression in bold print. But much more is involved when we try to define the reciprocal of a (square) matrix, called the inverse of the matrix. Remembering that pre-multiplication and post-multiplication may produce different results, let us pre-multiply matrix equation (N) by $(\mathbf{ZZ}')^{-1}$ where, since $\mathbf{ZZ}'$ is (4×4) or, more generally, $(\overline{q-1}\times\overline{q-1})$, we define

$$(\mathbf{ZZ}')^{-1}(\mathbf{ZZ}') = \mathbf{I} \qquad (\mathbf{I} \text{ being } 4\times 4)$$

The result is

$$(\mathbf{ZZ}')^{-1}(\mathbf{ZZ}')\,\hat{\boldsymbol{\beta}} = (\mathbf{ZZ}')^{-1}\mathbf{Zx}$$

i.e.,

$$\mathbf{I}\hat{\boldsymbol{\beta}} = \hat{\boldsymbol{\beta}} = (\mathbf{ZZ}')^{-1}\mathbf{Zx}$$

We have thus 'solved' the normal equations – in matrix notation!

It will be noticed that if we have some means of evaluating $\mathbf{A}^{-1}$ corresponding to the square (and, in our case, symmetric) $r\times r$ matrix $\mathbf{A}$, using the relation

$$\mathbf{A}^{-1}\mathbf{A} = \mathbf{I} \qquad [\mathbf{I} \text{ is } (r\times r)]$$

we can immediately solve any set of simultaneous equations involving the matrix of coefficients $\mathbf{A}$. Actually the numerical procedure is almost the exact opposite: the inverse of an $r\times r$ matrix $\mathbf{A}$ can be determined from the property that the solution of the r sets of equations

$$\mathbf{AC} = \mathbf{I}$$

where $\mathbf{C}$ is an $r\times r$ matrix of unknowns (and $\mathbf{I}$ allows for r sets of solutions) is

$$\mathbf{C} = \mathbf{A}^{-1}\mathbf{I} = \mathbf{A}^{-1}.$$

Now the solution of the equations

$$\mathbf{AC} = \mathbf{I}$$

may be obtained by determinantal methods (Cramer's Rule, p. 12) and the r sets of solutions thus provide $\mathbf{A}^{-1}$.

Notice that the right-hand side of any actual set of equations involving $\mathbf{A}$ on the left *is not involved in the determination of* $\mathbf{A}^{-1}$. And observe that we have to solve r sets of equations in r unknowns if we require $\mathbf{A}^{-1}$ rather than the solution of a single given set of r equations with $\mathbf{A}$ on the left. To an electronic computer the difference is a matter of seconds.

Computer procedure

Every electronic computer has available standard programs to multiply matrices and to obtain the inverse of a square symmetric matrix. This explains our insistence that the biologist should know that:

(1) When he is preparing a set of normal equations from his Ω or ω models he is performing two matrix multiplications, namely

$$\mathbf{ZZ}' \quad \text{and} \quad \mathbf{Zx}$$

the former being $(\overline{q-1} \times N)(N \times \overline{q-1})$ and the latter $(\overline{q-1} \times N)(N \times 1)$.

(2) The solution of the normal equations

$$\mathbf{ZZ}'\hat{\boldsymbol{\beta}} = \mathbf{Zx} \qquad (N)$$

written in the form

$$\hat{\boldsymbol{\beta}} = (\mathbf{ZZ}')^{-1}\mathbf{Zx}$$

merely requires, from the computer, the inversion of the matrix $\mathbf{ZZ}'$ and its pre-multiplication into the matrix $\mathbf{Zx}$.

In illustration of this we, once again, utilize Ryder's data. We have already shown that

$$\mathbf{ZZ}' = \begin{bmatrix} 10 & 0 & 0 & 0 \\ 0 & 40 & -10 & -10 \\ 0 & -10 & 40 & -10 \\ 0 & -10 & -10 & 40 \end{bmatrix} \quad \text{and} \quad \mathbf{Zx} = \begin{bmatrix} -7{\cdot}62 \\ -12{\cdot}72 \\ 19{\cdot}58 \\ 13{\cdot}33 \end{bmatrix}$$

When the former matrix is inverted the result is

$$(\mathbf{ZZ}')^{-1} = \begin{bmatrix} 0{\cdot}1 & 0 & 0 & 0 \\ 0 & 0{\cdot}03 & 0{\cdot}01 & 0{\cdot}01 \\ 0 & 0{\cdot}01 & 0{\cdot}03 & 0{\cdot}01 \\ 0 & 0{\cdot}01 & 0{\cdot}01 & 0{\cdot}03 \end{bmatrix}$$

On multiplying this matrix into $\mathbf{Zx}$ we obtain

$$\hat{\boldsymbol{\beta}} = \begin{bmatrix} -0{\cdot}7620 \\ -0{\cdot}0525 \\ 0{\cdot}5935 \\ 0{\cdot}4685 \end{bmatrix}$$

$\mathscr{S}^0_\Omega$ in matrix form

After 'fitting' the model Ω by Least Squares the N-component vector of residuals is

$$\mathbf{x} - \mathbf{Z}'\hat{\boldsymbol{\beta}}.$$

Since the sum of the squares of the components of a vector $\mathbf{a}$ is $\mathbf{a}'\mathbf{a}$ the sum of the squares of the residuals after 'fitting' Ω is

$$\begin{aligned} \mathscr{S}^0_\Omega &= (\mathbf{x}-\mathbf{Z}'\hat{\boldsymbol{\beta}})'(\mathbf{x}-\mathbf{Z}'\hat{\boldsymbol{\beta}}) \\ &= (\mathbf{x}'-(\mathbf{Z}'\hat{\boldsymbol{\beta}})')(\mathbf{x}-\mathbf{Z}'\hat{\boldsymbol{\beta}}) \\ &= (\mathbf{x}'-\hat{\boldsymbol{\beta}}'\mathbf{Z})(\mathbf{x}-\mathbf{Z}'\hat{\boldsymbol{\beta}}) \qquad [\text{Check that } (\mathbf{Z}'\hat{\boldsymbol{\beta}})' = \hat{\boldsymbol{\beta}}'\mathbf{Z}] \\ &= \mathbf{x}'\mathbf{x}-\mathbf{x}'\mathbf{Z}'\hat{\boldsymbol{\beta}}-\hat{\boldsymbol{\beta}}'\mathbf{Zx}+\hat{\boldsymbol{\beta}}'\mathbf{ZZ}'\hat{\boldsymbol{\beta}} \\ &= \mathbf{x}'\mathbf{x}-\mathbf{x}'\mathbf{Z}'\hat{\boldsymbol{\beta}}-\hat{\boldsymbol{\beta}}'\mathbf{Zx}+\hat{\boldsymbol{\beta}}'\mathbf{Zx} \quad \text{by } (N) \\ &= \mathbf{x}'\mathbf{x}-\mathbf{x}'\mathbf{Z}'\hat{\boldsymbol{\beta}} \end{aligned}$$

The latter is a succinct way of writing the expression for $\mathscr{S}^0_\Omega$ given on p. 70.

The variance–covariance matrix of $\hat{\boldsymbol{\beta}}$

As a final exercise in matrix multiplication let us find the expected value of the vector of $\hat{\beta}$'s and the variance–covariance matrix of the various products of these $\hat{\beta}$'s.

To do this we will have to remember that

$$(\mathbf{AB})\,\mathbf{C} = \mathbf{A}(\mathbf{BC})$$

and that

$$(\mathbf{AB})' = \mathbf{B}'\,\mathbf{A}'$$

as can easily be checked on any small numerical matrices. This means that

$$(\mathbf{ABC})' = ((\mathbf{AB})\,\mathbf{C})' = \mathbf{C}'(\mathbf{AB})' = \mathbf{C}'\,\mathbf{B}'\,\mathbf{A}'$$

Another useful notion is that the vector product

$$\underset{(p\times 1)}{\mathbf{y}}\,\underset{(1\times p)}{\mathbf{y}'}$$

is a $(p\times p)$ matrix. Supposing the expected value of each component of $\mathbf{y}$ is zero we may take the expected value of each of these $p\times p$ single products of which $\mathbf{yy}'$ is composed and obtain a so-called variance–covariance matrix. This is because each term is either a variance (on the diagonal) or a covariance. With these preliminaries we may proceed to the exercise.

□ □ □ Our model Ω states that

$$\mathbf{x} = \mathbf{Z}'\,\boldsymbol{\beta}+\mathbf{e} \quad \text{where } \mathscr{E}(\mathbf{e}) = \mathbf{0}$$

$\mathbf{0}$ being a column vector of zeros. Hence

$$\mathscr{E}(\mathbf{x}) = \mathbf{Z}'\,\boldsymbol{\beta}$$

Furthermore

$$\hat{\boldsymbol{\beta}} = (\mathbf{ZZ}')^{-1}\,\mathbf{Zx}$$

and, on taking the expected value of *each* of the components of $\mathbf{x}$, we may write

$$\begin{aligned}\mathscr{E}(\hat{\boldsymbol{\beta}}) &= (\mathbf{ZZ}')^{-1}\,\mathbf{Z}\mathscr{E}(\mathbf{x})\\ &= (\mathbf{ZZ}')^{-1}\,\mathbf{Z}(\mathbf{Z}'\,\boldsymbol{\beta})\\ &= (\mathbf{ZZ}')^{-1}(\mathbf{ZZ}')\,\boldsymbol{\beta} = \mathbf{I}\boldsymbol{\beta} = \boldsymbol{\beta}\end{aligned}$$

Comparing this derivation with that of p. 22 we can see the advantages of our 'shorthand' matrix notation. This is even more apparent at the next stage.

The variance–covariance of the components of $\hat{\boldsymbol{\beta}}$ is the expected value of $(\hat{\boldsymbol{\beta}}-\boldsymbol{\beta})(\hat{\boldsymbol{\beta}}-\boldsymbol{\beta})'$. Let us evaluate this product. We have

$$\begin{aligned}\hat{\boldsymbol{\beta}}-\boldsymbol{\beta} &= (\mathbf{ZZ}')^{-1}\mathbf{Zx}-\boldsymbol{\beta}\\ &= (\mathbf{ZZ}')^{-1}\mathbf{Z}(\mathbf{Z}'\boldsymbol{\beta}+\mathbf{e})-\boldsymbol{\beta}\\ &= (\mathbf{ZZ}')^{-1}\mathbf{Z}(\mathbf{Z}'\boldsymbol{\beta})+(\mathbf{ZZ}')^{-1}\mathbf{Ze}-\boldsymbol{\beta}\\ &= (\mathbf{ZZ}')^{-1}(\mathbf{ZZ}')\boldsymbol{\beta}+(\mathbf{ZZ}')^{-1}\mathbf{Ze}-\boldsymbol{\beta}\\ &= \mathbf{I}\boldsymbol{\beta}+(\mathbf{ZZ}')^{-1}\mathbf{Ze}-\boldsymbol{\beta}\\ &= (\mathbf{ZZ}')^{-1}\mathbf{Ze}\end{aligned}$$

and consequently

$$\begin{aligned}(\hat{\boldsymbol{\beta}}-\boldsymbol{\beta})' &= ((\mathbf{ZZ}')^{-1}\mathbf{Ze})' = \mathbf{e}'\mathbf{Z}'((\mathbf{ZZ}')^{-1})'\\ &= \mathbf{e}'\mathbf{Z}'(\mathbf{ZZ}')^{-1}\end{aligned}$$

since $(\mathbf{ZZ}')^{-1}$ is symmetric and transposing it leaves it unchanged. Hence

$$(\hat{\boldsymbol{\beta}}-\boldsymbol{\beta})(\hat{\boldsymbol{\beta}}-\boldsymbol{\beta})' = (\mathbf{ZZ}')^{-1}\mathbf{Zee}'\mathbf{Z}'(\mathbf{ZZ}')^{-1}$$

The only term in this expression that involves a random variable is $\mathbf{ee}'$ which is the $(N\times N)$ matrix of product-pairs of 'errors'. Since any two different 'errors' are independent the expectation of their product is zero. Hence the only non-zero terms in $\mathscr{E}(\mathbf{ee}')$ is the diagonal of squared errors, namely $\mathscr{E}(e_1^2)$, $\mathscr{E}(e_2^2)$, ... $\mathscr{E}(e_N^2)$. Each of these terms is σ^2, so that

$$\mathscr{E}(\mathbf{ee}') = \begin{bmatrix}\sigma^2 & 0 & \dots & 0\\ 0 & \sigma^2 & \dots & 0\\ \cdot & \cdot & \cdot & \cdot\\ 0 & 0 & \dots & \sigma^2\end{bmatrix} = \sigma^2\mathbf{I}$$

Thus, finally

$$\begin{aligned}\mathscr{E}(\hat{\boldsymbol{\beta}}-\boldsymbol{\beta})(\hat{\boldsymbol{\beta}}-\boldsymbol{\beta})' &= \sigma^2(\mathbf{ZZ}')^{-1}\mathbf{ZIZ}'(\mathbf{ZZ}')^{-1}\\ &= \sigma^2(\mathbf{ZZ}')^{-1}(\mathbf{ZZ}')(\mathbf{ZZ}')^{-1}\\ &= \sigma^2(\mathbf{ZZ}')^{-1}\end{aligned}$$

This result is very convenient. Once $(\mathbf{ZZ}')^{-1}$ has been obtained from the computer the vector of $\hat{\beta}$'s is obtained by a matrix multiplication, and the variances and covariances of these $\hat{\beta}$'s are given by the terms of $(\mathbf{ZZ}')^{-1}$ itself.

Thus, reverting to our numerical illustration, the variance–covariance matrix of the $\hat{\beta}$'s is

$$\sigma^2\begin{bmatrix}0{\cdot}1 & 0 & 0 & 0\\ 0 & 0{\cdot}03 & 0{\cdot}01 & 0{\cdot}01\\ 0 & 0{\cdot}01 & 0{\cdot}03 & 0{\cdot}01\\ 0 & 0{\cdot}01 & 0{\cdot}01 & 0{\cdot}03\end{bmatrix}$$

showing, as we already know, that $\hat{\beta}_1$ is uncorrelated with $\hat{\beta}_2$, $\hat{\beta}_3$ and $\hat{\beta}_4$ while the latter variates are interconnected.

The variance of $\hat{x}$

Suppose it is required to calculate the variance of $\hat{x}$, the estimate of x for a given set of values $z_0, z_1, z_2, \ldots z_{q-1}$. We have

$$\hat{x} = z_0\hat{\beta}_0 + z_1\hat{\beta}_1 + \ldots + z_{q-1}\hat{\beta}_{q-1}$$

and thus, by the theorem of p. 20,

$$\begin{aligned}\mathscr{V}(\hat{x}) = {} & z_0^2\mathscr{V}(\hat{\beta}_0) + z_1^2\mathscr{V}(\hat{\beta}_1) + \ldots + z_{q-1}^2\mathscr{V}(\hat{\beta}_{q-1}) \\ & + 2z_0z_1\mathscr{C}(\hat{\beta}_0, \hat{\beta}_1) + \ldots + 2z_{q-2}z_{q-1}\mathscr{C}(\hat{\beta}_{q-2}, \hat{\beta}_{q-1})\end{aligned}$$

where the variances and covariances of the $\hat{\beta}$'s are obtained as the appropriate terms of $\sigma^2(\mathbf{ZZ}')^{-1}$.

We may estimate σ^2 by $\mathscr{S}_\Omega/(N-q)$ and obtain the estimated variance of $\hat{x}$ for a given set of z-values. A $100\alpha\%$ confidence interval for $\hat{x}$ is then given by

$$\hat{x} \pm t_\alpha\sqrt{\{\text{Est.}\,\mathscr{V}(\hat{x})\}}$$

where t is the $100\alpha\%$ point of the t distribution with $N-q$ degrees of freedom.

Problems 4

1. Effect the following multiplication of two symmetric matrices:

$$\begin{bmatrix} 4 & 3 & 2 \\ 3 & 2 & 1 \\ 2 & 1 & 1 \end{bmatrix}\begin{bmatrix} -1 & 1 & 1 \\ 1 & 0 & -2 \\ 1 & -2 & 1 \end{bmatrix}$$

The result is also symmetrical. (*Answer: I_3*)

2. Evaluate

$$\begin{bmatrix} 5 & 2 & 0 & 0 \\ 2 & 1 & 0 & 0 \\ 0 & 0 & 8 & 3 \\ 0 & 0 & 5 & 2 \end{bmatrix}\begin{bmatrix} 1 & -2 & 0 & 0 \\ -2 & 5 & 0 & 0 \\ 0 & 0 & 2 & -3 \\ 0 & 0 & -5 & 8 \end{bmatrix}$$

(*Answer: I_4*)

Now partition each of these 4×4 matrices into four 2×2 matrices so that the above product appears as

$$\begin{bmatrix} \mathbf{A} & \mathbf{O} \\ \mathbf{O} & \mathbf{B} \end{bmatrix}\begin{bmatrix} \mathbf{C} & \mathbf{O} \\ \mathbf{O} & \mathbf{D} \end{bmatrix} = \begin{bmatrix} \mathbf{AC} & \mathbf{O} \\ \mathbf{O} & \mathbf{BD} \end{bmatrix}$$

Check that this symbolic procedure is valid in that it reproduces the original result.

3. Use the relation

$$\mathbf{ZZ'C} = \mathbf{I}$$

to obtain $(\mathbf{ZZ'})^{-1}$ from the $\mathbf{ZZ'}$ given on p. 76. Note that this involves the solution of four separate sets of equations in four unknowns and that these four sets of solutions are the four column vectors of $\mathbf{C}$.

4. Four measurements were made on 86 human male skulls, namely, C the cranial capacity (determined by packing the skull with mustard seed and weighing the seed), L the glabella-occipital length, B the maximum parietal breadth and H the basio-bregmatic height. The following results were obtained by C. R. Rao and D. C. Shaw (1948) using the common logarithms of each of the measurements and treating $\log C$ as x:

$$\mathbf{ZZ'} = \begin{bmatrix} 0{\cdot}01875 & 0{\cdot}00848 & 0{\cdot}00684 \\ & 0{\cdot}02904 & 0{\cdot}00878 \\ & & 0{\cdot}02886 \end{bmatrix} \qquad \mathbf{Zx} = \begin{bmatrix} 0{\cdot}03030 \\ 0{\cdot}04410 \\ 0{\cdot}03629 \end{bmatrix}$$

$$(\mathbf{x}-\bar{\mathbf{x}})'(\mathbf{x}-\bar{\mathbf{x}}) = 0{\cdot}12692$$

and we have computed

$$(\mathbf{ZZ'})^{-1} = \begin{bmatrix} 64{\cdot}201 & -15{\cdot}580 & -10{\cdot}476 \\ & 41{\cdot}704 & -8{\cdot}995 \\ & & 39{\cdot}869 \end{bmatrix}$$

Calculate (i) the vector $\hat{\boldsymbol{\beta}}$, (ii) the residual sum of squares $\mathscr{S}^0_\Omega$ after fitting $\log C$ by a linear relation in the logs of the three external measurements, and (iii) the 95% confidence intervals for the $\hat{\beta}$'s. Are you satisfied with these three intervals in view of the correlations between the $\hat{\beta}$'s?

5. The following excerpts were taken from B. H. Ketchum's preliminary report of the SCOR Chemistry Intercalibration Session of September, 1961.

'On Wednesday, 6 September, the [seven] analysts boarded the *Gascoyne* which then proceeded south and east of the island of Oahu until the depth of water was 1000 fathoms. Three separate casts with Nansen bottles were made between about 10.00 a.m. and 2.00 p.m. Five depths were sampled, selected so as to give the maximum range in oxygen concentration, namely 50 meters, 200 meters, 400 meters, 600 meters, 900 meters. At each of these depths three Nansen bottles were placed on the wire about 2 meters apart and three oxygen samples were drawn by different analysts from each of these three Nansen bottles. Thus nine oxygen samples were obtained from each depth on each cast.'

'The analytical results for oxygen are presented in Table 7 in the

Table 6. Plan of oxygen sampling aboard the *Gascoyne* on 6 September 1961.
The numbers in the table correspond to the analysts.
(X = no sample obtained)
(The three Nansen bottles are indicated by *a*, *b* and *c*, respectively, the order of sampling within a cast by the numbers 1, 2, 3)

Cast	Depth:	50 m *a*	50 m *b*	50 m *c*	200 m *a*	200 m *b*	200 m *c*	400 m *a*	400 m *b*	400 m *c*	600 m *a*	600 m *b*	600 m *c*	900 m *a*	900 m *b*	900 m *c*
I	1	1	7	5	3	X	2	6	1	7	5	3	4	2	6	1
	2	7	5	3	4	2	6	1	7	5	3	4	X	6	1	7
	3	X	3	4	2	X	1	7	5	3	4	2	X	1	7	X
II	1	3	4	2	6	1	7	5	3	4	2	6	1	7	5	3
	2	4	2	6	1	7	5	3	4	2	6	1	7	5	3	4
	3	2	6	1	7	5	3	4	2	6	1	7	5	3	4	2
III	1	6	1	7	5	3	4	2	6	1	7	5	3	4	2	6
	2	1	7	5	3	4	2	6	1	7	5	3	4	2	6	1
	3	7	5	3	4	2	6	1	7	5	3	4	2	6	1	7

Table 7. Oxygen concentration (ml/l) determined by the various analysts.

Cast	Depth:	50 m *a*	50 m *b*	50 m *c*	200 m *a*	200 m *b*	200 m *c*	400 m *a*	400 m *b*	400 m *c*	600 m *a*	600 m *b*	600 m *c*	900 m *a*	900 m *b*	900 m *c*
I	1	4·55	4·74	4·69	4·31	X	4·09	3·44	3·46	3·63	1·29	1·20	1·35	0·87	0·80	0·78
	2	4·73	4·61	4·53	4·34	4·20	4·34	3·54	3·63	3·56	1·19	1·34	X	0·82	0·78	1·10
	3	X	4·59	4·54	4·23	X	4·35	3·65	3·53	3·47	1·34	1·20	X	0·84	0·98	X
II	1	4·47	4·65	4·33	4·20	4·36	4·60	3·59	3·52	3·62	1·18	1·10	1·15	1·10	0·92	0·83
	2	4·65	4·36	4·34	4·37	4·55	4·48	3·55	3·56	3·36	1·14	1·15	1·27	0·88	0·90	0·88
	3	4·37	4·44	4·59	4·55	4·43	4·38	3·64	3·46	3·45	1·17	1·26	1·27	0·85	0·88	0·84
III	1	4·38	4·59	4·78	4·43	4·36	4·45	3·83	3·74	3·85	1·50	1·17	1·21	0·82	0·84	0·75
	2	4·59	4·74	4·69	4·32	4·43	4·24	3·76	3·88	4·04	1·11	1·26	1·26	0·78	0·73	0·75
	3	4·68	4·45	4·57	4·40	4·20	4·22	3·93	4·04	3·83	1·36	1·32	1·19	0·77	0·76	0·92

same order and arrangement as the identification of analysts is presented in Table 6. The range of oxygen observed in these samples was from roughly 0·8 to 4·6 ml oxygen per liter, thus achieving the broad range of concentrations that was planned.'

'Most analysts had relatively small variations which fluctuated between plus and minus values from the mean value. The only exception to this was the group from Woods Hole [No. 7] whose oxygen values are consistently high, averaging high by +0·14 ml/liter.'

The differences between the five depths will be represented by four β's and their corresponding vectors the components of each of which must sum to zero if we are to preserve the 'averaging' property of the first vector of units attached to β_0. Prior to reduction by the mean component of each column-vector the four 'depth' vectors may conveniently be given components proportional to d, d^2, d^3 and d^4, respectively, where d is the depth of the cast.

Two further β's may be used to designate the differences between the 'high', 'middle' and 'low' Nansen bottles at each depth. Two other β's will differentiate between the three casts and six more will be used for differences between the analysts. Finally, six β's can be employed to measure the possible interactions between the analysts and the first (linear) depth 'effect'.

Construct the foregoing 21-parameter model and test the significance of its groups of parameters using an electronic computer. The group of analyst β's will be found significant at the 1% level. Calculate the contrast expressing the difference between analyst No. 7 and the mean of the other six in terms of the six analyst β's. Obtain a 99% confidence interval for this contrast and compare your conclusions with that of the SCOR report.

(*Answer*: $0{\cdot}097 < \psi < 0{\cdot}293$)

References in Chapter IV

BARTLETT, M.S. (1934) 'The vector representation of a sample.' *Proc. Camb. Phil. Soc.* **30**, 327-340.

RAO, C. R. and SHAW, D. C. (1948) 'On a formula for the prediction of cranial capacity.' *Biometrics* **4**, 247–253.

PART B

Several Dependent Variates

CHAPTER FIVE

The p-Variate Linear Model

In previous chapters we have considered the application of a model in which a single random variable x is 'explained' by q supposedly error-free observations or measurements. Although these explanatory variables may have been interconnected the only source of chance variation in x has resided in the error term of the model which has been assumed (univariate) Normal with zero mean and invariant variance σ^2.

We now turn to the case where the q error-free observations are to be used to 'explain' p variates which may be supposed to be interconnected. Thus, for example, 10 $(=p)$ measurements could be made on a number of mice which have been subjected to various treatments and are of different genetic constitutions. These treatment and genetic differences would be used to 'explain' the 10 correlated measurements on a specified mouse. It may well be that a clearer picture of the treatment effects would emerge in this manner than if a single $(p = 1)$ measurement had been made on each mouse.

Before we consider an illustration we will generalize the notion of the residual error to be expected in such a p-variate estimate. In this we will be anticipating some of the results of the next chapter.

We require to generalize the assumption that a single typical residual is a random value from $N(0, \sigma^2)$. At first sight all we need to say is that a typical set of p variates measured on a single unit is drawn from p different Normal universes with means defined by the p appropriate linear functions of q β's and with variances σ_j^2 $(j = 1, 2, \ldots p)$. In other words the model will allow for p different means (by allowing for p different sets of q β's) and p different variances.

What is lacking in this generalization is that we must allow any pair of the p variates to be correlated in a specified manner that remains invariate throughout the sampling procedure. That is to say if x_i and x_j are two of the variates measured on a unit (e.g., a mouse) then $\mathscr{C}(x_i, x_j)$ has a fixed (though unknown) value which we will write succinctly as σ_{ij} where i and j assume any of the integer values 1, 2, ... p. In particular, $\sigma_{ii} \equiv \sigma_i^2$ $(i = 1, 2, \ldots p)$.

Thus, whereas we could summarize our distributional assumptions in the univariate case by saying that the residual (error) was distributed as

$N(0, \sigma^2)$ we now say that the p variates are distributed as $N(\mathbf{0}, \mathbf{\Sigma})$, where $\mathbf{0}$ is a p-component column vector of zeros and

$$\mathbf{\Sigma} \equiv \begin{bmatrix} \sigma_{11} & \sigma_{12} & \cdots & \sigma_{1p} \\ \sigma_{21} & \sigma_{22} & \cdots & \sigma_{2p} \\ \cdot & \cdot & \cdot & \cdot \\ \sigma_{p1} & \sigma_{p2} & \cdots & \sigma_{pp} \end{bmatrix} \qquad \sigma_{ij} \equiv \sigma_{ji}$$

The illustrative data

Sixteen men, each of whom was judged to be either over- or underweight, were subjected to urinalysis on two separate mornings and four measurements were made on each occasion to summarize the results. Two of these measurements, the volume in millilitres (which we will denote by z_2) and the specific gravity (which we will reduce by unity and then multiply by 1000 before denoting it by z_3), can be regarded as (non-random) co-variates used in partial explanation of the two variates, namely

$$x_1 = \text{pigment creatinine}$$

$$x_2 = \text{choline } \mu\text{g/ml}$$

which are likely to be correlated.

The data were 'selected' from the 11-variate analysis of observations on 17 males published by Smith, Gnanadesikan, and Hughes (1962) by omitting individual No. 16 who had only one urinalysis and by utilizing the first two urinalysis results where three were made. The figures that follow suggest that a 'replication effect' would have been a significant parameter. However, we are not informed whether the published data were actually collected as homogeneous replicates. It will be remembered that we are not allowed to invent 'effects' by inspection of the data.

The model Ω

Remembering that there are three explanatory variables (the man's weight, volume of urine, and specific gravity of urine) besides the general mean, and that any particular set of them applies to both the variate measurements, we may write our Ω-model in the form ($j = 1, 2, \ldots 32$):

$$x_{1j} = \beta_{10} z_{0j} + \beta_{11} z_{1j} + \beta_{12} z_{2j} + \beta_{13} z_{3j} + e_{1j}$$

$$x_{2j} = \beta_{20} z_{0j} + \beta_{21} z_{1j} + \beta_{22} z_{2j} + \beta_{23} z_{3j} + e_{2j}$$

We have, of course, allowed for different β-coefficients in the two variates since different entities are being 'explained' in terms of the same three variables. As usual, $z_{0j} \equiv 1$ while the variable z_1 represents the man's weight category.

Using this notation the numerical data are given on the next page. Note that we have arranged that the components of the z-vectors add to zero. The mean of the original z_2-values was 261·25, that of the z_3-values 25·5625.

x_{1j}	x_{2j}	z_{0j}	z_{1j}	z_{2j}	z_{3j}
17·6	7·5	1	7	−56·25	−1·5625
13·4	7·1	1	7	−101·25	6·4375
22·3	4·0	1	7	−31·25	4·4375
20·5	2·0	1	7	−26·25	4·4375
12·1	16·8	1	7	−46·25	−0·5625
12·0	14·5	1	7	−71·25	4·4375
14·7	2·0	1	7	−86·25	−1·5625
14·8	0·4	1	7	−116·25	0·4375
18·1	14·5	1	7	−41·25	5·4375
19·7	12·5	1	7	38·75	−2·5625
23·7	4·9	1	7	13·75	−5·5625
19·2	0·2	1	7	143·75	−7·5625
14·8	12·0	1	7	−91·25	5·4375
15·6	5·2	1	7	−26·25	2·4375
16·2	10·2	1	7	−76·25	−4·5625
14·1	8·5	1	7	−6·25	−5·5625
14·1	6·9	1	7	43·75	0·4375
19·1	4·7	1	7	178·75	−1·5625
17·0	1·9	1	−9	88·75	−7·5625
12·5	0·7	1	−9	213·75	−15·5625
21·5	8·3	1	−9	−66·25	7·4375
22·2	9·3	1	−9	113·75	−0·5625
13·0	18·3	1	−9	−21·25	7·4375
10·9	10·5	1	−9	−56·25	5·4375
22·8	3·3	1	−9	213·75	−9·5625
16·5	6·3	1	−9	168·75	5·4375
12·5	22·5	1	−9	−156·25	6·4375
8·7	19·5	1	−9	−146·25	−0·5625
15·0	20·0	1	−9	63·75	1·4375
12·9	1·0	1	−9	48·75	−2·5625
12·1	5·0	1	−9	−16·25	−0·5625
13·2	3·0	1	−9	−91·25	0·4375
512·8	263·5				

Let us write the two 32-component vectors of x-measurements as

$$\mathbf{x}_1 \equiv \begin{bmatrix} x_{11} \\ x_{12} \\ \cdots \\ x_{1,32} \end{bmatrix} \quad \text{and} \quad \mathbf{x}_2 \equiv \begin{bmatrix} x_{21} \\ x_{22} \\ \cdots \\ x_{2,32} \end{bmatrix}$$

and let

$$\mathbf{X} \equiv [\mathbf{x}_1 \quad \mathbf{x}_2]$$

We will use analogous notation for $\mathbf{e}_1$, $\mathbf{e}_2$ and $\mathbf{E}$.

As in the univariate case

$$\mathbf{Z} \equiv \begin{bmatrix} z_{01} & z_{02} & \cdots & z_{0,32} \\ z_{11} & z_{12} & \cdots & z_{1,32} \\ z_{21} & z_{22} & \cdots & z_{2,32} \\ z_{31} & z_{32} & \cdots & z_{3,32} \end{bmatrix}$$

We have now retained the first row of units in the symbolic description because we will be using electronic computers from this point. The computational advantages of measuring the x's about the sample mean and likewise for each of the z-vectors are no longer relevant.† However, as already indicated, we have continued to use this device (thus permitting the elimination of the first row in $\mathbf{Z}$ and the suppression of β_{10} and β_{20} from the model) in the numerical work on the illustrative example.

Further, we write

$$\boldsymbol{\beta}_1 \equiv \begin{bmatrix} \beta_{10} \\ \beta_{11} \\ \beta_{12} \\ \beta_{13} \end{bmatrix} \qquad \boldsymbol{\beta}_2 \equiv \begin{bmatrix} \beta_{20} \\ \beta_{21} \\ \beta_{22} \\ \beta_{23} \end{bmatrix}$$

and

$$\mathbf{B} \equiv [\boldsymbol{\beta}_1 \quad \boldsymbol{\beta}_2].$$

The whole set of 32 pairs of relations expressing the model may now be written succinctly in the form

$$\underset{(32\times 2)}{\mathbf{X}} = \underset{(32\times 4)}{\mathbf{Z}'}\ \underset{(4\times 2)}{\mathbf{B}} + \underset{(32\times 2)}{\mathbf{E}} \tag{1}$$

where the orders of the component matrices have been indicated. This form is completely analogous to that of the univariate case developed in Chapter Four. The only novelty is the addition of two matrices.

We note that

$$\mathscr{E}(\mathbf{E}) = \mathbf{0} \quad \text{and} \quad \mathscr{E}(\mathbf{E}'\mathbf{E}) = \mathbf{\Sigma}$$

where $\mathbf{0}$ is a (32×2) matrix of zeros and

$$\mathbf{\Sigma} = \begin{bmatrix} \sigma_{11} & \sigma_{12} \\ \sigma_{12} & \sigma_{22} \end{bmatrix}$$

† Nevertheless, by making all z-vectors add to zero $\hat{\boldsymbol{\beta}}_0$ becomes the vector of means of the x's and makes all the other β's into contrasts. Another advantage is that it tends to reduce the correlation between two z-vectors, one of which has the same elements as the other except that they are raised to a given power (see, e.g., number **5** of Problems **4**).

If we now pre-multiply equation (1) by **Z**, ignore **E** and thus replace **B** by $\hat{\mathbf{B}}$ its (Least Squares) estimate, we obtain

$$\underset{(4\times 32)}{\mathbf{Z}}\;\underset{(32\times 2)}{\mathbf{X}} = \underset{(4\times 32)}{\mathbf{Z}}\;\underset{(32\times 4)}{\mathbf{Z}'}\;\underset{(4\times 2)}{\hat{\mathbf{B}}} \tag{2}$$

and, on pre-multiplying both sides by $(\mathbf{ZZ}')^{-1}$,

$$\hat{\mathbf{B}} = (\mathbf{ZZ}')^{-1}\mathbf{ZX} \tag{3}$$

Once again this equation is exactly analogous to the corresponding univariate equation of Chapter Four.

Returning to the numerical example we have (with the first row of units in **Z** eliminated)

$$\mathbf{ZZ}' = \begin{bmatrix} 2016 & -5720 & 46 \\ -5720 & 325550 & -10082{\cdot}5 \\ 46 & -10082{\cdot}5 & 931{\cdot}875 \end{bmatrix}$$

and

$$\mathbf{ZX} = \begin{bmatrix} 216{\cdot}8 & -229{\cdot}1 \\ 5074 & -8068{\cdot}875 \\ -92{\cdot}95 & 496{\cdot}08125 \end{bmatrix}$$

From the former of these we obtain (using a standard matrix inversion program available on almost any electronic computer)

$$(\mathbf{ZZ}')^{-1} = \begin{bmatrix} 0{\cdot}0^{3}52973 & 0{\cdot}0^{4}12780 & 0{\cdot}0^{3}11213 \\ 0{\cdot}0^{4}12780 & 0{\cdot}0^{5}49281 & 0{\cdot}0^{4}52689 \\ 0{\cdot}0^{3}11213 & 0{\cdot}0^{4}52689 & 0{\cdot}0^{2}16376 \end{bmatrix}$$

and thus

$$\hat{\mathbf{B}} = (\mathbf{ZZ}')^{-1}\mathbf{ZX} = \begin{bmatrix} 0{\cdot}16927 & -0{\cdot}16886 \\ 0{\cdot}02288 & -0{\cdot}01655 \\ 0{\cdot}13944 & 0{\cdot}36155 \end{bmatrix} \equiv \hat{\mathbf{B}}_{\Omega}$$

The model ω

Now, the experiment was set up to determine whether knowledge of a man's weight would improve the prediction of his x_1 and x_2 values from the volume and specific gravity of his urine. We may thus write the ω-model as

$$\underset{(32\times 2)}{\mathbf{X}} = \underset{(32\times 3)}{\mathbf{Z}'}\;\underset{(3\times 2)}{\mathbf{B}} + \underset{(32\times 2)}{\mathbf{E}} \tag{4}$$

where β_{11} and β_{21} and the corresponding z-vector have been eliminated from equation (1).† As we found in the univariate case, the non-ortho-

† We have not yet eliminated the first row of **Z** and the corresponding β's.

gonality of $\mathbf{z}_1$ with the vectors $\mathbf{z}_2$ and $\mathbf{z}_3$ means that the estimates of the remaining β-values will now differ from the values we obtained under Ω.

Since there should be no misunderstanding we will retain the notation of Ω and write

$$\mathbf{ZZ}' = \begin{bmatrix} 325550 & -10082{\cdot}5 \\ -10082{\cdot}5 & 931{\cdot}875 \end{bmatrix}$$

and

$$\mathbf{ZX} = \begin{bmatrix} 5074 & -8068{\cdot}875 \\ -92{\cdot}95 & 496{\cdot}80125 \end{bmatrix}$$

We thus obtain

$$(\mathbf{ZZ}')^{-1} = \begin{bmatrix} 0{\cdot}0^5 46198 & 0{\cdot}0^4 49984 \\ 0{\cdot}0^4 49984 & 0{\cdot}0^2 16139 \end{bmatrix}$$

and

$$\hat{\mathbf{B}}_\omega = (\mathbf{ZZ}')^{-1}\mathbf{ZX} = \begin{bmatrix} 0{\cdot}01879 & -0{\cdot}01248 \\ 0{\cdot}10361 & 0{\cdot}39731 \end{bmatrix}$$

We notice that the $\hat{\beta}$-values are of the same relative size as the corresponding values in Ω. Our problem is now to test whether the two sets of residuals from Ω and ω, respectively, could be regarded as deriving from one and the same bivariate Normal universe.

Significance test of ω

It will be remembered that in the univariate case we computed the sum of the squares of the residuals under Ω, namely $\mathscr{S}^0_\Omega$, and the similar sum under ω, namely $\mathscr{S}^0_\omega$. The former of these was an estimate of $(N-q)\sigma^2$ and (when ω was justified) $\mathscr{S}^0_\omega$ was an estimate of $(N-s)\sigma^2$, where $(q-s)$ of the β's in Ω had been removed to form ω. It was therefore natural to compare $\mathscr{S}^0_\Omega$ and $\mathscr{S}^0_\omega$, taking due account of their different 'degrees of freedom'. This could have been done by computing 'critical' (e.g., 5% and 1%) values of the ratio $\mathscr{S}^0_\Omega/\mathscr{S}^0_\omega$. In fact, however, the traditional form of the F-tables comparing $\mathscr{S}^0_\Omega$ and $\mathscr{S}^0_\omega$ consists of critical values of

$$\frac{(\mathscr{S}^0_\omega - \mathscr{S}^0_\Omega) \div (q-s)}{\mathscr{S}^0_\Omega \div (N-q)}$$

Nevertheless, when generalizing this univariate procedure to the p-variate case it will be more convenient to think in terms of $\mathscr{S}^0_\Omega/\mathscr{S}^0_\omega$.

We notice that using the 32 pairs of residuals under Ω we could calculate a sum of squares for the x_1 variate, a sum of squares for the x_2 variate and a sum of products of corresponding x_1 and x_2 variates. When divided by the number of degrees of freedom $32-4 = 28$ these quantities are estimates of σ_{11}, σ_{22} and σ_{12} $(=\sigma_{21})$, respectively. Expressed another way we have now estimated the components of $\mathbf{\Sigma}$ and we may write them collectively as $\hat{\mathbf{\Sigma}}$.

However, in order to facilitate the machine computation of these components we may write them in vector and matrix form as follows:

$$28\hat{\mathbf{\Sigma}} = (\mathbf{X}-\mathbf{Z}'\hat{\mathbf{B}})'(\mathbf{X}-\mathbf{Z}'\hat{\mathbf{B}})$$

[The reader should check that the right-hand side of this equation is actually a 2×2 matrix]

$$\begin{aligned} &= (\mathbf{X}'-(\mathbf{Z}'\hat{\mathbf{B}})')(\mathbf{X}-\mathbf{Z}'\hat{\mathbf{B}}) \\ &= (\mathbf{X}'-\hat{\mathbf{B}}'\mathbf{Z})(\mathbf{X}-\mathbf{Z}'\hat{\mathbf{B}}) \\ &= \mathbf{X}'\mathbf{X}-\mathbf{X}'\mathbf{Z}'\hat{\mathbf{B}}-\hat{\mathbf{B}}'\mathbf{Z}\mathbf{X}+\hat{\mathbf{B}}'\mathbf{Z}\mathbf{Z}'\hat{\mathbf{B}} \end{aligned}$$

Now equation (2) shows that the third of these four terms is equal to $\hat{\mathbf{B}}'\mathbf{Z}\mathbf{Z}'\hat{\mathbf{B}}$ while the transposition of equation (2), namely

$$(\mathbf{Z}\mathbf{X})' = (\mathbf{Z}\mathbf{Z}'\hat{\mathbf{B}})'$$

i.e.,

$$\mathbf{X}'\mathbf{Z}' = \hat{\mathbf{B}}'(\mathbf{Z}\mathbf{Z}')' = \hat{\mathbf{B}}'\mathbf{Z}\mathbf{Z}',$$

shows that the second of the four terms is also equal to $\hat{\mathbf{B}}'\mathbf{Z}\mathbf{Z}'\hat{\mathbf{B}}$. Effecting the consequent cancellation we obtain

$$28\hat{\mathbf{\Sigma}} = \mathbf{X}'\mathbf{X}-\hat{\mathbf{B}}'\mathbf{Z}\mathbf{Z}'\hat{\mathbf{B}} \tag{5}$$

Affixing the suffix Ω or ω according as $\mathbf{B}$ has three or two rows, respectively, we find (after adjusting the components of $\mathbf{X}'\mathbf{X}$ to be 'about mean' sums of squares and products)

$$28\hat{\mathbf{\Sigma}}_\Omega = \begin{bmatrix} \begin{array}{r} 8689{\cdot}94 \\ -8217{\cdot}62 \\ \hline 472{\cdot}32 \end{array} & \begin{array}{r} 3950{\cdot}88 \\ -4222{\cdot}59 \\ \hline -271{\cdot}71 \end{array} \\ & \begin{array}{r} 3407{\cdot}59 \\ -2169{\cdot}76 \\ \hline \end{array} \\ -271{\cdot}71 & 1237{\cdot}83 \end{bmatrix} - \begin{bmatrix} 0{\cdot}16927 & 0{\cdot}02288 & 0{\cdot}13944 \\ -0{\cdot}16886 & -0{\cdot}01655 & 0{\cdot}36155 \end{bmatrix} \times$$

$$\times \begin{bmatrix} 2016 & -5720 & 46 \\ -5720 & 325550 & -10082{\cdot}5 \\ 46 & -10082{\cdot}5 & 931{\cdot}875 \end{bmatrix} \begin{bmatrix} 0{\cdot}16927 & -0{\cdot}16886 \\ 0{\cdot}02288 & -0{\cdot}01655 \\ 0{\cdot}13944 & 0{\cdot}36155 \end{bmatrix}$$

$$= \begin{bmatrix} 472{\cdot}32 & -271{\cdot}71 \\ -271{\cdot}71 & 1237{\cdot}83 \end{bmatrix} - \begin{bmatrix} 139{\cdot}84 & -154{\cdot}20 \\ -154{\cdot}20 & 351{\cdot}54 \end{bmatrix}$$

$$= \begin{bmatrix} 332{\cdot}48 & -117{\cdot}51 \\ -117{\cdot}51 & 886{\cdot}29 \end{bmatrix}$$

Notice that the result is a symmetric matrix – as it should be.

The similar calculations for ω result in

$$29\hat{\mathbf{\Sigma}}_{\omega} = \begin{bmatrix} 386{\cdot}63 & -171{\cdot}50 \\ -171{\cdot}50 & 940{\cdot}04 \end{bmatrix}$$

While direct comparison of $\hat{\mathbf{\Sigma}}_{\Omega}$ and $\hat{\mathbf{\Sigma}}_{\omega}$ suggests that little has been gained by the subdivision of the male subjects into over- and under-weight, it is possible to derive a test mathematically that has certain desirable properties.

The test criterion is the (univariate) variate obtained by dividing the determinant of the matrix $28\hat{\mathbf{\Sigma}}_{\Omega}$ by the determinant of the matrix $29\hat{\mathbf{\Sigma}}_{\omega}$. We will write

$$U_{2,1,28} = \frac{|28\hat{\mathbf{\Sigma}}_{\Omega}|}{|29\hat{\mathbf{\Sigma}}_{\omega}|}$$

where the first suffix of U denotes the number of (dependent) variates p, the third suffix is the degrees of freedom left after fitting Ω, and the middle suffix is the number of *rows* of $\mathbf{B}_{\Omega}$ that are equated to zero by ω. It can be proved that the distribution of $U_{p,q-s,N-q}$ is exactly the same as the distribution of $U_{q-s,p,N-s-p}$ and this result will prove useful later.

In the instant case

$$U_{2,1,28} = \frac{332{\cdot}48\times 886{\cdot}29-(-117{\cdot}51)^2}{386{\cdot}63\times 940{\cdot}04-(-171{\cdot}50)^2} = \frac{280865}{334035} = 0{\cdot}8408$$

Now Bartlett (1938) has shown that

$$\Pr[-\{f-\tfrac{1}{2}(p-q+s+1)\}\ln U_{p,q-s,f} < c] \approx \Pr(\chi^2_{p(q-s)} < c) \qquad (6)$$

where c is any arbitrary value, ln stands for the natural logarithm (which is 2·302585 times the common logarithm), and f is short for $N-q$. Applying this to our numerical illustration

$$p = 2 \qquad q-s = 1 \qquad f = 32-4 = 28$$

$$\log U_{2,1,28} = \bar{1}{\cdot}92469 = -0{\cdot}07531$$

and

$$-\ln U_{2,1,28} = 0{\cdot}17341$$

Thus

$$-(28-1)\ln U_{2,1,28} = 4{\cdot}682$$

and, on referring to a table of the chi-square distribution with $p(q-s) = 2\times 1 = 2$ degrees of freedom we see that the 5% point is 5·991. We conclude that the model ω is not significantly different from the model Ω. In other words, knowledge of a man's weight category† does

† Which is not necessarily the same as knowledge of his exact weight in pounds and ounces.

not add precision to a linear model predicting his pigment creatinine (x_1) and choline (x_2) from the volume (z_2) and specific gravity (z_3) of his urine.

It is of interest to note that the equivalence of $U_{p,q-s,N-q}$ and $U_{q-s,p,N-s-p}$ means that when $q-s=1$ (i.e., when we are testing an ω that deletes a single row of $\mathbf{B}_\Omega$) the variate U is that appropriate to the univariate linear model and permits an exact (instead of an approximate) test to be made. In the illustrative example

$$0{\cdot}8408 = U_{2,1,28} = U_{1,2,27} = \frac{\mathscr{S}^0_\Omega \text{ with 27 degrees of freedom}}{\mathscr{S}^0_\omega \text{ with } 27-2 = 25 \text{ degrees of freedom}}$$

Thus

$$\frac{1}{0{\cdot}8408} = \frac{\mathscr{S}^0_\omega}{\mathscr{S}^0_\Omega}$$

and

$$\frac{1-0{\cdot}8408}{0{\cdot}8408} = \frac{\mathscr{S}^0_\omega - \mathscr{S}^0_\Omega}{\mathscr{S}^0_\Omega}$$

so that

$$\frac{(\mathscr{S}^0_\omega - \mathscr{S}^0_\Omega) \div 2}{\mathscr{S}^0_\Omega \div 27} = \frac{0{\cdot}1592}{0{\cdot}8408} \times \frac{27}{2} = 2{\cdot}556$$

and this is an F-variate with 2 and 27 degrees of freedom. Reference to an F-table confirms the conclusion we drew from the approximate chi-square value.

The general case

The foregoing illustration can be generalized without difficulty. The computational procedure is as follows:

(i) Formulate a general linear hypothesis Ω involving N p-variate observations and q β's per variate, namely

$$\underset{(N\times p)}{\mathbf{X}} = \underset{(N\times q)}{\mathbf{Z}'}\ \underset{(q\times p)}{\mathbf{B}_\Omega} + \underset{(N\times p)}{\mathbf{E}} \tag{1}$$

(ii) Calculate the matrix products $\mathbf{ZX}$ and $\mathbf{ZZ}'$ and invert the latter.

(iii) Obtain the estimate of $\mathbf{B}_\Omega$ from

$$\hat{\mathbf{B}}_\Omega = (\mathbf{ZZ}')^{-1}\mathbf{ZX} \tag{3}$$

(iv) Proceed analogously with the 'reduced' model ω in which only s rows of $\mathbf{B}_\Omega$ remain.

(v) To test the validity of the 'reduced' model calculate

$$(N-q)\hat{\mathbf{\Sigma}}_\Omega \quad \text{and} \quad (N-s)\hat{\mathbf{\Sigma}}_\omega$$

where

$$f\hat{\mathbf{\Sigma}} = \mathbf{X}'\mathbf{X} - \hat{\mathbf{B}}'\mathbf{ZZ}'\hat{\mathbf{B}} \tag{5}$$

and $\hat{\mathbf{B}}$ and $\mathbf{Z}$ can refer either to Ω or ω provided f is adjusted appropriately. The ratio of the determinants, namely

$$|(N-q)\hat{\mathbf{\Sigma}}_{\Omega}| \quad \text{to} \quad |(N-s)\hat{\mathbf{\Sigma}}_{\omega}|$$

is written $U_{p,\,q-s,f}$ and the variate

$$-\{f-\tfrac{1}{2}(p-q+s+1)\}\ln U_{p,\,q-s,f} \qquad f = N-q$$

is distributed approximately as chi-square with $p(q-s)$ degrees of freedom. If the value of $U_{p,\,q-s,f}$ obtained from the data is suspiciously large the significance of the $p(q-s)$ omitted β-values is considered proved.

Extension of the *S*-method to the multivariate case

The model ω eliminates p sets of $q-s$ betas from the general model Ω. Let us write these betas as a matrix $\underset{(q-s\times p)}{\mathbf{B}_D}$ where the 'D' stands for 'deleted'. We suppose that the U-test has shown that, as a whole, these betas cannot be equated to zero. Our objective is to find confidence intervals for an arbitrary set of 'contrasts' which we form from the elements of $\mathbf{B}_D$. Since such a 'contrast' is to be a scalar quantity (i.e., a 1×1 matrix) it will have to assume the form

$$\underset{(1\times 1)}{\psi} = \underset{(1\times p)}{\mathbf{a}'}\ \underset{(p\times \overline{q-s})}{\mathbf{B}_D'}\ \underset{(\overline{q-s}\times 1)}{\mathbf{c}}$$

where the components of both $\mathbf{a}'$ and $\mathbf{c}$ are selected by the experimenter.

Before providing a confidence interval for the estimated value of ψ, namely for

$$\hat{\psi} = \mathbf{a}'\hat{\mathbf{B}}_D'\mathbf{c},$$

we will state some results for the $\hat{\beta}$'s of Ω. We write

$$\underset{(q\times p)}{\hat{\mathbf{B}}_{\Omega}} = \{\hat{\boldsymbol{\beta}}_1 \ \ \hat{\boldsymbol{\beta}}_2 \ \ \ldots \ \ \hat{\boldsymbol{\beta}}_p\}$$

where $\hat{\boldsymbol{\beta}}_i$ $(i = 1, 2, \ldots p)$ is a q-component column vector of $\hat{\beta}$'s.

Now the expected value of $\hat{\boldsymbol{\beta}}_i$ can be shown to be $\boldsymbol{\beta}_i$ and the covariance of the two vectors $\hat{\boldsymbol{\beta}}_i$, $\hat{\boldsymbol{\beta}}_j$ is the $(q\times q)$ matrix $\sigma_{ij}(\mathbf{ZZ}')^{-1}$ with $i,j = 1, 2, \ldots p$. Consider the p-component column vector of variates $\hat{\mathbf{B}}_D'\mathbf{c}$. The $(q-s)$-component vector $\mathbf{c}$ multiplies each of the p rows of $\hat{\mathbf{B}}_D'$ (or each of the p columns of $\hat{\mathbf{B}}_D$). Hence the covariance of two typical rows of $\hat{\mathbf{B}}_D'\mathbf{c}$ is the covariance of $\mathbf{c}'\hat{\boldsymbol{\beta}}_i$ and $\mathbf{c}'\hat{\boldsymbol{\beta}}_j$ and is thus

$$\mathbf{c}'\mathscr{C}(\hat{\boldsymbol{\beta}}_i, \hat{\boldsymbol{\beta}}_j)\,\mathbf{c} = \sigma_{ij}\ \underset{(1\times\overline{q-s})}{\mathbf{c}'}\ \underset{(\overline{q-s}\times\overline{q-s})}{(\mathbf{ZZ}')_D^{-1}}\ \underset{(\overline{q-s}\times 1)}{\mathbf{c}}$$

a scalar quantity, where $(\mathbf{ZZ}')_D^{-1}$ is the symmetrical matrix of deleted rows and columns in $(\mathbf{ZZ}')_\Omega^{-1}$. The $(p \times p)$ variance–covariance matrix of $\hat{\mathbf{B}}'_D \mathbf{c}$ thus consists of the elements of $\mathbf{\Sigma}$ each multiplied by $\mathbf{c}'(\mathbf{ZZ}')_D^{-1}\mathbf{c}$. It may be written $\mathbf{\Sigma}^*$, i.e.,

$$\mathbf{\Sigma}^* = \{\mathbf{c}'(\mathbf{ZZ}')_D^{-1}\mathbf{c}\}\mathbf{\Sigma}$$

It has been shown by S. N. Roy (1957) that the whole set of statements

$$\hat{\psi} - \left\{\frac{\theta_\alpha}{1-\theta_\alpha}\mathbf{a}'\hat{\mathbf{\Sigma}}^*\mathbf{a}(N-q)\right\}^{1/2} \leqslant \psi \leqslant \hat{\psi} + \left\{\frac{\theta_\alpha}{1-\theta_\alpha}\mathbf{a}'\hat{\mathbf{\Sigma}}^*\mathbf{a}(N-q)\right\}^{1/2}$$

where

$$\hat{\psi} = \mathbf{a}'\hat{\mathbf{B}}'_D\mathbf{c},$$

$\hat{\mathbf{\Sigma}}^*$ is obtained from $\mathbf{\Sigma}^*$ by substituting $\hat{\mathbf{\Sigma}}$ for $\mathbf{\Sigma}$, and $\mathbf{a}$ and $\mathbf{c}$ are arbitrarily chosen vectors of coefficients, is true with probability $1-\alpha$ (where, e.g., $\alpha = 0{\cdot}05$).

In the foregoing θ_α is the upper $100\alpha\%$ point of the distribution of the largest root of a determinantal equation involving $\hat{\mathbf{B}}_D$ and $\hat{\mathbf{\Sigma}}$. This distribution has been called the Generalized Beta distribution and the 80%, 85%, 90%, 95% and 99% points have been tabulated by F. G. Foster and D. H. Rees (1957) for

$$\min(p, q-s) = 2, \quad \nu_1 = 5\,(2)\,41\,(10)\,101,\ 121,\ 161$$

and

$$\nu_2 = 2,\ 3\,(2)\,21;$$

by F. G. Foster (1957) for

$$\min(p, q-s) = 3, \quad \nu_1 = 4\,(2)\,194 \quad \text{and} \quad \nu_2 = 3\,(1)\,10;$$

and by F. G. Foster (1958) for

$$\min(p, q-s) = 4, \quad \nu_1 = 5\,(2)\,195, \quad \text{and} \quad \nu_2 = 4\,(1)\,11.$$

A shorter collection of 5% and 1% points for $\min(p, q-s) = 2\,(1)\,6$ is to be found in K. C. S. Pillai (1960). In the foregoing $\nu_1 = N-q$ and $\nu_2 = q-s$.

As a numerical example we will suppose that the 2 $(=p)$ vectors of β's which correspond to the observational ('explanatory') vectors $\mathbf{z}_2$ and $\mathbf{z}_3$ have been found significant at the 5% level and we will construct a 'contrast' from their estimates. Here $q-s = 2$ and

$$(\mathbf{ZZ}')_D^{-1} = \begin{bmatrix} 0{\cdot}0^5 49281 & 0{\cdot}0^4 52689 \\ 0{\cdot}0^4 52689 & 0{\cdot}0^2 16376 \end{bmatrix}$$

being the $(\mathbf{ZZ}')^{-1}$ of Ω with the first column and first row eliminated (since the weight category, and the general mean, were the only z-vectors left in ω). Furthermore, from $\hat{\mathbf{B}}_\Omega$,

$$\hat{\mathbf{B}}_D = \begin{bmatrix} 0{\cdot}02288 & -0{\cdot}01655 \\ 0{\cdot}13944 & 0{\cdot}36155 \end{bmatrix}$$

Purely to illustrate the procedure we choose

$$\mathbf{c}' = \{1 \quad -1\} \qquad \text{and} \qquad \mathbf{a}' = \{1 \quad 0\}$$

so that

$$\hat{\psi} = \{1 \quad 0\}\begin{bmatrix} 0{\cdot}02288 & -0{\cdot}01655 \\ 0{\cdot}13944 & 0{\cdot}36155 \end{bmatrix}\begin{bmatrix} 1 \\ -1 \end{bmatrix}$$

$$= [0{\cdot}02288 \quad -0{\cdot}01655]\begin{bmatrix} 1 \\ -1 \end{bmatrix} = 0{\cdot}03943$$

$$\mathbf{c}'(\mathbf{ZZ}')_D^{-1}\mathbf{c} = \{1 \quad -1\}\begin{bmatrix} 0{\cdot}0^5 49281 & 0{\cdot}0^4 52689 \\ 0{\cdot}0^4 52689 & 0{\cdot}0^2 16376 \end{bmatrix}\begin{bmatrix} 1 \\ -1 \end{bmatrix}$$

$$= [-0{\cdot}0^4 47761 \quad -0{\cdot}0^2 15849]\begin{bmatrix} 1 \\ -1 \end{bmatrix}$$

$$= 0{\cdot}0016327$$

Thus

$$\hat{\mathbf{\Sigma}}^* = 0{\cdot}0016327 \times (28)^{-1}\begin{bmatrix} 332{\cdot}48 & -117{\cdot}51 \\ -117{\cdot}51 & 886{\cdot}29 \end{bmatrix}$$

$$= \begin{bmatrix} 0{\cdot}019387 & -0{\cdot}0068521 \\ -0{\cdot}0068521 & 0{\cdot}051680 \end{bmatrix}$$

and

$$\mathbf{a}'\hat{\mathbf{\Sigma}}^*\mathbf{a}(N-q) = \{1 \quad 0\}\begin{bmatrix} 0{\cdot}019387 & -0{\cdot}0^2 68521 \\ -0{\cdot}0^2 68521 & 0{\cdot}051680 \end{bmatrix}\begin{bmatrix} 1 \\ 0 \end{bmatrix} \times 28$$

$$= [0{\cdot}019387 \quad -0{\cdot}0^2 68521]\begin{bmatrix} 1 \\ 0 \end{bmatrix} \times 28$$

$$= 0{\cdot}019387 \times 28 = 0{\cdot}54284$$

Now $\min(p, q-s) = \min(2, 2) = 2$ and turning to Foster and Rees' tables we have, for $\nu_1 = N-q = 28$ and $\nu_2 = q-s = 2$,

$$\theta_{0{\cdot}95} = \tfrac{1}{2}(0{\cdot}2771 + 0{\cdot}2604) \text{ approx.}$$
$$= 0{\cdot}2688$$

Hence, finally,

$$0{\cdot}03943-\left(\frac{0{\cdot}2688}{0{\cdot}7312}\times 0{\cdot}54284\right)^{1/2} \leqslant \psi \leqslant 0{\cdot}03943+(0{\cdot}19956)^{1/2}$$

i.e.,

$$-0{\cdot}40729 \leqslant \psi \leqslant 0{\cdot}48615$$

Applications

It will be appreciated that the foregoing technique is applicable when we are interested in explaining or predicting a number p of (multivariate Normally) correlated variates by means of q instrumental variables and covariates. Relatively few examples of its use are known to the writer and all of these, with the sole exception of the recent article by Smith *et al.* (*loc. cit.*), are based on $p = 2$, 3 or 4.

Thus two of the numerical illustrations (Tukey, 1949; Steel, 1955) provided a regression analysis of two years' crop yields ($p = 2$) on variety and location (or replicate) differences. Because of the design of the experiments orthogonality of the z-vectors permitted a substantial simplification in computation. These examples have been strongly criticized (Finney, 1956) on the grounds that such crop yields are not legitimate predictands. Bartlett's (1934) original illustration of the bivariate linear model escapes this criticism because it was used to 'explain' two (correlated) constituents of cereal yield in terms of block and treatment differences ($q = 15$).

A further two of the illustrations (Bartlett, 1939; Dutton, 1954) were concerned with the regression of calculated univariate regression *coefficients* (the 'linear', 'quadratic' and 'cubic' $\hat{\beta}$'s in the earlier paper, and the first two in the later) on a number of differences in the experimental set-up. In these cases p was thus 3 or 2 and the $\hat{\beta}$'s are multivariate Normal with invariant $\mathbf{\Sigma}$ provided the original samples had the same residual variances.

Two of the quadrivariate examples (Box, 1950; Dutton, 1954) were based on weight gains or losses, respectively, of a number of rats distinguished by their initial weights and, in the later illustration, by differences in experimental conditions. The only other illustration of a linear model with $p = 4$ is that of Bartlett (1947) which considered (in effect) the regression of four skull measurements on the times to which the four separate samples pertained. This material was later reworked by Rao (1952), Kendall (1957), Williams (1959), and Kshirsagar (1962).

The paucity of these examples and the small p-values involved has, we think, been due to computational difficulties and the consequent lack of incentive for biologists to learn the technique. Now that electronic machines can easily invert matrices of the order of 50 or more, and rapidly perform the subsequent matrix multiplications, biologists have a tool that should be useful to them in a number of fields of application.

Problems 5

1. Twenty-four rats were divided into two groups of twelve, each group consisting of 3 young females, 3 adult females, 3 young males and 3 adult males. One group was subjected to 500 r whole-body radiation and the other group was subjected to 600 r. The initial weights and the cumulative weight losses in grammes at 1, 3, 6 and 7 days after radiation were recorded for each rat in this 2^3 experiment (Dutton, 1954, *loc. cit.*).

A quadrivariate model Ω to 'explain' the weight losses by using nine parameters per variate resulted in

$$(N-q)\hat{\mathbf{\Sigma}}_\Omega = \begin{bmatrix} 95{\cdot}00 & 51{\cdot}60 & 51{\cdot}53 & 51{\cdot}79 \\ & 350{\cdot}23 & 103{\cdot}38 & 77{\cdot}12 \\ & & 339{\cdot}34 & 280{\cdot}87 \\ & & & 379{\cdot}12 \end{bmatrix}$$

while an ω that eliminated the β's for the treatment difference gave

$$(N-s)\hat{\mathbf{\Sigma}}_\omega = \begin{bmatrix} 95{\cdot}95 & 56{\cdot}67 & 45{\cdot}14 & 44{\cdot}21 \\ & 377{\cdot}40 & 69{\cdot}08 & 36{\cdot}48 \\ & & 382{\cdot}59 & 332{\cdot}17 \\ & & & 439{\cdot}92 \end{bmatrix}$$

Does the stronger radiation produce different weight losses from the weaker radiation?

2. Six pigs (3 hogs and 3 gilts) from each of five litters were given different protein concentrations in their diets (A = low, B = medium, C = high) over a 16-week experimental period. A second degree polynomial was fitted to the successive weights of each pig separately and the results are shown below in the form of three coefficients w, g and h denoting, respectively, the initial weight in pounds, the average growth rate in pounds per week, and half the rate of change of growth rate in pounds per week per week (Wishart, 1938). Fit a bivariate linear model to 'explain' each of g and h in terms of eleven parameters per variate (including the general mean and the interaction between treatment and sex) which summarize the experimental design, and test whether the parameters for dietary differences are significantly different from zero. In constructing Ω allow for a 'linear' and a 'quadratic' effect in dietary differences and test for each separately using the S-method. Summarize the results for a pig breeder interested in the best protein concentration.

Litter	Treatment	Sex	w	g	h
I	A	G	48	9·94	0·199
	B	G	48	10·00	0·146
	C	G	48	9·75	0·136
	A	H	38	9·52	0·209
	B	H	39	8·51	0·154
	C	H	48	9·11	0·139
II	A	G	32	9·48	0·194
	B	G	32	9·24	0·147
	C	G	28	8·66	0·181
	A	H	35	8·21	0·119
	B	H	38	9·95	0·178
	C	H	37	8·50	0·144
III	A	G	35	9·32	0·176
	B	G	41	9·34	0·182
	C	G	33	7·63	0·176
	A	H	41	9·32	0·176
	B	H	46	8·43	0·171
	C	H	42	8·90	0·155
IV	A	G	46	10·98	0·193
	B	G	46	9·68	0·213
	C	G	50	10·37	0·207
	A	H	48	10·56	0·126
	B	H	40	8·86	0·157
	C	H	42	9·51	0·130
V	A	G	32	8·82	0·199
	B	G	37	9·67	0·192
	C	G	30	8·57	0·189
	A	H	43	10·42	0·200
	B	H	40	9·20	0·192
	C	H	40	8·76	0·177

References in Chapter Five

BARTLETT, M. S. (1934) 'The vector representation of a sample.' *Proc. Camb. Phil. Soc.* **30**, 327–340.

BARTLETT, M. S. (1938) Further aspects of the theory of multiple regression.' *Proc. Camb. Phil. Soc.* **34**, 33–40.

BARTLETT, M. S. (1939) Discussion of J. Wishart's 'Statistical treatment of animal experiments'. *J. R. Statist. Soc.* B, **6**, 18–20.

BARTLETT, M. S. (1947) 'Multivariate analysis.' *J. R. Statist. Soc.* B, **9** 176–197.

BOX, G. E. P. (1950) 'Problems in the analysis of growth and wear curves.' *Biometrics*, **6**, 362–389.

DUTTON, A. M. (1954) 'Application of some multivariate analysis techniques to data from radiation experiments.' Chapter 5 of *Statistics and Mathematics in Biology* (Ed. O. Kempthorne *et al.*, Ames, Iowa).

FINNEY, D. J. (1956) 'Multivariate analysis and agricultural experiments.' *Biometrics* **12**, 67–71.

FOSTER, F. G. (1957–58) 'Upper percentage points of the generalized Beta distribution, II and III.' *Biometrika* **44**, 441–453; **45**, 492–503.

FOSTER, F. G. and REES, D. H. (1957) 'Upper percentage points of the generalized Beta distribution, I.' *Biometrika* **44**, 237–247.

KENDALL, M. G. (1957) *A Course in Multivariate Analysis*. London.

KSHIRSAGAR, A. M. (1962) 'A note on direction and collinearity factors in canonical analysis.' *Biometrika* **49**, 255–259.

PILLAI, K. C. S. (1960) *Statistical Tables for Tests of Multivariate Hypothesis.* Manila, P.I.

RAO, C. R. (1952) *Advanced Statistical Methods in Biometric Research*. New York.

ROY, S. N. (1957) *Some Aspects of Multivariate Analysis*. New York.

SMITH, H., GNANADESIKAN, R. and HUGHES, J. B. (1962) 'Multivariate analysis of variance (MANOVA).' *Biometrics* **18**, 22–41.

STEEL, R. G. D. (1955) 'An analysis of perennial crop data.' *Biometrics* **11**, 201–212.

TUKEY, J. W. (1949) 'Dyadic anova, an analysis of variance for vectors.' *Hum. Biol.* **21**, 65–110.

WILLIAMS, E. J. (1959) *Regression Analysis*. New York.

WISHART, J. (1938) 'Growth-rate determinations in nutrition studies with the bacon pig, and their analysis.' *Biometrika* **30**, 16–28.

CHAPTER SIX

Principal Components

The bivariate Normal

Let us now try to picture what a univariate Normal distribution $N(\mu, \sigma^2)$ becomes when we are concerned with $p = 2$ Normally distributed variates instead of one. To every pair of measurements (x_1, x_2) there will correspond a frequency of appearance – larger or smaller depending on the closeness of x_1 and x_2 to their means μ_1 and μ_2 – and in order to represent

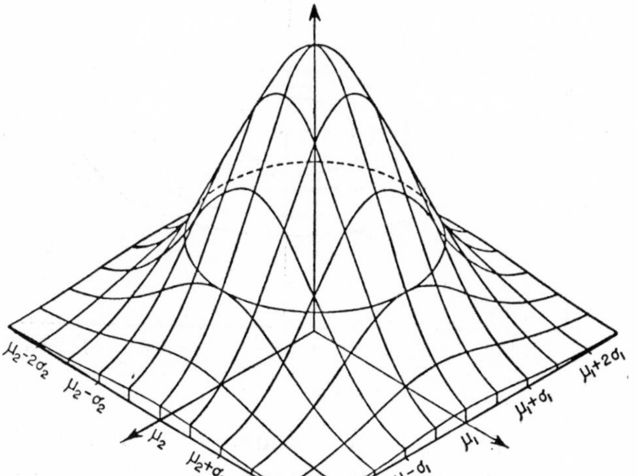

Fig. 1

this geometrically we must draw the frequency axis perpendicular to the plane of the X_1 and X_2 axes. The resulting solid model would look something like Fig. 1.

Notice particularly in this figure that for a given value of x_1, say $\mu_1 - \sigma_1$, namely the value one standard deviation below the mean, there is a Normal distribution of x_2 values. Similarly for a given fixed value of x_2 (e.g., $\mu_2 + \sigma_2$ in the figure).

If we look down on this 'hill' from directly above and work outwards from the (x_1, x_2)-origin – shown as (μ_1, μ_2) in the figure – we can draw in a set of closed contour lines on the (X_1, X_2) plane such that 50% of the whole frequency distribution lies inside the first line, 70% of it lies inside the second and so on. The result is a series of nested concentric ellipses in the (X_1, X_2) plane as shown in Fig. 2. If we were actually plotting a set of N pairs of measurements (x_1, x_2) we would find that about 50% of our 'dots' lay within the 50% contour, 70% of them lay within the 70% contour, and so on. This new method of representation is more important to us than that of Fig. 1, as we realize when we try to extend the foregoing ideas to $p = 3$ Normally distributed variates – a triplet, instead of a pair, of observations in each vector.

Now, what caused the elliptical shape of the probability (frequency) contours of Fig. 2 is that σ_1 and σ_2 have different values. These ellipses

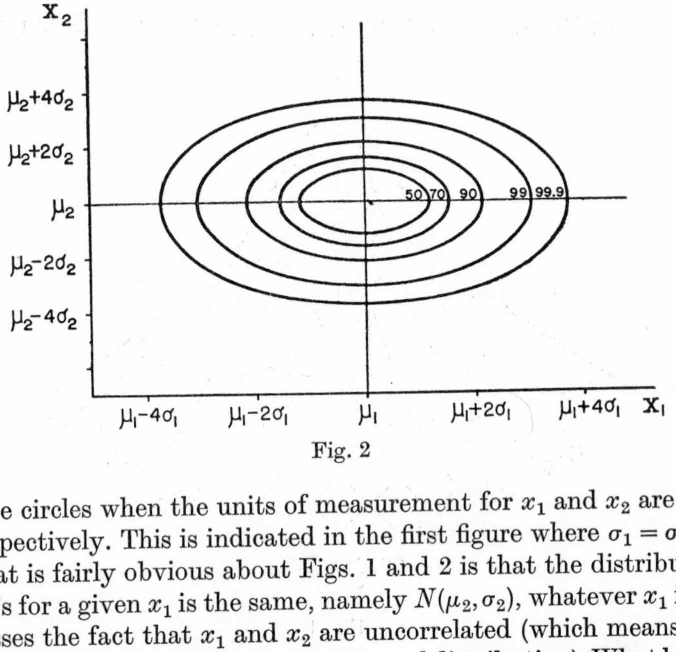

Fig. 2

become circles when the units of measurement for x_1 and x_2 are σ_1 and σ_2, respectively. This is indicated in the first figure where $\sigma_1 = \sigma_2$.

What is fairly obvious about Figs. 1 and 2 is that the distribution of the x_2's for a given x_1 is the same, namely $N(\mu_2, \sigma_2)$, whatever x_1 is. This expresses the fact that x_1 and x_2 are uncorrelated (which means 'independent' in the case of the bivariate Normal distribution). What happens when x_1 and x_2 are correlated is that the two axes of the ellipses in the second figure are rotated rigidly into a position depending on the covariance of x_1 and x_2. The result – with only one of the concentric equiprobability ellipses shown – is given in Fig. 3. Note that the actual pairs of correlated observations are measured along the horizontal and vertical axes, X_1 and X_2, respectively.

□□□ This type of rotation is tremendously important in what follows so it is worth trying to follow it through analytically. The original correlated measures x_1 and x_2 have been transformed into

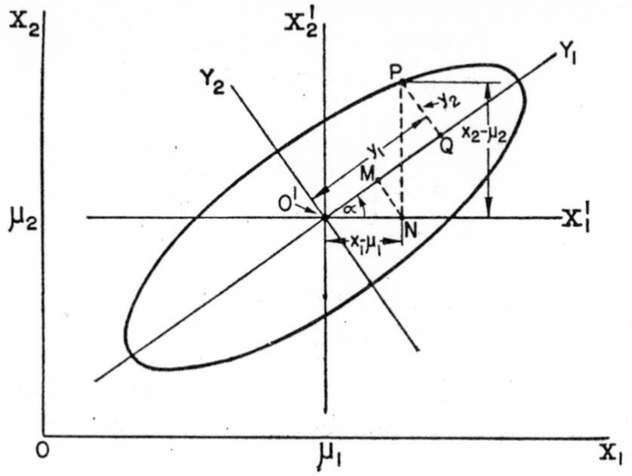

Fig. 3

new uncorrelated measures y_1 and y_2, respectively. Figure 3 shows that the point (x_1, x_2) on the ellipse becomes a point (y_1, y_2) where

$$y_1 = (x_1 - \mu_1)\cos\alpha + (x_2 - \mu_2)\sin\alpha$$

$$y_2 = -(x_1 - \mu_1)\sin\alpha + (x_2 - \mu_2)\cos\alpha$$

These relations should be clear from the figure. Thus, for example, $O'Q$ of length y_1 is made up of two parts:

(i) OM which is the projection of $O'N$, of length $x_1 - \mu_1$, on $O'Y_1$; and

(ii) MQ which is the projection of PN, of length $x_2 - \mu_2$, on $O'Y_1$.

The first of these projections is of length

$$(x_1 - \mu_1)\cos\alpha$$

and the second projection is of length

$$(x_2 - \mu_2)\sin\alpha$$

Figure 3 shows the angle α as that particular angle through which $O'X_1'$ must be rotated in order that its new position $O'Y_1$ coincides (in direction) with the major axis of the family of ellipses generated by the given bivariate Normal distribution. $O'Y_2$ then coincides with the minor axis of this family. Let us ignore this for the moment and discover some of the properties of a rigid rotation of the (X_1, X_2) axes through an arbitrary angle α.

In matrix notation this general linear transformation of the x's may be written

$$\mathbf{y} = \mathbf{A}(\mathbf{x} - \boldsymbol{\mu})$$

where

$$\mathbf{y} = \begin{bmatrix} y_1 \\ y_2 \end{bmatrix} \qquad \mathbf{x}-\boldsymbol{\mu} = \begin{bmatrix} x_1-\mu_1 \\ x_2-\mu_2 \end{bmatrix}$$

and

$$\mathbf{A} = \begin{bmatrix} \cos\alpha & \sin\alpha \\ -\sin\alpha & \cos\alpha \end{bmatrix}$$

We notice that

$$\begin{aligned} \mathbf{AA}' &= \begin{bmatrix} \cos\alpha & \sin\alpha \\ -\sin\alpha & \cos\alpha \end{bmatrix} \begin{bmatrix} \cos\alpha & -\sin\alpha \\ \sin\alpha & \cos\alpha \end{bmatrix} \\ &= \begin{bmatrix} \cos^2\alpha+\sin^2\alpha & -\cos\alpha\sin\alpha+\sin\alpha\cos\alpha \\ -\sin\alpha\cos\alpha+\cos\alpha\sin\alpha & \sin^2\alpha+\cos^2\alpha \end{bmatrix} \\ &= \begin{bmatrix} 1 & 0 \\ 0 & 1 \end{bmatrix} = \mathbf{I} \end{aligned} \qquad (1)$$

On pre-multiplying by $\mathbf{A}^{-1}$ we obtain

$$\mathbf{A}' = \mathbf{A}^{-1} \qquad (2)$$

It may also be confirmed that

$$\mathbf{A}'\mathbf{A} = \mathbf{I} \qquad (3)$$

so that

$$\mathbf{A} = (\mathbf{A}')^{-1} \qquad (4)$$

These four relations characterize a so-called *orthogonal* transformation of x's into y's. Note that by pre-multiplying the transformation by $\mathbf{A}^{-1}$ we obtain

$$\mathbf{A}^{-1}\mathbf{y} = \mathbf{I}(\mathbf{x}-\boldsymbol{\mu})$$

or, by relation (2),

$$\mathbf{A}'\mathbf{y} = \mathbf{x}-\boldsymbol{\mu}$$

This shows that the x's can be obtained from the y's just as easily as the y's from the x's.

Observe that although the trigonometrical functions of $\mathbf{A}$ emerge naturally from the axis-rotation of Fig. 3 we can write the orthogonality conditions in algebraic symbols. In this case we require

$$\mathbf{A} \equiv \begin{bmatrix} a_{11} & a_{12} \\ a_{21} & a_{22} \end{bmatrix}$$

to satisfy

$$\mathbf{AA}' = \mathbf{I}$$

Exercising due care with plus and minus signs the reader may verify for himself that the latter equality implies

$$a_{21} = \pm a_{12} \quad \text{and} \quad a_{22} = \mp a_{11}$$

the minus sign of a_{11} being used when $a_{21} = +a_{12}$.

Furthermore,

$$a_{11}^2 + a_{12}^2 = 1$$

Notice that these relations leave one element, say a_{11}, of **A** undetermined. This corresponds to the arbitrariness of α in the trigonometric transformation.

When we move to $p = 3$ we will abandon the trigonometric functions and consider transformations based on matrices with elements such that

$$\mathbf{AA'} = \mathbf{I}$$

As we have seen, this condition of orthogonality is not sufficient by itself to determine all the elements of **A**. Corresponding to the arbitrary angle α in the bivariate case, with three variables (x_1, x_2, x_3) there will be two such angles; with four variables, three angles; and so on. Shortly we will consider methods of eliminating the indeterminacy of an orthogonal transformation.

□ □ □ Finally, let us consider the expected value of the transformed vector **y** and the variance–covariance matrices of the x's and the y's. We have

$$\mathscr{E}\mathbf{y} = \mathbf{A}\mathscr{E}(\mathbf{x} - \boldsymbol{\mu}) = \mathbf{A0} = \mathbf{0}$$

where **0** is a two-component vector of zeros. Thus the variance–covariance matrix of the y's is given by $\mathscr{E}(\mathbf{yy}')$, a 2×2 matrix. Now

$$\begin{aligned}
\mathscr{E}(\mathbf{x} - \boldsymbol{\mu})(\mathbf{x} - \boldsymbol{\mu})' &= \mathscr{E}\begin{bmatrix} (x_1 - \mu_1)^2 & (x_1 - \mu_1)(x_2 - \mu_2) \\ (x_2 - \mu_2)(x_1 - \mu_1) & (x_2 - \mu_2)^2 \end{bmatrix} \\
&= \begin{bmatrix} \mathscr{E}(x_1 - \mu_1)^2 & \mathscr{E}(x_1 - \mu_1)(x_2 - \mu_2) \\ \mathscr{E}(x_1 - \mu_1)(x_2 - \mu_2) & \mathscr{E}(x_2 - \mu_2)^2 \end{bmatrix} \\
&\equiv \begin{bmatrix} \sigma_{11} & \sigma_{12} \\ \sigma_{21} & \sigma_{22} \end{bmatrix} \equiv \boldsymbol{\Sigma}
\end{aligned}$$

The notation for the elements of $\boldsymbol{\Sigma}$ has already been used in Chapter Five. It is occasionally useful to write $\sigma_{12}/(\sigma_{11}\sigma_{22})^{1/2} = \rho$ where ρ is, by definition, the correlation coefficient between x_1 and x_2.

Hence

$$\begin{aligned}
\mathscr{E}(\mathbf{yy}') &= \mathscr{E}\{\mathbf{A}(\mathbf{x} - \boldsymbol{\mu})(\mathbf{A}(\mathbf{x} - \boldsymbol{\mu}))'\} \\
&= \mathscr{E}\{\mathbf{A}(\mathbf{x} - \boldsymbol{\mu})(\mathbf{x} - \boldsymbol{\mu})'\mathbf{A}'\} \\
&= \mathbf{A}\{\mathscr{E}(\mathbf{x} - \boldsymbol{\mu})(\mathbf{x} - \boldsymbol{\mu})'\}\mathbf{A}' = \mathbf{A\Sigma A}'
\end{aligned}$$

The results of the foregoing mathematics may be summed up as follows. A rigid rotation of two rectangular coordinate axes, after suitable translation to a new centre of coordinates (if desired), is equivalent to a linear transformation of the original coordinate values (x_1, x_2). If the 2×2 matrix of coefficients applied to the vector $\mathbf{x}$ is $\mathbf{A}$ then $\mathbf{AA}' = \mathbf{I}$, and this implies that the four elements of $\mathbf{A}$ are related in a manner indicated on pp. 104–105. The variance–covariance matrix of the transformed variates (y_1, y_2) is given by $\mathbf{A\Sigma A}'$ where $\mathbf{\Sigma}$ is the variance–covariance matrix of the x's.

These results are perfectly general and will extend very easily to values of p in excess of 2. In fact the remaining material in this Part B relies heavily on the concept of a translation of the origin and a rigid rotation of rectangular coordinate axes.

Numerical illustration

Using the individual measurements of cranial lengths x_1, and breadths x_2, of mature specimens of *Rana esculenta* published in a study by Kauri, Reyment (1961) obtained the following results:

	♀♀	♂♂
N	35	14
$\hat{\mu}$	$\begin{bmatrix} 22{\cdot}860 \\ 24{\cdot}397 \end{bmatrix}$	$\begin{bmatrix} 21{\cdot}821 \\ 22{\cdot}843 \end{bmatrix}$
$\hat{\mathbf{\Sigma}}$	$\begin{bmatrix} 17{\cdot}683 & 20{\cdot}290 \\ 20{\cdot}290 & 24{\cdot}407 \end{bmatrix}$	$\begin{bmatrix} 18{\cdot}479 & 19{\cdot}095 \\ 19{\cdot}095 & 20{\cdot}755 \end{bmatrix}$

where $\hat{\mathbf{\Sigma}}$ was obtained by dividing the elements of the sample sums of squares and products (about the means) matrix by $N-1$.

We notice that the average lengths and breadths of the female crania are larger than the corresponding means for the male frogs. However, the sample variance–covariance matrices do not appear to be systematically different. We will later provide a statistical test of the homogeneity of two or more sample variance–covariance matrices but for the time being let us amalgamate the foregoing $\hat{\mathbf{\Sigma}}$'s into a single matrix. This is done by (i) multiplying throughout the first matrix by 34 (i.e., $N-1$), and throughout the second matrix by 13; (ii) aggregating the corresponding elements; and (iii) dividing the results by $34+13 = 47$. We thus obtain

$$\hat{\mathbf{\Sigma}} = \begin{bmatrix} 17{\cdot}903 & 19{\cdot}959 \\ 19{\cdot}959 & 23{\cdot}397 \end{bmatrix}$$

Notice that the covariance between x_1 and x_2 is substantial so that we have an illustration of Fig. 3 rather than of Fig. 2.

Now, suppose we want the angle α to be such that the new y-variables are uncorrelated. If we write λ_1 and λ_2 for the variances of y_1 and y_2, respectively, this means that the variance–covariance matrix of the y's is

$$\begin{bmatrix} \lambda_1 & 0 \\ 0 & \lambda_2 \end{bmatrix}$$

Hence

$$\mathbf{A\Sigma A'} = \begin{bmatrix} \lambda_1 & 0 \\ 0 & \lambda_2 \end{bmatrix} = \mathbf{\Lambda} \text{ (say)} \tag{5}$$

Post-multiplying relation (5) by $\mathbf{A}$ we obtain

$$\mathbf{A\Sigma} = \begin{bmatrix} \lambda_1 & 0 \\ 0 & \lambda_2 \end{bmatrix}\mathbf{A} = \begin{bmatrix} \lambda_1 & 0 \\ 0 & \lambda_2 \end{bmatrix}\begin{bmatrix} a_{11} & a_{12} \\ a_{21} & a_{22} \end{bmatrix}$$

where we have retained the general form for $\mathbf{A}$ since its particular form will emerge from what follows. Multiplying out the two pairs of matrices on the right- and left-hand sides, respectively,

$$\begin{bmatrix} a_{11}\sigma_{11}+a_{12}\sigma_{21} & a_{11}\sigma_{12}+a_{12}\sigma_{22} \\ a_{21}\sigma_{11}+a_{22}\sigma_{21} & a_{21}\sigma_{12}+a_{22}\sigma_{22} \end{bmatrix} = \begin{bmatrix} \lambda_1 a_{11} & \lambda_1 a_{12} \\ \lambda_2 a_{21} & \lambda_2 a_{22} \end{bmatrix}$$

i.e.,

$$\begin{bmatrix} a_{11}(\sigma_{11}-\lambda_1)+a_{12}\sigma_{21} & a_{11}\sigma_{12}+a_{12}(\sigma_{22}-\lambda_1) \\ a_{21}(\sigma_{11}-\lambda_2)+a_{22}\sigma_{21} & a_{21}\sigma_{12}+a_{22}(\sigma_{22}-\lambda_2) \end{bmatrix} = \mathbf{0} \tag{6}$$

where $\mathbf{0}$ is a 2×2 matrix of zero elements.

Two equations in two 'unknowns' a_{11} and a_{12} are obtained by equating the elements of the first rows on the left- and right-hand sides of equation (6). A theorem in algebra states that if a set of homogeneous linear equations (i.e., linear in a number of unknowns and with zeros on the right-hand sides) is to have a non-zero solution – and in this case if all four a's were zero we would have no transformation! – the determinant of the coefficients must be zero. That is to say

$$\begin{vmatrix} \sigma_{11}-\lambda_1 & \sigma_{21} \\ \sigma_{12} & \sigma_{22}-\lambda_1 \end{vmatrix} = 0 \tag{7}$$

Similar considerations hold for the second pair of equations (in a_{21} and a_{22}) in equation (6) so that

$$\begin{vmatrix} \sigma_{11}-\lambda_2 & \sigma_{21} \\ \sigma_{12} & \sigma_{22}-\lambda_2 \end{vmatrix} = 0 \tag{8}$$

Since σ_{11}, σ_{22} and $\sigma_{21}=\sigma_{12}$ are given quantities the only 'freedom' in satisfying the two relations (7) and (8) is provided by the possibility of varying λ_1 and λ_2. In other words, λ_1 and λ_2 are derivable from (7) and (8).

It is no coincidence that if we subsume both relations (7) and (8) under one, namely

$$\begin{vmatrix} \sigma_{11}-\lambda & \sigma_{21} \\ \sigma_{12} & \sigma_{22}-\lambda \end{vmatrix} = 0 = |\,\mathbf{\Sigma}-\lambda\mathbf{I}\,| \tag{9}$$

and attempt to solve for λ we obtain a quadratic in λ, namely

$$\lambda^2-(\sigma_{11}+\sigma_{22})\lambda+\sigma_{11}\sigma_{22}-\sigma_{12}\sigma_{21} = 0 \quad (10)$$

and a quadratic equation always has two roots (solutions)! These two roots, which we have written λ_1 and λ_2, are called the *eigenvalues* (or latent roots, or characteristic roots) of the variance–covariance matrix $\mathbf{\Sigma}$. As we have seen, they are obtained by solving the determinantal equation

$$|\mathbf{\Sigma}-\lambda\mathbf{I}| = 0$$

A very important consequence of (10) follows from the well-known algebraic theorem that if

$$x^2-bx+c = 0$$

then b is the sum of the roots of the quadratic in x, and c is their product. Applying this to equation (10)

$$\lambda_1+\lambda_2 = \sigma_{11}+\sigma_{22} \quad (11)$$

and

$$\lambda_1\lambda_2 = \sigma_{11}\sigma_{22}-\sigma_{12}^2 \quad (12)$$

Relation (11) states that the aggregate of the original variances $(\sigma_{11}, \sigma_{22})$ is preserved by the orthogonal transformation to *uncorrelated* variates. Since λ_1 is the variance of the variable y_1 measured along the major axis of the ellipse of Fig. 3 it is never less than – and may be much greater than – λ_2. Relation (12), on the other hand, shows that the product of the roots of (10) is obtained by putting $\lambda = 0$ on the left-hand side of (10); the result is $|\mathbf{\Sigma}|$, from (9).

Returning to the numerical example we will use the estimate $\hat{\mathbf{\Sigma}}$ of $\mathbf{\Sigma}$ and obtain estimated values of λ_1 and λ_2. We have

$$\begin{vmatrix} 17{\cdot}903-\lambda & 19{\cdot}959 \\ 19{\cdot}959 & 23{\cdot}397-\lambda \end{vmatrix} = 0$$

i.e.,

$$\lambda^2-41{\cdot}300\lambda+20{\cdot}5148 = 0$$

$$\lambda = (41{\cdot}300\pm\sqrt{1623{\cdot}631})/2 = 40{\cdot}797 \text{ or } 0{\cdot}503$$

Thus

$$\hat{\lambda}_1 = 40{\cdot}797 \quad\text{and}\quad \hat{\lambda}_2 = 0{\cdot}503$$

showing that almost 99% of the aggregate variability in x_1 and x_2 (as measured by the sum of their variances, 41·300) is represented in the first of the new y-variables. In fact Fig. 3 has become a very long and thin ellipse and we may conveniently ignore the variable y_2 since it adds very little to the knowledge provided by y_1.

But we have now obtained the (estimated) variances of the two new

y-variates without having determined the elements of the $\mathbf{A}$ matrix which satisfy the relations

$$\mathbf{AA'} = \mathbf{I} \tag{13}$$

and

$$\mathbf{A\Sigma A'} = \mathbf{\Lambda} \tag{14}$$

Post-multiplying (14) by $\mathbf{A}$ we have

$$\mathbf{A\Sigma} = \mathbf{\Lambda A} \tag{15}$$

Because of the diagonality of $\mathbf{\Lambda}$ the right-hand side of equation (15) is a matrix whose first row involves λ_1 and the elements only of the first row of $\mathbf{A}$. Similarly λ_2 is involved only with the elements of the second row of $\mathbf{A}$. Inserting our estimated variances and covariances the first pair of equations, deriving from the two elements of the first row of equation (15) and rewritten in the form of equation (6), is

$$\begin{aligned} (17{\cdot}903 - 40{\cdot}797)\,a_{11} \quad &+ 19{\cdot}959\,a_{12} &= 0 \\ 19{\cdot}959\,a_{11} \quad &+ (23{\cdot}397 - 40{\cdot}797)\,a_{12} &= 0 \end{aligned}$$

Both of these equations lead to the same result, namely

$$a_{12} = 1{\cdot}1471\,a_{11}$$

However, on introducing the equation provided bv the first element of relation (13) we see that

$$a_{11}^2 + a_{12}^2 = 1$$

i.e.,

$$a_{11}^2 + (1{\cdot}1471\,a_{11})^2 = 1$$

or

$$a_{11}^2 = 1/2{\cdot}3158 = 0{\cdot}4318 = (0{\cdot}6571)^2$$

Thus

$$a_{11} = 0{\cdot}6571 \quad \text{and} \quad a_{12} = 0{\cdot}7538$$

Although our comments earlier in this chapter show that we do not need to solve the equations involving λ_2 we note that they are

$$\begin{aligned} (17{\cdot}903 - 0{\cdot}503)\,a_{21} + \quad &19{\cdot}959\,a_{22} &= 0 \\ 19{\cdot}959\,a_{21} \quad &+ (23{\cdot}397 - 0{\cdot}503)\,a_{22} &= 0 \end{aligned}$$

supplemented by

$$a_{21}^2 + a_{22}^2 = 1$$

We have now found that

$$\mathbf{A} = \begin{bmatrix} 0{\cdot}6571 & 0{\cdot}7538 \\ -0{\cdot}7538 & 0{\cdot}6571 \end{bmatrix}$$

which, of course, satisfies the relation

$$\mathbf{AA'} = \mathbf{I}$$

When the new independent variates y have been obtained from the original variates x by means of **A** they are known as 'principal components'.

Now, if both samples of *Rana* had derived from a single bivariate Normal distribution the best estimate of its mean vector would be

$$\hat{\mu} = \frac{1}{49}\begin{bmatrix} 35 \times 22{\cdot}860 + 14 \times 21{\cdot}821 \\ 35 \times 24{\cdot}397 + 14 \times 22{\cdot}843 \end{bmatrix} = \begin{bmatrix} 22{\cdot}563 \\ 23{\cdot}953 \end{bmatrix}$$

With the upper end of this vector as origin we may rigidly rotate the coordinate axes into new positions determined by the orthogonal transformation matrix **A**. In fact the transformed vectors of sample means are given by

$$\bar{\mathbf{y}}^{(1)} = \mathbf{A}\begin{bmatrix} 22{\cdot}860 - 22{\cdot}563 \\ 24{\cdot}397 - 23{\cdot}953 \end{bmatrix} = \mathbf{A}\begin{bmatrix} 0{\cdot}297 \\ 0{\cdot}444 \end{bmatrix}$$

$$= \begin{bmatrix} 0{\cdot}5298 \\ 0{\cdot}0679 \end{bmatrix}$$

and

$$\bar{\mathbf{y}}^{(2)} = \mathbf{A}\begin{bmatrix} -0{\cdot}742 \\ -1{\cdot}110 \end{bmatrix} = \begin{bmatrix} -1{\cdot}3243 \\ -0{\cdot}1701 \end{bmatrix}$$

We have indicated that the second of the two y-variables is of little importance so we can summarize the positions of the females and males on our Y_1-axis by the figures:

♀♀	♂♂
$0{\cdot}5298 \pm 1{\cdot}0796$	$-1{\cdot}3243 \pm 1{\cdot}7071$

where, e.g., $1{\cdot}0796 = (\hat{\lambda}_1/35)^{1/2}$.

In fact we could test whether the difference between these two means is zero by calculating Student's t, namely

$$t = (0{\cdot}5298 + 1{\cdot}3243)/\{\hat{\lambda}_1(\tfrac{1}{35} + \tfrac{1}{14})\}^{1/2} = 0{\cdot}918$$

with $34 + 13 = 47$ degrees of freedom. This difference is not significant and males and females are thus indistinguishable by their cranial lengths and breadths.†

The trivariate Normal

We can summarize the foregoing discussion and at the same time extend it to $p = 3$, the trivariate Normal.

Suppose that the observations are made in triplets (e.g., the length,

† Owing to a numerical error, Reyment's (*loc. cit.*) test criterion is almost five times what it should be and he concludes that there is 'definite sexual dimorphism in the two dimensions studied'.

breadth and height of a turtle's carapace). Suppose that each of the three variates x_1, x_2, x_3 is distributed Normally; such an assumption is consonant with – though it does not require as a mathematical consequence – a trivariate Normal distribution of the variates as a group.

The trivariate Normal may be pictured by referring to Fig. 2, imagining the ellipses there shown to become solid (so-called) ellipsoids looking rather like a set of concentric, flattened (because the cross-section is elliptical, rather than circular) rugby footballs. The two reference axes OX_1, OX_2 now become three, OX_1, OX_2, OX_3, mutually perpendicular to one another.

The trivariate Normal distribution is completely specified by the vector of means

$$\boldsymbol{\mu} = \begin{bmatrix} \mu_1 \\ \mu_2 \\ \mu_3 \end{bmatrix}$$

and the 3×3 variance–covariance matrix

$$\boldsymbol{\Sigma} = \begin{bmatrix} \sigma_{11} & \sigma_{12} & \sigma_{13} \\ \sigma_{21} & \sigma_{22} & \sigma_{23} \\ \sigma_{31} & \sigma_{32} & \sigma_{33} \end{bmatrix} \qquad \sigma_{ij} = \sigma_{ji}$$

This means that a sample of N from a trivariate Normal universe may be replaced by the estimates of $\boldsymbol{\mu}$ and $\boldsymbol{\Sigma}$ derived therefrom. In other words, there is no more 'information' in the N trivariate Normal observations than there is in the sample mean vector and in the sample variance–covariance matrix.

Any linear transformation of the three variates x may be written

$$\underset{(3\times 1)}{\mathbf{y}} = \underset{(3\times 3)}{\mathbf{A}}\ \underset{(3\times 1)}{\mathbf{x}}$$

where, for convenience, we have assumed that each of the x's is measured from its universal mean. That is $\boldsymbol{\mu} = \mathbf{0}$, where $\mathbf{0}$ is a three-component vector of zeros. Such a linear transformation is equivalent to a *rigid* rotation of the three axes OX_1, OX_2, OX_3, if

$$\mathbf{AA}' = \mathbf{I} = \mathbf{A}'\mathbf{A} \qquad (1)'$$

A transformation satisfying relation (1)′ is called an orthogonal transformation.

The variance–covariance matrix of the transformed variates y is given by

$$\mathscr{E}(\mathbf{yy}') = \mathbf{A\Sigma A}'$$

and the three y-variates will be uncorrelated (which means independent in the Normal case) if this matrix is a diagonal matrix (i.e., one in which only the diagonal elements are non-zero). We then write

$$\mathbf{A\Sigma A'} = \mathbf{\Lambda} \tag{5)'$$

where

$$\mathbf{\Lambda} = \begin{bmatrix} \lambda_1 & 0 & 0 \\ 0 & \lambda_2 & 0 \\ 0 & 0 & \lambda_3 \end{bmatrix}$$

and it is convenient to arrange this matrix so that $\lambda_1 > \lambda_2 > \lambda_3$.

The values of the λ's may be determined as the three roots of the cubic equation

$$| \mathbf{\Sigma} - \lambda \mathbf{I} | = 0 \qquad (9)'$$

It can be proved that these three roots will always be non-negative (as they must be if they are to be variances). They may be obtained numerically by trial and error. That is to say, a value of λ is 'guessed' and the left-hand side of (9)′ is evaluated. Another value of λ is chosen and once again the left-hand side of (9)′ is evaluated. If these two evaluations have opposite signs then a root of equation (9)′ lies between the two chosen λ-values. By continually 'bracketing' a root in this manner an approximation to each of the three roots may be obtained. However, this laborious procedure may be avoided by using a computer routine for eigenvalues, or 'latent' roots, λ.

An important property of the set of three roots is that

$$\lambda_1 + \lambda_2 + \lambda_3 = \sigma_{11} + \sigma_{22} + \sigma_{33} \qquad (11)'$$

Since λ_1 is assumed to be the largest of the three roots we say that λ_1 'absorbs' a certain (hopefully, large) percentage of the 'total variance'. Another property of the roots is that

$$\lambda_1 \lambda_2 \lambda_3 = |\mathbf{\Sigma}| \qquad (12)'$$

Once the three λ's have been calculated the elements of

$$\mathbf{A} = \begin{bmatrix} \mathbf{a}_1' \\ \mathbf{a}_2' \\ \mathbf{a}_3' \end{bmatrix}$$

where the *eigenvector* $\mathbf{a}_i'$ is a three-component row vector ($i = 1, 2, 3$), may be obtained from the three sets of relations

$$\mathbf{a}_i' \mathbf{\Sigma} = \lambda_i \mathbf{a}_i' \qquad (i = 1, 2, 3) \qquad (15)'$$

each of which consists of three homogeneous, simultaneous equations for the three components of $\mathbf{a}'_i$. Because of the lack of 'constant' terms in (15)' these equations will have to be supplemented by the equation

$$\mathbf{a}'_i \mathbf{a}_i = 1$$

which is obtained from (1)'.

The result of these computations is to produce a linearly transformed set of variates y_1, y_2, y_3, called 'principal components' of the x's, which are mutually independent and can thus be considered separately. Because of the decreasing order of variance associated with the principal components it is possible that only one, or only two, of the variates is needed to summarize the whole of the variability and covariability of the original variates x_1, x_2, x_3. The objective of the analysis is thus *parsimonious summarization of a mass of observations*. In fact $3N$ measurements have been condensed into a mean vector $\mathbf{A}\hat{\mu}$ and three variances $\hat{\lambda}_1$, $\hat{\lambda}_2$, $\hat{\lambda}_3$, of which only one or two tell most of the story.

Numerical illustration

Jolicoeur and Mosimann (1960) measured the length, width and height in millimetres of the carapaces of 24 male and 24 female specimens of *Chrysemys picta marginata* collected in a single day from a small stagnant pond in the St. Lawrence Valley. The resulting mean vectors and variance–covariance estimates were:

$$
\begin{array}{cc}
\vec{\text{♂♂}} & \text{♀♀} \\
\end{array}
$$

$$
\hat{\mu} \quad
\begin{bmatrix} 113\cdot38 \\ 88\cdot29 \\ 40\cdot71 \end{bmatrix}
\qquad
\begin{bmatrix} 136\cdot00 \\ 102\cdot58 \\ 51\cdot96 \end{bmatrix}
$$

$$
\hat{\Sigma} \quad
\begin{bmatrix} 138\cdot77 & 79\cdot15 & 37\cdot38 \\ & 50\cdot04 & 21\cdot65 \\ & & 11\cdot26 \end{bmatrix}
\qquad
\begin{bmatrix} 451\cdot39 & 271\cdot17 & 168\cdot70 \\ & 171\cdot73 & 103\cdot29 \\ & & 66\cdot65 \end{bmatrix}
$$

A principal component analysis resulted in

$$
\hat{\lambda}' \qquad 195\cdot28 \qquad 3\cdot69 \qquad 1\cdot10 \qquad\qquad 680\cdot40 \qquad 6\cdot50 \qquad 2\cdot86
$$

and

$$
\mathbf{A}
\begin{bmatrix}
0\cdot84012 & 0\cdot49190 & 0\cdot22854 \\
-0\cdot48811 & 0\cdot86938 & -0\cdot07696 \\
-0\cdot23654 & -0\cdot04690 & 0\cdot97049
\end{bmatrix}
\begin{bmatrix}
0\cdot81263 & 0\cdot49549 & 0\cdot30676 \\
-0\cdot54537 & 0\cdot83213 & 0\cdot10062 \\
-0\cdot20540 & -0\cdot24907 & 0\cdot94645
\end{bmatrix}
$$

so that

$$
\mathbf{A}\hat{\mu} \quad
\begin{bmatrix} 147\cdot99 \\ 18\cdot28 \\ 8\cdot55 \end{bmatrix}
\qquad\qquad
\begin{bmatrix} 177\cdot28 \\ 16\cdot42 \\ -4\cdot31 \end{bmatrix}
$$

It is easy to check the correctness of these results. We note, for example, that

$\hat{\sigma}_{11}+\hat{\sigma}_{22}+\hat{\sigma}_{33}$	200·07	689·77
$\hat{\lambda}_1+\hat{\lambda}_2+\hat{\lambda}_3$	200·07	689·76
$\lvert\hat{\mathbf{\Sigma}}\rvert$	794·05	12639·89
$\hat{\lambda}_1\hat{\lambda}_2\hat{\lambda}_3$	792·64	12648·64

$$\mathbf{AA}' \quad \begin{bmatrix} 1{\cdot}00000 & -0{\cdot}00001 & 0{\cdot}00000 \\ & 1{\cdot}00000 & -0{\cdot}00001 \\ & & 1{\cdot}00000 \end{bmatrix} \quad \begin{bmatrix} 0{\cdot}99998 & -0{\cdot}00001 & 0{\cdot}00001 \\ & 0{\cdot}99999 & -0{\cdot}00001 \\ & & 0{\cdot}99999 \end{bmatrix}$$

When we try to interpret the results in biological terms we notice that 97·6% of the male variability, and 98·6% of the female, is accounted for in y_1, the first of the transformed variates. We could arbitrarily decide that this meant we could ignore the other two (uncorrelated) transformed variates but a more scientific approach would be as follows.

The statement that the second and third λ-values are 'small' should not be taken to mean that they are 'zero' because this implies that there is no variation at all along the second and third Y-axes. This, in turn, means that two of our original variates can be expressed in terms of the third – or, in other words, that we are dealing with a univariate Normal distribution. Such would be the case if, for example, x_1 was the animal's temperature expressed in Centigrade, x_2 was its temperature in Fahrenheit, and x_3 its temperature in Réaumur. Instead, we will consider the possibility that $\lambda_2 = \lambda_3 \neq 0$.

Revert, for the moment, to the case where $p = 2$ and the variates have equal variances and are uncorrelated. In such a situation Fig. 2 becomes a set of concentric circles and no particular rigid rotation of the co-ordinate axes is to be preferred to any other.

In the three-dimensional case if the rotation of the first axis along the principal axis of the ellipsoid leads to equality of λ_2 and λ_3 this means that OY_2 and OY_3, at right angles to one another, could be rotated arbitrarily in any direction in their plane which is perpendicular to the principal axis OY_1. There would be little point, and some danger, in interpreting a given set of vectors $\mathbf{a}_i'$ ($i = 2, 3$) deriving from a sample when, in fact, these are approximations to a situation in which no interpretation (or any interpretation) is valid.

We therefore consider the hypothesis $\lambda_2 = \lambda_3$ and test it by means of a criterion devised by Bartlett and slightly modified by Lawley (1956). We will state the test procedure for the general case where the first k eigenvalues are significant and it is desired to test whether the remaining

$p-k$ eigenvalues are equal to a common (unknown) value λ. Under these circumstances the quantity

$$\left[N-k-\frac{2(p-k)+7+2/(p-k)}{6}+\sum_{j=1}^{k}\left(\frac{\hat{\lambda}}{\hat{\lambda}_j-\hat{\lambda}}\right)^2\right]$$
$$\times\left[-\ln(\hat{\lambda}_{k+1}\hat{\lambda}_{k+2}\ldots\hat{\lambda}_p)+(p-k)\ln\hat{\lambda}\right] \quad (16)$$

where $\hat{\lambda}=(\hat{\lambda}_{k+1}+\hat{\lambda}_{k+2}+\ldots+\hat{\lambda}_p)/(p-k)$, is approximately distributed as chi-square with $(p-k-1)(p-k+2)/2$ degrees of freedom. Note that $p-k \geqslant 2$.

Inserting the 'male' numerical quantities

$$N = 24 \qquad k = 1 \qquad p = 3 \qquad \hat{\lambda} = (3{\cdot}69+1{\cdot}10)/2 = 2{\cdot}395$$

$$\left(\frac{\hat{\lambda}}{\hat{\lambda}_1-\hat{\lambda}}\right)^2 = \left(\frac{2{\cdot}395}{192{\cdot}885}\right)^2 = 0{\cdot}00015$$

$$-\ln(\hat{\lambda}_2\hat{\lambda}_3) = -\ln 4{\cdot}059 = -2{\cdot}302585\times 0{\cdot}60842 = -1{\cdot}40094$$

$$2\ln\hat{\lambda} = 4{\cdot}60517\times 0{\cdot}37931 = 1{\cdot}74679$$

and thus

$$(23-2+0{\cdot}00015)\times 0{\cdot}34585 = 7{\cdot}263$$

is a variate from chi-square with two degrees of freedom. This nearly reaches significance at the 2% level so we conclude that $\hat{\lambda}_2$ and $\hat{\lambda}_3$ cannot be replaced by $\hat{\lambda}=2{\cdot}395$. However, when we make similar calculations for the females we find $\chi_2^2=3{\cdot}444$ which is not significant even at the 5% level. In order to adopt a uniform interpretation for both sexes we aggregate the two independent chi-square values and obtain $\chi_4^2=10{\cdot}707$ which is significant at the 5% level.

We thus conclude that all three principal components should be used in the interpretation of the trivariate measurements on these painted turtles. As to that interpretation, Jolicoeur and Mosimann (*loc. cit.*) point out that in both males and females the first principal component is a measure of general size since the coefficients $\mathbf{a}_1'$ are all positive. On the other hand the second principal component is mainly a contrast of length and width since the coefficients of $\mathbf{a}_2'$ applied to these measurements are of opposite signs while the coefficient of height is relatively small. Finally, the last principal component contrasts length with height in males, and length plus width with height in females. The second and third principal components are thus indicators of 'shape'.

[See p. 200]

The *p*-variate Normal

The extension of the foregoing concepts and techniques to any integer value of $p > 3$ is immediate even though the p-dimensional geometry it envisages is an abstraction without concrete analogy in the real world.

However, while it was merely convenient with $p = 2$ or 3 to utilize an electronic computer for the calculation of the sums of squares and products involved in the variance–covariance matrix, and for the subsequent computation of the eigenvalues and eigenvectors, it is absolutely essential to use such a machine once p exceeds 4 or 5. For example, it was estimated by Holzinger and Harman (1941) that a principal component analysis of a (positive definite) symmetrical matrix of the twenty-fourth order would take over 1000 hours on a hand calculator. Such an analysis could be completed in about 10 minutes on an IBM 709 using 'double precision' arithmetic and in about one-fifth of that time on an IBM 7090.

Of course the purpose of such an analysis is not merely to demonstrate the capacities of the larger computers. It is, rather to take advantage of the relations

$$\lambda_1+\lambda_2+\ldots+\lambda_p = \sigma_{11}+\sigma_{22}+\ldots+\sigma_{pp}$$

with $\lambda_1 > \lambda_2 > \ldots > \lambda_p$, and the assumed p-variate Normality of the universe to reduce the N observational p-tuples to perhaps half a dozen uncorrelated Normal variates with estimates of their means and variances. Furthermore, it may be possible to interpret the elements of the first few row vectors of the transformation matrix $\mathbf{A}$ in a biologically meaningful manner. Examples of the technique and the subsequent biological evaluation are found in the references given at the end of this chapter.

As p becomes larger it is increasingly difficult to find features of the animal or plant that can be made in the same units (e.g., millimetres) as the other measurements. Let us, therefore, examine the effect on a principal components analysis of changing the scale of measurement of some of the variates. Write

$$\underset{(p\times 1)}{\mathbf{y}} = \underset{(p\times p)}{\mathbf{K}}\ \underset{(p\times 1)}{\mathbf{x}}$$

where $\mathbf{K}$ is a diagonal matrix of scale changes. Thus $\mathbf{K}' = \mathbf{K}$. If, for convenience, the original x's were all measured from their universal means

$$\mathscr{E}(\mathbf{y}) = \mathbf{K}\mathscr{E}(\mathbf{x}) = \mathbf{0}$$

and

$$\begin{aligned}\mathscr{E}(\mathbf{y}\mathbf{y}') &= \mathscr{E}\{(\mathbf{Kx})(\mathbf{Kx})'\} = \mathbf{K}\mathscr{E}(\mathbf{x}\mathbf{x}')\mathbf{K}' \\ &= \mathbf{K\Sigma K}' = \mathbf{K\Sigma K}\end{aligned}$$

Making a principal components analysis of the y-measurements thus means obtaining the p roots of the determinantal equation in ν

$$|\mathbf{K\Sigma K}-\nu\mathbf{I}| = 0$$

Pre-multiplying by $\mathbf{K}^{-1}$ and post-multiplying by $\mathbf{K}^{-1}$ within the determinant we obtain

$$|\mathbf{\Sigma} - \nu\mathbf{K}^{-2}| = 0$$

Clearly the p roots $\nu_1, \nu_2, \ldots \nu_p$ are not, in general, the same as the p roots $\lambda_1, \lambda_2, \ldots \lambda_p$ of

$$|\mathbf{\Sigma} - \lambda\mathbf{I}| = 0$$

Of course if all the diagonal components of $\mathbf{K}$ are the same constant the result is only to change the eigenvalues and eigenvectors by a given multiple. However, if the diagonal components of $\mathbf{K}$ differ, the changed roots produce a new transformation matrix $\mathbf{A}$. It is thus doubtful whether a principal component analysis should be applied to x-variates measuring different entities, e.g., a combination of lengths, weights and dichotomous variates (namely, variates scored as 0 or 1).

An attempt to avoid this difficulty has been made by standardizing all p variates by dividing each by its estimated standard deviation. This is equivalent to making

$$\mathbf{K} = \begin{bmatrix} \hat{\sigma}_1^{-1} & 0 & \ldots & 0 \\ 0 & \hat{\sigma}_2^{-1} & \ldots & 0 \\ \ldots & \ldots & \ldots & \ldots \\ 0 & 0 & \ldots & \hat{\sigma}_p^{-1} \end{bmatrix}$$

and thus

$$\mathbf{K}\hat{\mathbf{\Sigma}}\mathbf{K} = \begin{bmatrix} 1 & \hat{\rho}_{12} & \hat{\rho}_{13} & \ldots & \hat{\rho}_{1p} \\ \hat{\rho}_{21} & 1 & \hat{\rho}_{23} & \ldots & \hat{\rho}_{2p} \\ \ldots & \ldots & \ldots & \ldots & \ldots \\ \hat{\rho}_{p1} & \hat{\rho}_{p2} & \hat{\rho}_{p3} & \ldots & 1 \end{bmatrix}$$

where $\hat{\rho}_{ij}$ is the estimated correlation coefficient between x_i and x_j. One disadvantage of this is that if the original observations are p-variate Normal the new, standardized observations are not. Or rather, they are only approximately Normal as N becomes large. Another difficulty is that this device distorts the original measurements which, for example, took due account of the fact that the head is a portion of a much larger body. In the new standardized scale the head and the body lengths are on an equal footing.

Illustration

R. E. Blackith and M. I. Roberts (1958) report the collection of 375 grasshoppers of the genera *Omocestus* and *Stenobothrus* and the subsequent measurement of 10 characters on each. The resulting 10×10 variance–covariance matrix with 367 degrees of freedom (because the insects were subdivided into eight groups and the 'within group' sums of squares and products aggregated†) was calculated and printed (*loc. cit.*) with six decimal places. We made four different principal component analyses using these published variances and covariances.

The 10 characters used by Blackith and Roberts and their variances were:

	Variance
1. Number of antennal segments	0·553112
2. Width of head in mm	0·013786
3. Pronotal width in mm	0·014966
4. Hind femoral length in mm	0·254456
5. Hind femoral width in mm	0·019775
6. Prozonal length in mm	0·009744
7. Metazonal length in mm	0·019693
8. Front femoral width in mm	0·001464
9. Elytron length in mm	0·415498
10. Dry weight (in mg) of head, thorax and appendages with abdomen cut away	15·772500
Total	17·074994

It is clear that variate No. 10 will dominate the analysis and that this would not have occurred if the unit of weight had been one-tenth of a gram instead of a milligram. A similar arbitrariness exists with respect to the count made for variate No. 1.

As an alternative approach the 10×10 matrix of correlation coefficients was calculated (to five decimal places) from the original variance–covariance matrix with the following (three decimals only) results:

$$\begin{bmatrix}
1{\cdot}000 & 0{\cdot}272 & 0{\cdot}250 & 0{\cdot}288 & 0{\cdot}194 & 0{\cdot}165 & 0{\cdot}172 & 0{\cdot}082 & 0{\cdot}161 & 0{\cdot}269 \\
 & 1{\cdot}000 & 0{\cdot}790 & 0{\cdot}657 & 0{\cdot}525 & 0{\cdot}506 & 0{\cdot}488 & 0{\cdot}390 & 0{\cdot}420 & 0{\cdot}723 \\
 & & 1{\cdot}000 & 0{\cdot}570 & 0{\cdot}463 & 0{\cdot}434 & 0{\cdot}425 & 0{\cdot}390 & 0{\cdot}354 & 0{\cdot}636 \\
 & & & 1{\cdot}000 & 0{\cdot}510 & 0{\cdot}286 & 0{\cdot}482 & 0{\cdot}360 & 0{\cdot}550 & 0{\cdot}722 \\
 & & & & 1{\cdot}000 & 0{\cdot}314 & 0{\cdot}246 & 0{\cdot}369 & 0{\cdot}341 & 0{\cdot}657 \\
 & & & & & 1{\cdot}000 & 0{\cdot}306 & 0{\cdot}201 & 0{\cdot}195 & 0{\cdot}443 \\
 & & & & & & 1{\cdot}000 & 0{\cdot}185 & 0{\cdot}375 & 0{\cdot}419 \\
 & & & & & & & 1{\cdot}000 & 0{\cdot}326 & 0{\cdot}473 \\
 & & & & & & & & 1{\cdot}000 & 0{\cdot}509 \\
 & & & & & & & & & 1{\cdot}000
\end{bmatrix}$$

When we base a transformation to principal components on a correlation matrix it is advisable to bear in mind what happens when all the correlation coefficients have the same value, i.e., $\rho_{ij} = \rho$, all $i \neq j$. In that case the determinantal equation (9)′ has only two roots, $\lambda_1 = 1 + (p-1)\rho$

† Without, apparently, a prior test of homogeneity of the eight variance–co-variance matrices. Note that we use $N = 368$ in Bartlett's criterion (16).

and $\lambda_2 = 1-\rho$, of which the smaller has multiplicity $p-1$ (i.e., the $p-1$ smallest roots are all equal). This, in turn, means that we are in a 'spheroidal' situation where any set of rigid rotations of $p-1$ axes is as valid as any other. That is to say, after finding that $\mathbf{a}_1' = \{p^{-1/2}, p^{-1/2}, \ldots p^{-1/2}\}$ we may write $\mathbf{a}_i' = \{a_1, a_2, \ldots a_p\}$, $i = 2, 3, \ldots p$, where the components a_j are quite arbitrary subject to

$$\mathbf{a}_i' \mathbf{a}_i = 1 \quad \text{and} \quad \sum_{j=1}^{p} a_j = 0$$

This arbitrariness in the second (and later) components renders a principal component analysis of little interpretive value.

If we eliminate the first row and last column of elements in the above matrix we are eliminating variates 1 and 10 from the analysis. The result is a matrix of correlation coefficients the majority of which lie fairly close to 0·4, the average value of the 28 coefficients. We may thus forecast that the eigenvalues of this 8×8 correlation matrix will all be of a similar size and that there will be little hope of reducing the number of transformed variates to less than eight unless seven of them can be regarded as equal, in which case the analysis will break down.

To illustrate the foregoing remarks we made four principal component analyses:

(a) Using the whole 10×10 variance–covariance matrix as published (*loc. cit.*);
(b) Using the above 10×10 correlation matrix derived from the published variance–covariance matrix;
(c) Eliminating variates Nos. 1 and 10 and using the resulting 8×8 variance–covariance matrix;
(d) Operating on the 8×8 correlation matrix that corresponds to the variance–covariance matrix of (c).

The resulting eigenvalues are shown below together with a statement indicating which may be considered equal according to Bartlett's criterion (16).

We may draw the following conclusions from this and the earlier principal component analyses:

(i) A principal component analysis should not be based on variates measured on different scales. Completely different types of result are obtained when the units are changed or when the variates are standardized (e.g., (a) and (b) below).
(ii) The first eigenvalue usually accounts for a considerable proportion of the total variability. In fact this proportion is 94·2%, 48·0%, 73·2%, and 49·5%, respectively, in the four illustrative analyses.

Eigenvalue no.	(a)	(b)	(c)	(d)
1	16·0867	4·8018	0·5487	3·9587
2	0·5157	0·9703	0·1449	0·9236
3	0·3206	0·8984	0·0211	0·8669
4	0·1031	0·8521	0·0149	0·6340
5	0·0172	0·6365	0·0095	0·5876
6	0·0121	0·5869	0·0064	0·5012
7	0·0095	0·4992	0·0027	0·3386
8	0·0063	0·3507	0·0011	0·1894
9	0·0027	0·2178		
10	0·0011	0·1863		
Totals	17·0750	10·0000	0·7493	8·0000
Equality	—†	9, 10	—	—

(iii) Although there is no evidence that the smaller eigenvalues are equal in the above analyses nevertheless 90% or more of the total variability is accounted for by one, seven, two and six, respectively, of the transformed variates. This is a general type of result when p is large.

(iv) The variance–covariance matrix provides a simpler summarization than the correlation matrix in the case of the eight variates measured on the same scale. It is reasonable to suppose that with such a single scale the use of the direct measurements (rather than their standardized equivalents) is biologically more meaningful.

(v) When most of the covariances are positive the first eigenvector will generally have only positive components and will thus be an indicator of general 'size'. This suggests that the biologist will require at least two eigenvectors – which, it will be remembered, are uncorrelated – to summarize his data. In case (c) the first two eigenvalues account for 92·6% of the total variability even though the remaining six all provide additional information about the eight measured variates.

(vi) If the off-diagonal elements of a correlation matrix are approximately equal the interpretive value of a principal components analysis of this matrix is dubious.

It is thus important to remember the limitations of a principal components summarization. Nevertheless the procedure does give the biologist a useful tool in the study of multivariate data.

† Blackith's published principal component analysis of the (a)-matrix (1960) includes a statement of the first three eigenvalues (which agree with those shown above). He gives the corresponding eigenvectors but does not normalize them, i.e., $\mathbf{a}_i'\mathbf{a}_i \neq 1$. His statement that the last three eigenvalues are not significantly different does not agree with our own conclusion.

Problems 6

1. Twenty-three female specimens of the Cretaceous ostracod *Ovocytheridea apiformis* sp. nov. were measured as to their carapace lengths and breadths in millimetres and provided the following estimated mean vector and variance–covariance matrix (Reyment, 1960)

$$\hat{\boldsymbol{\mu}} = \begin{bmatrix} 0{\cdot}954 \\ 0{\cdot}502 \end{bmatrix} \qquad \hat{\boldsymbol{\Sigma}} = \frac{1}{22}\begin{bmatrix} 0{\cdot}0069 & 0{\cdot}0025 \\ 0{\cdot}0025 & 0{\cdot}0032 \end{bmatrix}$$

Using a desk machine find the eigenvalues of the matrix $\hat{\boldsymbol{\Sigma}}$ and use them to determine the orthogonal transformation matrix **A** which will result in a pair of uncorrelated variates y_1 and y_2.

2. Sewall Wright (1954) computed the following statistics based on bone measurements of 276 White Leghorns.

	$\hat{\mu}$ in mm	$\hat{\sigma}$ in mm	$(\hat{\rho}_{ij})$					
Skull length	38·77	1·26	1·000	0·584	0·615	0·601	0·570	0·600
Skull breadth	29·81	0·93		1·000	0·576	0·530	0·526	0·555
Humerus length	74·64	2·84			1·000	0·940	0·875	0·878
Ulna length	68·74	2·73				1·000	0·877	0·886
Femur length	77·34	3·20					1·000	0·924
Tibia length	114·84	5·00						1·000

Make a principal components analysis of this correlation matrix and test for the 'significance' of the minor axes using criterion (16) with the first of its two factors replaced by N (because the approximation is much cruder for correlation matrices). Interpret biologically (so far as possible) the significant rows of **A**.

Repeat the procedure (including the interpretation) using $\hat{\boldsymbol{\Sigma}}$ instead of the correlation matrix. Discuss the differences in the two approaches.

3. Apply the procedures of Problem **2** to the following statistics calculated (by approximate methods) from the natural logarithms of eight

	$\hat{\mu}$	$\hat{\sigma}$	$(\hat{\rho}_{ij})$							
P_0	4·7837	0·2268	1·0000	0·9933	0·9926	0·9785	0·9752	0·9722	0·9674	0·9601
C_0	4·1224	0·1978		1·0000	0·9973	0·9835	0·9805	0·9768	0·9719	0·9675
M_0	4·2575	0·1972			1·0000	0·9869	0·9831	0·9796	0·9746	0·9661
M_1	4·4249	0·1582				1·0000	0·9975	0·9947	0·9905	0·9697
M_2	4·3079	0·1515					1·0000	0·9979	0·9949	0·9708
M_3	4·1604	0·1459						1·0000	0·9973	0·9723
M_4	3·9591	0·1410							1·0000	0·9694
L	5·1403	0·1106								1·0000

measurements (in millimetres) made on 303 specimens of *Maïa squinado* (Teissier, 1955).

In the foregoing table the following designations have been used: L is the overall length of the cephalothorax; M_0, C_0 and P_0 are the three principal parts of the claw, namely the meropod, the carpopod and the propod; while M_1, M_2, M_3 and M_4 denote the four meropods of the locomotor feet numbered from the front to the rear.

References to the Use of Principal Components in Biological Articles

BLACKITH, R. E. (1960) 'A synthesis of multivariate techniques to distinguish patterns of growth in grasshoppers.' *Biometrics* **16**, 28–40.

BURT, C. and BANKS C. (1947) 'A factor analysis of body measurements for British adult males.' *Ann. Eugen., Lond.* **13**, 238–256.

CASSIE, R. M. (1963) 'Multivariate analysis in the interpretation of numerical plankton data.' *N.Z.J. Sci.* **6**, 36–59.

GOODALL, D. W. (1954) 'Objective methods for the classification of vegetation. III: An essay in the use of factor analysis.' *Aust. J. Bot.* **2**, 304–324.

JOLICOEUR, P. and MOSIMANN, J. E. (1960) 'Size and shape variation in the painted turtle. A principal component analysis.' *Growth* **24**, 339–354.

KRAUS, B. S. and CHOI, S. C. (1958) 'A factorial analysis of the prenatal growth of the human skeleton.' *Growth* **22**, 231–242.

PEARCE, S. C. and HOLLAND, D. A. (1960) 'Some applications of multivariate methods in Botany.' *Appl. Statist.* **9**, 1–7.

PEARCE, S. C. and HOLLAND, D. A. (1961) 'Analyse des composantes, outil en recherche biometrique.' *Biom.-Prax.* **2**, 159–177.

TEISSIER, G. (1955) 'Allométrie de taille et variabilité chez *Maïa squinado*.' *Arch. Zool. exp. gén.* **92**, 221–264.

WILLIAMSON, M. H. (1961) 'An ecological survey of a Scottish herring fishery. Part IV: Changes in the plankton during the period 1949 to 1959.' *Bull. Mar. Ecol.* **5**, 208–229.

Other References in Chapter Six

BLACKITH, R. E. and ROBERTS, M. I. (1958) 'Farbenpolymorphismus bei einigen Feldheuschrecken.' *Z. Vererbungs.* **89**, 328–337.

HOLZINGER, K. J. and HARMAN, H. H. (1941) *Factor Analysis*. Chicago, Ill.

LAWLEY, D. N. (1956) 'Tests of significance for the latent roots of covariance and correlation matrices.' *Biometrika* **43**, 128–136.

REYMENT, R. A. (1960) 'Studies on Nigerian Upper Cretaceous and Lower Tertiary *Ostracoda*. Part 1: Senonian and Maestrichtian *Ostracoda*.' *Stockh. Contr. Geol.* **7**.

REYMENT, R. A. (1961) 'A note on geographical variation in European *Rana*.' *Growth* **25**, 219–227.

WRIGHT, S. (1954) 'The interpretation of multivariate systems.' Chapter 2 of *Statistics and Mathematics in Biology*, Kempthorne, O. *et al.*, Eds., Ames, Iowa.

CHAPTER SEVEN

Canonical Analysis

In the preceding chapter we discussed a useful method of summarizing a sample of N observational p-tuples. This summary sometimes led to a useful interpretation in biological terms but was, in turn, subject to some arbitrariness of decision between competing scales of measurement.

We now consider the case where several samples of N p-variate observations are available and where it is desired to compare or, better, arrange the samples in some biologically meaningful manner. The method we will develop here is due essentially to M. S. Bartlett (1938) and has the great advantage that the p-variates may be different types of measurements (e.g., one a length, another a volume, a third a score, and so on) since changing the scale of any one of them throughout all the samples does not affect the results. Furthermore, experience suggests that the number of 'dimensions' required for a comparison of groups of p-variate observations will generally be less than that required for the summarization of any one of the groups by principal component analysis.

Let us, therefore, consider h p-variate Normal universes represented by samples. Making use of the concepts developed in Chapter Six we may think of the first universe as represented by a swarm of points in p-dimensional (Cartesian) space centred at a point characterized by a vector $\boldsymbol{\mu}^{(1)}$ and dispersed about this point in an ellipsoidal shape characterized by the variance–covariance matrix $\boldsymbol{\Sigma}^{(1)}$.

Using the same p variates the second universe is represented in this p-dimensional space by a second swarm of points which overlaps the first swarm to a greater or lesser extent. The second vector of means, $\boldsymbol{\mu}^{(2)}$, will in all probability lie at some non-zero distance away from $\boldsymbol{\mu}^{(1)}$ and the spread of the swarm, measured by $\boldsymbol{\Sigma}^{(2)}$, may or may not differ from that of the first swarm.

Similar ideas apply to the other $h-2$ p-variate universes. Once we have assumed that the p-variates are distributed Normally the whole swarm of points of any universe is replaceable by the vector $\boldsymbol{\mu}^{(l)}$ and the matrix $\boldsymbol{\Sigma}^{(l)}$, $l = 1, 2, \ldots h$. Our object is thus to obtain a clear picture of the mutual positions and orientations of these p-variate (Normal) swarms. As usual, we think in terms of $p = 3$ and argue inductively for $p > 3$.

The first point to make is that if, for example, $\boldsymbol{\Sigma}^{(1)} \neq \boldsymbol{\Sigma}^{(2)}$ the corresponding ellipsoids will be oriented in different directions whether or not the mean vectors $\boldsymbol{\mu}^{(1)}$ and $\boldsymbol{\mu}^{(2)}$ coincide. Standardization of each variate by division by that sample's corresponding estimated standard deviation merely changes $\mathbf{\Sigma}^{(l)}$ into the correlation matrix $\mathbf{\Sigma}_R^{(l)}$, say, and does not secure isoclinic ellipsoids unless $\mathbf{\Sigma}_R^{(l)} = \mathbf{\Sigma}_R^{(m)}$, all $l \neq m$.

Now, when the biologist talks of comparing two subspecies of ducks, for example, he is thinking in terms of the means (or modes) of the various features he can observe. He is not generally visualizing the possible differences in dispersion about these means, but he probably believes that the correlation (considered intuitively) between any two features is approximately the same in each species. Unfortunately there is presently no criterion available to test the hypothesis

$$\mathbf{\Sigma}_R^{(1)} = \mathbf{\Sigma}_R^{(2)} = \ldots = \mathbf{\Sigma}_R^{(h)} \tag{1}$$

though the hypothesis

$$\mathbf{\Sigma}^{(1)} = \mathbf{\Sigma}^{(2)} = \ldots = \mathbf{\Sigma}^{(h)} \tag{2}$$

can be tested relatively easily and accurately if all samples are p-variate Normal. Nevertheless if relation (2) is rejected mainly because of differences in the variances, and relation (1) is accepted by inspection of the corresponding elements of $\mathbf{\Sigma}_R^{(l)}$, $l = 1, 2, \ldots h$, the technique we will develop below – based on the truth of (2) – is still correctly applicable without actual standardization of the variates.

If neither (1) nor (2) holds the comparison we are hoping to facilitate is nugatory. Our first step will thus be to describe a test of the hypothesis (2) which will be independent of the mean vectors $\boldsymbol{\mu}^{(1)}, \boldsymbol{\mu}^{(2)}, \ldots \boldsymbol{\mu}^{(h)}$.

The test for equality of variance–covariance matrices

If $\hat{\mathbf{\Sigma}}^{(l)}$ is the estimated variance–covariance matrix of the lth sample, supposed to be based on N_l observational p-tuples, then (analogously with the univariate case) the set of $\hat{\mathbf{\Sigma}}^{(l)}$, $l = 1, 2, \ldots h$, is to be compared with the estimate of $\mathbf{\Sigma}$ based on all $N = N_1 + N_2 + \ldots + N_h$ observations, each sample's deviations being taken from its own estimated mean vector $\hat{\boldsymbol{\mu}}^{(l)}$. Thus the element $\hat{\sigma}_{ij}$ of $\hat{\mathbf{\Sigma}}$ is obtained from

$$\hat{\sigma}_{ij} = (N-h)^{-1} \sum_{l=1}^{h} (N_l - 1)\,\hat{\sigma}_{ij}^{(l)} \qquad (i, j = 1, 2, \ldots p)$$

where $\hat{\sigma}_{ij}^{(l)}$ is the estimate of σ_{ij} derived from the N_l observations of the lth sample.

Now the comparison of matrices is conveniently effected by comparing their determinants. We will write

$$|\hat{\mathbf{\Sigma}}^{(l)}| \equiv \hat{\Delta}_l \qquad (l = 1, 2, \ldots h)$$

and

$$|\hat{\mathbf{\Sigma}}| \equiv \hat{\Delta}$$

then the required test criterion is

$$-2\left[1-\left\{\sum_{l=1}^{h}\frac{1}{N_l-1}-\frac{1}{N-h}\right\}\frac{2p^2+3p-1}{6(p+1)(h-1)}\right]\ln\left\{\frac{\prod_{l=1}^{h}\hat{\Delta}_l^{(N_l-1)/2}}{\hat{\Delta}^{(N-h)/2}}\right\} \qquad (3)$$

and is distributed approximately as chi-square with $(h-1)p(p+1)/2$ degrees of freedom.

In illustration let us reconsider the Jolicoeur and Mosimann (1960) data on male and female painted turtles (p. 113). Comparing the $\mathbf{\Sigma}$-values for the two sexes we have

$$h = 2, \qquad p = 3, \qquad N_1 = N_2 = 24,$$
$$\hat{\Delta}_1 = 794{\cdot}05, \qquad \hat{\Delta}_2 = 12639{\cdot}89$$

and

$$\hat{\mathbf{\Sigma}} = \begin{bmatrix} 295{\cdot}08 & 175{\cdot}16 & 103{\cdot}04 \\ & 110{\cdot}86 & 62{\cdot}47 \\ & & 38{\cdot}96 \end{bmatrix}$$

so that

$$\hat{\Delta} = 5567{\cdot}03$$

Hence the value of the criterion (3) is

$$-2\left[1-\left(\frac{2}{23}-\frac{1}{46}\right)\frac{26}{24}\right]\ln\left\{\frac{(794{\cdot}05)^{11{\cdot}5}(12639{\cdot}89)^{11{\cdot}5}}{(5567{\cdot}03)^{23}}\right\}$$
$$= -2\times 0{\cdot}92935\times 2{\cdot}302585(33{\cdot}34825+47{\cdot}17005-86{\cdot}14934)$$
$$= 24{\cdot}09981\dagger$$

and, on the null hypothesis, is a χ^2 variate with six degrees of freedom. This is highly significant and we conclude that the sizes and/or orientations of the concentric density ellipsoids are different for the two sexes.

As mentioned, we may eliminate differences in ellipsoid sizes by changing $\mathbf{\Sigma}$ to $\mathbf{\Sigma}_R$ and in this case we get

$$\hat{\mathbf{\Sigma}}_R \quad \overset{\text{Males}}{\begin{bmatrix} 1{\cdot}0000 & 0{\cdot}9498 & 0{\cdot}9456 \\ & 1{\cdot}0000 & 0{\cdot}9121 \\ & & 1{\cdot}0000 \end{bmatrix}} \qquad \overset{\text{Females}}{\begin{bmatrix} 1{\cdot}0000 & 0{\cdot}9740 & 0{\cdot}9726 \\ & 1{\cdot}0000 & 0{\cdot}9655 \\ & & 1{\cdot}0000 \end{bmatrix}}$$

The sexual dimorphism is quite marked and militates against the use of the techniques now to be developed. However, in the particular case where $h = 2$ special methods are available to deal with the situation $\mathbf{\Sigma}^{(1)} \neq \mathbf{\Sigma}^{(2)}$ (Reyment, 1962).

† This is less than half the value calculated in Reyment (1962).

Comparison of h multivariate universes

Let us suppose that we have accepted the hypothesis expressed by (2), namely that $\mathbf{\Sigma}^{(l)} = \mathbf{\Sigma}^{(m)}$, all l, m. Our purpose is now to develop a method of comparing the h universal mean vectors $\boldsymbol{\mu}^{(l)}$, $l = 1, 2, \ldots h$, which will make clear the relative closeness of any pair of vectors and will exhibit any ordering of these vectors if such exists.

At first sight the most promising approach is to transform the original p axes of coordinates to the *common* principal component axes. For this purpose we would calculate the common estimate of the variance–covariance matrix, namely

$$\hat{\mathbf{\Sigma}} = (N-h)^{-1}\left\{\sum_{l=1}^{h} (N_l-1)\,\hat{\mathbf{\Sigma}}^{(l)}\right\} \tag{4}$$

and proceed to find its eigenvalues and eigenvectors (principal axes). The h transformed mean vectors could then be compared quite easily since they each consist of p variate values which are mutually independent and which are ranked in descending order of variance size. A notable advantage of this method would be that if the last $p-k$ of the p eigenvalues are deemed to be equal (by using (16) of Chapter Six) the comparison of the h mean vectors would be limited to the first k components (dimensions).

The foregoing procedure has been formalized by Rao (1952) utilizing the concept of the distances between the end-points of the h standardized mean vectors in k-dimensional space. Each of the $\binom{h}{2}$ distances between these standardized means (where, for example, the ith component of any mean vector is standardized by dividing it by $\lambda_i^{1/2}$) is calculated from the formula

$$D^2 = d_1^2 + d_2^2 + \ldots + d_p^2 \tag{5}$$

where d_i is the difference between the ith components of the specified pair of (estimated) mean vectors, and D is the required distance. The mutual relationships connecting the distances between any group of two, three, four, ... of the h samples then form the basis of a subdivision into 'group constellations' describing the affinities of the h samples.

Besides computing the $\binom{h}{2}$ distances Blackith (1960) recommends the calculation of the angles between any pair of vectors joining the end of a given mean vector to the ends of two other mean vectors in other groups. If $d_1, d_2, \ldots d_p$ are defined as above and if $\delta_1, \delta_2, \ldots \delta_p$ be the corresponding values measured from the first mean to a third sample mean, the angle between the two 'distance' vectors is θ given by

$$\cos\theta = (d_1\delta_1 + d_2\delta_2 + \ldots + d_p\delta_p)/D_1 D_2 \tag{6}$$

D_1 and D_2 being the two distances under consideration.

Although this technique has been used in a number of biological articles (see references at end of chapter†) it suffers from the following defect. Suppose that p is fairly large and that $h = 2$. Clearly the whole of the comparison between the two universes is contained in the one-dimensional comparison of two points on a straight line, these points representing the ends of the two (estimated) mean vectors. In other words, the ends of the mean vectors can be compared in a single dimension, a sub-space of the original p-dimensional space.

This argument extends quite simply to the case where $h = 3$ and the comparison of the three p-dimensional mean vectors is made by plotting the projections of the ends of the three vectors on a plane (i.e., in two dimensions). This plotting is conveniently done by using a pair of axes at right angles to one another. In general, the comparison of a number of universes $h < p$ should be made in a space of $h-1$ dimensions rather than a space of p dimensions.

Another criticism of the 'distance' technique is that its rationalization depends heavily on all p variates being measured in the same units. Furthermore, while no published analyses exist for $p > 10$ our modest experience with these larger values suggests that the dimensionality of the D^2 comparisons with biometric data will generally be greater (even for $h > p$) than that of the method now to be described.

Finally, we mention that a recent paper by N. A. Rahman (1962) indicates that a simple approximate method of calculating D^2-values which bypasses the computation of the principal axes, is an accurate substitute for the exact procedure.

Canonical axes

Consider the whole p-dimensional sample space of the h universes. Since the variance–covariance matrices of these universes are supposed equal we could represent the differences between the mean vectors of these h universes by a model of the form

$$\underset{(N\times p)}{\mathbf{X}} = \underset{(N\times h)}{\mathbf{Z}'}\;\underset{(h\times p)}{\mathbf{B}} + \underset{(N\times p)}{\mathbf{E}} \tag{7}$$

which is entirely analogous to (1) of Chapter Five. Note that h rows of $\mathbf{B}$ are needed to account for (i) the general mean of the whole sample of N, where $N = N_1 + N_2 + \ldots + N_h$, and (ii) the $h-1$ differences between the means of the h different universes. Observe that the variance–covariance matrix of each of the p-variate sample 'errors' is $\mathbf{\Sigma}_\Omega$, and that this common value for the h universes is estimated by relation (4).

† The paper by Sokal (1961) advocates a measure which ignores the correlations between the p variates and uses relation (5) on the original mean vectors. This 'distance' will be very different from the distance determined by Rao's suggested method and may well lead to unjustifiable conclusions.

Our objective is to derive a transformation

$$\mathbf{y} = \mathbf{C}\mathbf{x} \tag{8}$$

which will emphasize the differences between the means of the h universes (or, rather, of their sample estimates). For example, if $h = 2$ the first axis along which to measure the first component of $\mathbf{y}$ should be the line joining the ends of the two mean vectors of these universes, or a line parallel thereto. When $h = 3$ this first axis should pass as closely as possible through all three points representing the ends of the mean vectors of the three universes.

Now, suppose that the Ω-model represented by (7) is replaced by a model in which the $\mathbf{B}$ matrix has degenerated into a single row of β's representing the p means of all the N x's. We may write the estimated variance–covariance matrix of this model as $\hat{\mathbf{\Sigma}}_\omega$. Our interest then resides in the variance–covariance matrix of the difference between the models Ω and ω for this measures the variability 'between' the h groups. It is estimated by

$$\{(N-1)\hat{\mathbf{\Sigma}}_\omega - (N-h)\hat{\mathbf{\Sigma}}_\Omega\}/(h-1)$$

or, in the notation of (5) of Chapter Five by

$$\{\hat{\mathbf{B}}'_\Omega \mathbf{Z}\mathbf{Z}'\hat{\mathbf{B}}_\Omega - \hat{\mathbf{B}}'_\omega \mathbf{Z}\mathbf{Z}'\hat{\mathbf{B}}_\omega\}/(h-1) \tag{9}$$

We will write this matrix as $\hat{\mathbf{\Xi}}$.

We note, in passing, that both Ω and ω could include other explanatory z-vectors. For example, we could compare the means of h groups of fish after allowing for age differences by a linear or quadratic function.

In Chapter Six we found a transformation

$$\mathbf{y} = \mathbf{A}\mathbf{x}$$

such that the first axis was inclined along the direction of the maximum variability among the N p-dimensional observations. Then a second axis, at right angles to the first, was inclined in the direction of the next greatest variability. And so on. The procedure we developed could have been arrived at by determining the components of $\mathbf{a}'_1$, the first row of $\mathbf{A}$, so as to maximize the variance of the first transformed variate, namely $\mathbf{a}'_1\mathbf{x}$. This variance is $\mathbf{a}'_1\mathbf{\Sigma}\mathbf{a}_1$ and (since an unrestricted maximization leads to infinite components for $\mathbf{a}'_1$) we would have had to require the maximization to be subject to $\mathbf{a}'_1\mathbf{a}_1 = 1$. We would then have arrived at the same conclusion as we did on p. 112 namely that the components of $\mathbf{a}'_1$ were obtainable from the p equations (15)', viz.,

$$\mathbf{a}'_1\mathbf{\Sigma} = \lambda_1\mathbf{a}'_1$$

where λ_1 is the largest root of

$$|\mathbf{\Sigma} - \lambda\mathbf{I}| = 0$$

This process could then have been repeated for $\mathbf{a}_2'$ corresponding to the second largest root λ_2; and so on.

We may express the whole series of maximizations in matrix form by saying that we were required to maximize the variance–covariance matrix

$$\mathbf{A\Sigma A'}$$

subject to

$$\mathbf{AA'} = \mathbf{I}$$

and that the elements of $\mathbf{A}$ were then determinable by the p sets of p equations

$$\mathbf{A\Sigma} = \mathbf{\Lambda A} \qquad \text{(15) of Chapter Six}$$

where the elements of the diagonal matrix $\mathbf{\Lambda}$ are obtained as the p roots of the determinantal equation

$$|\mathbf{\Sigma} - \lambda\mathbf{I}| = 0 \qquad \text{(9) of Chapter Six}$$

Although we can no longer think in terms of directed ellipsoids of variation and their major and minor axes our present problem is nevertheless quite similar. We wish our first transformed axis to be inclined in the direction of the greatest variability 'between' the h means; then our second axis, at right angles to the first, is to be inclined in the direction of next greatest variability and so on. And whereas in our first problem we operated with a $(p \times p)$ variance–covariance matrix $\mathbf{\Sigma}$ we are now using a $(p \times p)$ variance–covariance matrix $\mathbf{\Xi}$.

Our transformation matrix $\mathbf{C}$ of (8) thus has a first row $\mathbf{c}_1'$ which maximizes the 'between' variance of y_1, namely

$$\mathbf{c}_1' \mathbf{\Xi} \mathbf{c}_1 \tag{10}$$

Since this maximization would lead to infinite components for $\mathbf{c}_1'$ we must impose restrictions on the transformation matrix. We thus stipulate that the variates $\mathbf{y}$ shall be uncorrelated (i.e., have zero covariances) and each be of unit variance. But the variance–covariance matrix of the transformation (8) is $\mathbf{C\Sigma}_\Omega\mathbf{C}'$ and we are thus making the maximization of (10) subject to

$$\mathbf{c}_1' \mathbf{\Sigma}_\Omega \mathbf{c}_1 = 1 \tag{11}$$

□□□ The foregoing requirements for the first row of $\mathbf{C}$ can be extended to the second, third, ... rows so that we may finally state our problem in matrix form as follows: To maximize the 'between' variance–covariance matrix

$$\mathbf{C\Xi C'} \qquad (10)'$$

subject to

$$\mathbf{C\Sigma}_\Omega\mathbf{C}' = \mathbf{I} \qquad (11)'$$

Now we may write (11)′ in the form

$$(\mathbf{C}\boldsymbol{\Sigma}_{\Omega}^{1/2})(\boldsymbol{\Sigma}_{\Omega}^{1/2}\mathbf{C}') = (\mathbf{C}\boldsymbol{\Sigma}_{\Omega}^{1/2})(\mathbf{C}\boldsymbol{\Sigma}_{\Omega}^{1/2})' = \mathbf{I}$$

and putting

$$\mathbf{C}\boldsymbol{\Sigma}_{\Omega}^{1/2} = \mathbf{F}$$

this is the same as

$$\mathbf{F}\mathbf{F}' = \mathbf{I} \tag{12}$$

With this notation (10)′ becomes

$$(\mathbf{C}\boldsymbol{\Sigma}_{\Omega}^{1/2})\boldsymbol{\Sigma}_{\Omega}^{-1/2}\boldsymbol{\Xi}\boldsymbol{\Sigma}_{\Omega}^{-1/2}(\mathbf{C}\boldsymbol{\Sigma}_{\Omega}^{1/2})'$$
$$= \mathbf{F}(\boldsymbol{\Sigma}_{\Omega}^{-1/2}\boldsymbol{\Xi}\boldsymbol{\Sigma}_{\Omega}^{-1/2})\mathbf{F}' \tag{13}$$

The maximization of (13) subject to (12) is now on all fours with the maximization of a matrix $\mathbf{A}\boldsymbol{\Sigma}\mathbf{A}'$ subject to $\mathbf{A}\mathbf{A}' = \mathbf{I}$.

Our procedure is then as follows. We first find the roots $\nu_1 > \nu_2 > \nu_3 > \ldots$ of the pth degree polynomial equation

$$|\boldsymbol{\Sigma}_{\Omega}^{-1/2}\boldsymbol{\Xi}\boldsymbol{\Sigma}_{\Omega}^{-1/2} - \nu\mathbf{I}| = 0 \tag{14}$$

and then determine the p components of $\mathbf{f}_i'$ the ith row of $\mathbf{F}$ from the p equations

$$\mathbf{f}_i'\boldsymbol{\Sigma}_{\Omega}^{-1/2}\boldsymbol{\Xi}\boldsymbol{\Sigma}_{\Omega}^{-1/2} = \nu_i\mathbf{f}_i' \tag{15}$$

supplemented by the relation

$$\mathbf{f}_i'\mathbf{f}_i = 1 \tag{16}$$

Finally, we find the p components of $\mathbf{c}_i'$ from the p relations

$$\mathbf{c}_i'\boldsymbol{\Sigma}_{\Omega}^{1/2} = \mathbf{f}_i' \tag{17}$$

Although this is formally correct we may telescope some of these steps by substituting (17) into (15) and (16). That is to say, having found the roots $\nu_1, \nu_2 \ldots$ of (14) we obtain the p components of $\mathbf{c}'$ from

$$\mathbf{c}_i'\boldsymbol{\Xi}\boldsymbol{\Sigma}_{\Omega}^{-1/2} = \nu_i\mathbf{c}_i'\boldsymbol{\Sigma}_{\Omega}^{1/2}$$

or, better, on post-multiplication by $\boldsymbol{\Sigma}_{\Omega}^{1/2}$, from

$$\mathbf{c}_i'\boldsymbol{\Xi} = \nu_i\mathbf{c}_i'\boldsymbol{\Sigma}_{\Omega} \tag{15$'$}$$

supplemented by

$$\mathbf{c}_i'\boldsymbol{\Sigma}_{\Omega}\mathbf{c}_i = 1 \tag{16$'$}$$

When carrying out the numerical computations it is unnecessary to make the final divisions by $N-h$ or by $h-1$ to obtain $\hat{\boldsymbol{\Sigma}}_{\Omega}$ or $\hat{\boldsymbol{\Xi}}$, respectively. Writing **P** ('parametric') for the matrix of sums of squares and products 'between' the h groups, and **W** for the corresponding 'within' matrix we have

$$\mathbf{P} = (h-1)\hat{\boldsymbol{\Xi}} \quad \text{and} \quad \mathbf{W} = (N-h)\hat{\boldsymbol{\Sigma}}_{\Omega}$$

and (14) becomes, after division of every element of both its $(p \times p)$ matrices by $(N-h)/(h-1)$,

$$|\mathbf{W}^{-1/2}\mathbf{P}\mathbf{W}^{-1/2} - \phi\mathbf{I}| = 0 \qquad (14)''$$

where

$$\phi = \frac{h-1}{N-h}\nu$$

Then (15)′ and (16)′ become

$$\mathbf{c}_i'\mathbf{P} = \phi_i \mathbf{c}_i'\mathbf{W} \qquad (15)''$$

and

$$\mathbf{c}_i'\mathbf{W}\mathbf{c}_i = N-h \qquad (16)''$$

respectively.

As we might suspect, the p roots of (14) are only distinguishable when $p \leqslant h-1$. When $p > h-1$ there are $(p-\overline{h-1})$ zero roots and $h-1$ distinguishable other roots. It is very important to remember this when (14)″ is treated as a polynomial equation in ϕ.

The special case $h = 2$

In order to clarify the procedure adumbrated in general terms above let us reconsider Kauri's frog data used to illustrate the transformation to principal axes in Chapter Six.

Our first step is to put the numerical results into the form of a multivariate ANOVA. We obtain from the vectors $\hat{\boldsymbol{\mu}}$ and the single composite matrix $\hat{\boldsymbol{\Sigma}}$ given on p. 106:

	d.f.	Length	Breadth
P matrix	1	10·80	16·15
		16·15	24·15
W matrix	47	841·45	938·09
$= 47\hat{\boldsymbol{\Sigma}}_\Omega$		938·09	1099·65
'Total' matrix	48	852·25	954·24
$= 48\hat{\boldsymbol{\Sigma}}_\omega$		954·24	1123·80

The **W** matrix is obtained directly from $\hat{\boldsymbol{\Sigma}}$ while, e.g., the sum of squares of cranial lengths 'between' the sexes is

$$\frac{(35 \times 22{\cdot}860)^2}{35} + \frac{(14 \times 21{\cdot}821)^2}{14} - \frac{(35 \times 22{\cdot}860 + 14 \times 21{\cdot}821)^2}{49}$$

As a matter of interest we may calculate the ratio of the determinants $|47\hat{\boldsymbol{\Sigma}}_\Omega|$ to $|48\hat{\boldsymbol{\Sigma}}_\omega|$, namely $45{,}288/47{,}185 = 0{\cdot}9598$. Reference to

p. 92 shows that this is a $U_{2,1,47}$ variate (since $p = 2$, $q = 2$, $s = 1$ and $N = 49$) which has the same distribution as a $U_{1,2,46}$ variate. Hence

$$\frac{1-0{\cdot}9598}{0{\cdot}9598} \times \frac{46}{2} = 0{\cdot}963$$

is an F-variate with 2 and 46 degrees of freedom. This is far from being significant, indicating that there is no sexual dimorphism (as already concluded on p. 110). Let us, however, proceed as if such dimorphism had been proved to exist.

For computations on a desk calculator the determinantal equation (14)″ is best pre- and post-multiplied by $\mathbf{W}^{1/2}$ giving

$$|\mathbf{P}-\phi\mathbf{W}| = 0 \qquad (14)'''$$

We have stated that when $p > h-1$ (as it is here) this equation in ϕ will only have $h-1$ non-zero roots. This is easily verified here ($h = 2$) when we insert the numerical values of $\mathbf{P}$ and $\mathbf{W}$ into the quadratic (14)‴, for the term not involving ϕ (namely $10{\cdot}80 \times 24{\cdot}15 - 16{\cdot}15 \times 16{\cdot}15$) vanishes. Let us, however, proceed less directly in a manner that extends quite easily to larger values of p.

Let us write

$$\Delta(\phi) \equiv |\mathbf{P}-\phi\mathbf{W}| \equiv \phi^{p-1}(\alpha+\beta\phi)$$

where α and β are determinable coefficients. Then the equation

$$\Delta(\phi) = 0$$

has the solution $\phi = 0$ ($p-1$ roots) or $\alpha+\beta\phi = 0$. The required non-zero root is thus $\phi_1 = -\alpha/\beta$.

Suppose we evaluate $\Delta(\phi)$ at $\phi = \pm 1$; this provides two points on the curve of $\Delta(\phi)$ and enables us to calculate ϕ_1.

In this case

$$\alpha+\beta = \Delta(1) = |\mathbf{P}-\mathbf{W}| = \begin{vmatrix} -830{\cdot}65 & -921{\cdot}94 \\ -921{\cdot}94 & -1075{\cdot}50 \end{vmatrix} = 43390{\cdot}7$$

$$-\alpha+\beta = \Delta(-1) = |\mathbf{P}+\mathbf{W}| = \begin{vmatrix} 852{\cdot}25 & 954{\cdot}24 \\ 954{\cdot}24 & 1123{\cdot}80 \end{vmatrix} = 47184{\cdot}6$$

and thus

$$\phi_1 = -\frac{\alpha}{\beta} = \frac{3793{\cdot}9}{90575{\cdot}3} = 0{\cdot}041887$$

There is thus only one vector of c-components and, since $p = 2$, there are two components in the vector. Writing these two components as a and b the two equations of (15)′ are

$$[a \quad b]\begin{bmatrix} 10{\cdot}80 & 16{\cdot}15 \\ 16{\cdot}15 & 24{\cdot}15 \end{bmatrix} = (0{\cdot}041887)\,[a \quad b]\begin{bmatrix} 841{\cdot}45 & 938{\cdot}09 \\ 938{\cdot}09 & 1099{\cdot}65 \end{bmatrix}$$

Both lead to the same result so we write only the first one, namely

$$10{\cdot}80a + 16{\cdot}15b = 352{\cdot}46a + 392{\cdot}94b$$

i.e.,

$$341{\cdot}66a + 376{\cdot}79b = 0 \quad \text{or} \quad a = -1{\cdot}10282b$$

To supplement this (16)′ provides

$$[a \quad b]\begin{bmatrix} 841{\cdot}45 & 938{\cdot}09 \\ 938{\cdot}09 & 1099{\cdot}65 \end{bmatrix}\begin{bmatrix} a \\ b \end{bmatrix} = 47$$

i.e.,

$$841{\cdot}45a^2 + 1876{\cdot}18ab + 1099{\cdot}65b^2 = 47$$

and substituting for a this becomes

$$53{\cdot}943b^2 = 47$$

whence

$$b = \pm 0{\cdot}93343$$

and thus

$$a = \mp 1{\cdot}02941$$

Note that we may choose whether to make b positive or negative but that the sign of a is then fixed as the opposite to what we have chosen.

The canonical transformation (8) has thus become

$$y = [1{\cdot}02941 \quad -0{\cdot}93343]\mathbf{x}$$

This axis clearly passes through the origin of the x-measurements since

$$\mathbf{x} = \begin{bmatrix} 0 \\ 0 \end{bmatrix} \text{ implies } y = 0$$

It is, however, more helpful to move the origin of the y's to the grand mean of all $N = 49$ observations. This may be done by writing

$$y = [1{\cdot}02941 \quad -0{\cdot}93343]\begin{bmatrix} x_1 - 22{\cdot}563 \\ x_2 - 23{\cdot}953 \end{bmatrix}$$

On this axis the mean of the female cranial measurements is

$$\bar{y}_{♀} = [1{\cdot}02941 \quad -0{\cdot}93343]\begin{bmatrix} 0{\cdot}297 \\ 0{\cdot}444 \end{bmatrix} = -0{\cdot}1087$$

while

$$\bar{y}_{♂} = [1{\cdot}02941 \quad -0{\cdot}93343]\begin{bmatrix} -0{\cdot}742 \\ -1{\cdot}110 \end{bmatrix} = 0{\cdot}2723$$

The single linear function $\mathbf{c}_1'(\mathbf{x}-\bar{\mathbf{x}})$ obtained when $h = 2$ is known as the discriminant function. Having calculated $\mathbf{c}_1'$ and $\bar{\mathbf{x}}$ from two (large) groups of observations a new observational vector $\mathbf{x}$ may be inserted into the discriminant function and the observational unit allocated to one or other of the two groups (universes) depending on whether the result is positive or negative, respectively.

Numerical illustration with $p = 3$

Reeve (1941) has published a series of trivariate measurements on skulls of six collections (four subspecies) of *Tamandua tetradactyla.* The features chosen for measurement were: (i) the basal length excluding the premaxilla, (ii) the occipito-nasal length, and (iii) the greatest length of the nasals. Considering only complete sets of measurements and using the common logarithms of Reeve's published individual millimetre measurements, the following mean vectors and variance–covariance matrices were obtained by hand and checked on Yale's IBM 709.

Subspecies	Locality	No. of skulls	Mean vector	'Within' variance–covariance matrix		
instabilis	Sta. Marta,	21	2·054	0·0002091	0·0001916	0·0003106
	Colombia		2·066		0·0001902	0·0003106
			1·621			0·0008108
chapadensis	Minas Geraes,	6	2·097	0·0007920	0·0008437	0·0010458
	Brazil		2·100		0·0008961	0·0011404
			1·625			0·0014915
chapadensis	Matto Grosso,	9	2·091	0·0004916	0·0004271	0·0003486
	Brazil		2·095		0·0003973	0·0003239
			1·624			0·0005544
chapadensis	Sta. Cruz,	3	2·099			
	Bolivia		2·102		$N-1$ less than p	
			1·643			
chiriquensis	Panama	4	2·092	0·0000865	0·0000745	0·0001418
			2·110		0·0001249	0·0002962
			1·703			0·0008450
mexicana	Mexico	5	2·099	0·0003103	0·0002738	0·0004547
			2·107		0·0002637	0·0004653
			1·671			0·0012275
All six		48	2·077	0·0003245	0·0003040	0·0003914
			2·086		0·0003077	0·0004080
			1·636			0·0008608

Inspection of the mean vectors suggests that all six groups of skulls could well derive from the same universe while the opposite conclusion could be drawn from a visual comparison of the five 'within sample' variance–covariance matrices.

In fact, the value of the criterion (3) (omitting the fourth sample) was found to be 22·588 which is below the expected value of chi-square with $4 \times 3 \times 4/2$, i.e., 24 degrees of freedom. Furthermore, the determinants of the 'within' and 'total' sums of squares and products matrices, which were obtained from the matrices shown below, are $0{\cdot}0^6 17276$ and $0{\cdot}0^5 11766$, respectively, so that $U_{3,5,42} = 0{\cdot}1468$ and

$$-42{\cdot}5 \times 2{\cdot}302585 \times (\bar{1}{\cdot}16673) = 81{\cdot}54$$

which is a highly significant χ^2 variate with $3 \times 5 = 15$ degrees of freedom.

$$\mathbf{W} = \begin{bmatrix} 0{\cdot}0136309 & 0{\cdot}0127691 & 0{\cdot}0164379 \\ & 0{\cdot}0129227 & 0{\cdot}0171355 \\ & & 0{\cdot}0361519 \end{bmatrix}$$

$$\mathbf{P} = \begin{bmatrix} 0{\cdot}0200211 & 0{\cdot}0174448 & 0{\cdot}0130811 \\ & 0{\cdot}0158517 & 0{\cdot}0150665 \\ & & 0{\cdot}0306818 \end{bmatrix}$$

This verifies that there are differences between the mean vectors of the six groups and we now proceed to compare them along canonical axes.

The first step is to find the $p = 3$ roots of (14)″ or (14)‴. Actually the computer program uses the former equation (see Appendix I) while the desk machine computations were made on (14)‴. In both cases the roots were found to be

$$\phi_1 = 2{\cdot}4001 \qquad \phi_2 = 0{\cdot}9050 \qquad \phi_3 = 0{\cdot}0515$$

Now the third of these roots is very small in comparison with the other two. While it could be ignored as contributing little to the comparison of the groups a more suitable procedure is to test whether all the roots after the kth, say, can be given zero values. Bartlett's (1947) test of this hypothesis is based on the fact that

$$\{(N-1)-(p+h)/2\} \ln \left\{ \prod_{j=k+1}^{m} (1+\phi_j) \right\} \tag{17}$$

is approximately a chi-square variable with $(p-k) \times (h-k-1)$ degrees of freedom when $\phi_{k+1} = \phi_{k+2} = \ldots = \phi_m = 0$. Here m is the smaller of p and $h-1$.

An attractive feature of this test is that it analyses the U-variate which tests the overall significance of the differences between the group mean vectors. Since

$$\{U_{p,h-1,N-h}\}^{-1} = \prod_{j=1}^{m} (1+\phi_j)$$

Bartlett's criterion can be used to decide how many of the roots contribute significantly to the significant U-value the calculation of which preceded the canonical analysis.

In the case we are considering we have:

j	ϕ	$\prod_j^m (1+\phi_j)$	$42{\cdot}5 \ln \prod_j^m (1+\phi_j)$	d.f. for χ^2
1	2·4001	6·8108	81·54	15
2	0·9050	2·0031	29·52	8
3	0·0515	1·0515	2·13	3

This shows that the first two roots are significant.

The final step is to express the mean vectors of the six groups in canonical form. While measuring from the grand mean of all 48 observational triplets would locate the origin in the 'middle' of the six points

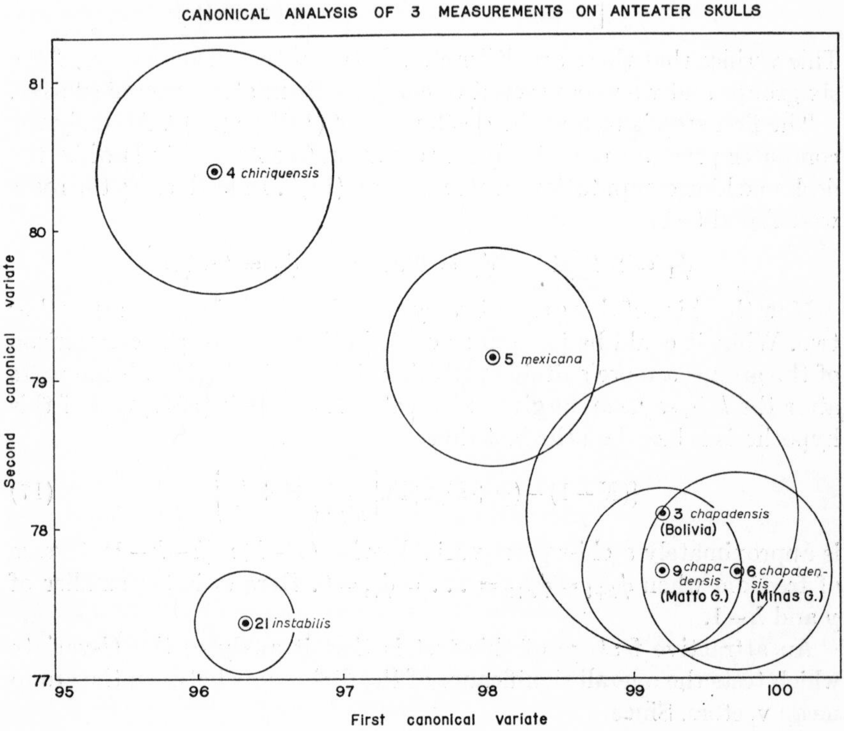

Fig. 4

we find it more convenient to utilize the original measured values. However, we change the sign of any row of **C** which results in negative $\bar{y}$-values.

The result of solving (15)″ and (16)″ for each of the roots ϕ_1 and ϕ_2 is

$$\begin{bmatrix} y_1 \\ y_2 \end{bmatrix} = \begin{bmatrix} 108{\cdot}918 & -33{\cdot}823 & -35{\cdot}497 \\ -40{\cdot}608 & 59{\cdot}952 & 22{\cdot}821 \end{bmatrix} \begin{bmatrix} x_1 \\ x_2 \\ x_3 \end{bmatrix}$$

Applying this transformation to the six mean vectors we obtain the following pairs of coordinates:

$$(96{\cdot}3, 77{\cdot}4), \quad (99{\cdot}7, 77{\cdot}8), \quad (99{\cdot}2, 77{\cdot}8),$$
$$(99{\cdot}2, 78{\cdot}2), \quad (96{\cdot}1, 80{\cdot}4), \quad (98{\cdot}0, 79{\cdot}2)$$

These have been plotted in Fig. 4. If $\mathbf{\Sigma}_\Omega$ and $\mathbf{\Xi}$ had been known exactly, instead of estimated from the samples, we would have had

$$\mathscr{V}(y_1) = 1 = \mathscr{V}(y_2) \quad \text{and} \quad \mathscr{C}(y_1, y_2) = 0$$

As a rough indication of the relative uncertainty of each of the means we have surrounded it with a '90% confidence' circle of radius $1{\cdot}645/\sqrt{N_l}$ ($l = 1, 2, 3, 4, 5, 6$). The graph does not confirm Reeve's conclusions (*loc. cit.*) namely:

'Comparison of ranges and means suggests that only *chapadensis* and *mexicana* have any claim to be distinct subspecies on the basis of skull proportions.'

'*Instabilis* appears to be a small edition of *mexicana* and *chiriquensis* ...'

Testing an arbitrary linear compound

Suppose, in the foregoing illustration, a biologically meaningful linear compound of the observational triplets had been to offset the first variate (basal length) against the mean of the other two. In other words, suppose it were desired to utilize a transformation vector the coefficients of which are in the ratio $1 : -\frac{1}{2} : -\frac{1}{2}$.†

If this compound were satisfactory its scale factor to ensure unit variance would be determined from equation (16)″. However, in testing to what extent this compound can replace the first of the canonical axes we do not need to make this normalization.

Let us, therefore, investigate the compound $x_1 - \frac{1}{2}x_2 - \frac{1}{2}x_3$ as a possible replacement of the first of the canonical axes in the *Tamandua* illustration. Our first step is to find the ratio of the 'total' sum of squares to the 'within' sum of squares of the 'compounded' observations.

If we write $\mathbf{m}' = \{1 \ -\frac{1}{2} \ -\frac{1}{2}\}$ these sums of squares are

$$\mathbf{m}'(\mathbf{W}+\mathbf{P})\mathbf{m} = 0{\cdot}01392945 \quad \text{and} \quad \mathbf{m}'\mathbf{W}\mathbf{m} = 0{\cdot}0052603,$$

respectively. Their ratio is accordingly $2{\cdot}6480 = 1 + \phi$, say.

† When p is large it is often tempting to inspect the significant rows of $\mathbf{C}$ and replace the small elements by zeros. The results cannot be tested in the manner here described.

It can, in fact, be shown (Bartlett, 1952) that this ratio can be treated approximately as if it were a factor in the product $\prod_{j=1}^{m}(1+\phi_j)$. Thus, corresponding to the original product

$$\prod_{j=1}^{3}(1+\phi_j) = 81{\cdot}54 = U^{-1}_{3,5,42} = \frac{|\mathbf{W}+\mathbf{P}|}{|\mathbf{W}|}$$

we have a product

$$\frac{\prod_{j=1}^{3}(1+\phi_j)}{1+\phi} = \frac{81{\cdot}54}{2{\cdot}6480} = 30{\cdot}79 = U^{-1}_{2,5,41}$$

where the reduction by a unit in the first and third suffices of U is justified by Bartlett (*loc. cit.*).

Hence, the use of the vector **m** as a linear compound has left a variability that, if it were purely random, would make

$$\left(41 - \frac{2-5+1}{2}\right)\ln U^{-1}_{2,5,41}$$

a χ^2 variate with $2\times 5 = 10$ degrees of freedom. Inserting the numerical value of U^{-1} we obtain 143·9 which is a highly significant value. This shows that the single compound $\mathbf{m}'\mathbf{x}$ cannot adequately represent the three variates.

An illustration with quantal variates

In studies of the artificial production of vaginal cornification by oestrogenic stimulation of ovariectomized mice, a standard procedure is to examine vaginal smears taken at three fixed times after the administration of the oestrogens. On each of these occasions the score *zero* is allotted to a smear in which there are leucocytes, mucin, and nucleated or cornified cells, while the score *unity* is reserved for smears in which there are only nucleated and/or cornified cells.

The resulting trivariate reaction patterns are of eight possible types:

Pattern no.	x_1-value	x_2-value	x_3-value
1	0	0	0
2	0	0	1
3	0	1	0
4	0	1	1
5	1	0	0
6	1	0	1
7	1	1	0
8	1	1	1

In this case, where cornification is unlikely to reappear after its earlier cessation, pattern number 5 is ruled out.

Claringbold (1958) has reported the results of a 12-fold replicated 3^4 experiment of this type. One of the factors was the logarithm of the dose, uniformly spaced. The other three were not specified but might reasonably be supposed to be: (i) the 'line' of mice used, (ii) the method of administration of the oestrogen, and (iii) the source of the oestrogen. For simplicity we have ignored one of Claringbold's unspecified factors so that the observations recorded as frequencies below represent a 3^3 experiment replicated 36 times. For illustrative purposes we will suppose that we have eliminated factor (iii) above, that the lines of mice are denoted by A, B and C, and that the methods of administration are designated M_1, M_2 and M_3. We then have $h = 27$ groups of trivariate observations to compare.

The 972 observations are then shown in the table on the following page.

Now the distribution of a (0, 1) variate is clearly not Normal or even approximately so. Yet the distribution of a linear function of numerous variates is approximately Normal (unless the coefficients applied to one or two of the variates allow them to dominate the result). Although three variates is not a very large number nevertheless a linear transformation

$$\mathbf{y} = \mathbf{C}\mathbf{x}$$

will result in a set of variates more Normally distributed than the original x's. With this *caveat* in mind we will 'pretend' that the quantal variates are Normal.

The 972 observational triplets summarized on the following page could, of course, be treated in the ordinary way. Thus, for example, the 18 observations (0, 0, 0) shown at the beginning of the table could be entered 18 times on punched cards with the appropriate 'line', method and dose identification. However, we will show that the necessary sums of squares and products can be obtained so easily on a desk calculator that this punching of the original observations is not warranted. It is only when we come to (14)″, (15)″ and (16)″ that an electronic computer may be desirable (particularly if $p > 3$).

Let us write (x_1, x_2, x_3) for the *frequency* with which the triplet of observations x_1, x_2, x_3 occurred, and let a full point stand for addition over all observed values of the corresponding variate. Thus $(x_1, x_2, .)$ means that all the frequencies in which x_1 and x_2 had the assigned values have been aggregated. Then, e.g.,

$$\hat{\sigma}_{13} = \{(\,.\,.\,.\,)-1\}^{-1}\left[\sum (x_1\,.\,x_3)\,x_1 x_3 - \frac{\{\sum (x_1\,.\,.\,)\,x_1\}\{\sum (\,.\,.\,x_3)\,x_3\}}{(\,.\,.\,.\,)}\right]$$

'Line'	Method	Log dose	Frequency of occurrence of pattern no. 1	2	3	4	6	7	8
A	M_1	0	18	0	7	1	2	7	1
		1	15	0	8	2	2	9	0
		2	6	1	11	1	2	15	0
	M_2	0	13	2	5	2	3	11	0
		1	6	2	12	0	1	14	1
		2	2	0	15	1	3	14	1
	M_3	0	20	2	6	2	3	3	0
		1	14	1	12	1	0	8	0
		2	10	2	10	1	2	10	1
B	M_1	0	23	0	9	1	1	2	0
		1	9	3	11	5	2	6	0
		2	9	2	9	8	2	4	2
	M_2	0	15	1	7	7	1	4	1
		1	11	0	10	5	1	9	0
		2	1	3	11	12	2	6	1
	M_3	0	25	1	7	2	0	1	0
		1	14	1	11	1	3	5	1
		2	8	3	5	5	2	12	1
C	M_1	0	25	5	2	2	1	1	0
		1	18	8	4	5	1	0	0
		2	12	6	7	4	1	4	2
	M_2	0	22	4	7	2	1	0	0
		1	7	6	12	6	0	4	1
		2	5	7	8	12	0	2	2
	M_3	0	23	2	7	2	0	1	1
		1	17	3	6	9	0	0	1
		2	7	6	8	5	1	7	2
		Totals	355	71	227	104	37	159	19

where $\sum$ means that the sum is taken over all values of the variables x appearing thereafter. Since x_1 and x_3 can only assume zero and unit values we obtain

$$\hat{\sigma}_{13} = \{(\,.\,.\,.\,)-1\}^{-1}\left[(1\,.\,1)-\frac{(1\,.\,.\,)(\,.\,.\,1)}{(\,.\,.\,.\,)}\right]$$

Similarly

$$\hat{\sigma}_{11} = \{(\,.\,.\,.\,)-1\}^{-1}\left[(1\,.\,.\,)-\frac{(1\,.\,.\,)^2}{(\,.\,.\,.\,)}\right]$$

The element in the first row, third column of **P** is, in an obvious notation,

$$\sum_{j=1}^{h} \frac{(1\,.\,.)^{(j)}(.\,.\,1)^{(j)}}{(.\,.\,.)^{(j)}} - \frac{(1\,.\,.)(.\,.\,1)}{(.\,.\,.)}$$

In the illustrative case

$$(.\,.\,.)^{(j)} = 36, \quad j = 1, 2, \ldots 27, \quad \text{and} \quad (.\,.\,.) = 27 \times 36 = 972$$

The 27 values of $(1\ 1\ .)^{(j)}$, for example, are obtained by adding together the frequencies of pattern 7, namely (1 1 0), and pattern 8, namely (1 1 1), for each of the 27 lines of the frequency table. Utilizing formulae of the type displayed above we eventually obtain the following matrix, each of whose elements has 26 degrees of freedom

$$\mathbf{P} = \begin{bmatrix} 19{\cdot}58230 & 19{\cdot}16255 & -6{\cdot}71708 \\ & 33{\cdot}31687 & 3{\cdot}99280 \\ & & 20{\cdot}11317 \end{bmatrix}$$

A simple calculation made on the 'Totals' line of the frequency table produces the 'total' matrix of sums of squares and products which in this case is $971\hat{\boldsymbol{\Sigma}}_{\omega}$. Subtraction of **P** from this gives

$$\mathbf{W} = \begin{bmatrix} 147{\cdot}8611 & 46{\cdot}25000 & -17{\cdot}19444 \\ & 209{\cdot}13889 & 17{\cdot}41667 \\ & & 135{\cdot}16667 \end{bmatrix}$$

with 945 degrees of freedom.

Solving the equation (14)‴ produces three roots which are tested for significance below. The straightforward application of the criterion (17)

j	ϕ_j	$956 \ln \prod_j^m (1+\phi_i)$	d.f.	First differences of χ^2 values	d.f.
1	0·20460	339·2	78	178·0	28
2	0·15583	161·2	50	138·4	26
3	0·02414	22·8	24		

shows that the third root is not significantly different from zero. But on differencing the (dependent) significant chi-square values into (independent) chi-squares where

$$178{\cdot}0 + 138{\cdot}4 + 22{\cdot}8 = 339{\cdot}2$$

it is seen that the first and second roots account for roughly equal parts of the total. The ratio of independent χ^2-values being an F-variate we see that $F_{28,26} = 178{\cdot}0/138{\cdot}4 = 1{\cdot}29$ implies that the hypothesis $\phi_1 = \phi_2$ is acceptable. As we saw in Chapter Six, when two roots of the characteristic equation are equal we may choose any pair of axes at right angles to one another in the plane of the axes corresponding to those roots. In general the arbitrariness of any particular choice is a disadvantage; however, if one (or both) of the axes has a 'natural' interpretation there is every reason to use it. We will illustrate the procedure.

An 'interesting' transformed variate y_1 would be a multiple of the difference between the measurements (scores) made at the first and third examinations after the administration of the oestrogen. This is equivalent to choosing $\mathbf{c}_1' = \{-a \ 0 \ a\}$ where a is to be determined from the unit variance requirement of equation (16)″. Inserting the elements of **W** and putting $N-h = 945$ we obtain $a = 1{\cdot}72544$.

Now the second transformation vector $\mathbf{c}_2' = \{b \ c \ d\}$, say, is subject to two constraints. Applying (16)″ in its more general form of (11)′ we see that the requirement

$$\mathbf{CWC}' = (N-h)\mathbf{I}$$

means that the result of the product on the left is a matrix with a zero element in the first row, second column and also in the second row, first column. On inserting the components of $\mathbf{c}_2'$ both these result in

$$-165{\cdot}05555b - 28{\cdot}83333c + 152{\cdot}36111d = 0$$

This relation of course expresses the fact that y_1 and y_2 are uncorrelated. The unit variance of y_2 is implied in the second element of the second row of the matrix product, namely

$$147{\cdot}86111b^2 + 209{\cdot}18889c^2 + 135{\cdot}16667d^2 + \\ 2 \times 46{\cdot}25bc - 2 \times 17{\cdot}19444bd + 2 \times 17{\cdot}41667cd = 945$$

Since these two equations leave open the choice of one of the unknowns we put $c = 1$ and reach the alternative solutions

$$\mathbf{c}_2' = \{-2{\cdot}006 \quad 1 \quad -1{\cdot}984\}$$

or

$$\mathbf{c}_2' = \{1{\cdot}341 \quad 1 \quad 1{\cdot}642\}$$

The latter of these is not far from a vector of units and we can consider the corresponding y_2 as a kind of 'mean' of the three observed measurements. We will use this alternative in what follows.

We have now obtained two coordinate axes on which the 27 different factorial combinations of the experiment could be plotted. However, since the transformed variates y_1 and y_2 are orthogonal linear combinations of the variates which do not depend on the relation of **P** to **W** (because equation (15)″ has not been used to determine **C**), we may make two separate ANOVA's of the data using y_1 and y_2 as independent single variates. We will illustrate the computations using y_1.

The table below gives the frequencies of each of the three possible y_1-values (i.e., $-1{\cdot}725$ from pattern 7, zero from patterns 1, 3, 6 and 8, and $1{\cdot}725$ from patterns 2 and 4) and the total y_1 obtained for each of the 27 factorial combinations. The total sum of squares about the mean is

$$159 \times (-1{\cdot}725)^2 + 175 \times (1{\cdot}725)^2 - \frac{(27{\cdot}600)^2}{972} = 993{\cdot}075$$

and the sum of squares between 'treatments' is

$$\frac{(-10{\cdot}350)^2 + (-12{\cdot}075)^2 + \ldots + (6{\cdot}900)^2}{36} - \frac{(27{\cdot}600)^2}{972} = 138{\cdot}409$$

The latter is to be analysed into its constituent parts.

'Line'	Method	Log dose	Frequency of y_1-values shown $-1{\cdot}725$	0	$1{\cdot}725$	Total of y_1-values
A	M_1	0	7	28	1	−10·350
		1	9	25	2	−12·075
		2	15	19	2	−22·425
	M_2	0	11	21	4	−12·075
		1	14	20	2	−20·700
		2	14	21	1	−22·425
	M_3	0	3	29	4	1·725
		1	8	26	2	−10·350
		2	10	23	3	−12·075
B	M_1	0	2	33	1	− 1·725
		1	6	22	8	3·450
		2	4	22	10	10·350
	M_2	0	4	24	8	6·900
		1	9	22	5	−6·900
		2	6	15	15	15·525
	M_3	0	1	32	3	3·450
		1	5	29	2	−5·175
		2	12	16	8	−6·900
C	M_1	0	1	28	7	10·350
		1	0	23	13	22·425
		2	4	22	10	10·350
	M_2	0	0	30	6	10·350
		1	4	20	12	13·800
		2	2	15	19	29·325
	M_3	0	1	31	4	5·175
		1	0	24	12	20·700
		2	7	18	11	6·900
		Totals	159	638	175	27·600

Restricting ourselves to the main effects we easily find:

Variability:	d.f.	s.s.	m.s.
Between lines	2	96·989	48·494
Between methods	2	0·171	0·086
Between doses:			
(a) Linear	1	0·041	
(b) Quadratic	1	0·075	
Interactions	20	41·133	2·057
Residual	945	854·666	0·904
Totals	971	993·075	

Little significance can be attached to the actual figures since we arbitrarily assigned titles to Claringbold's (*loc. cit.*) factors.

Problems 7

1. Matthew and De Couto (1959) provide the following measurements in millimetres of lengths and widths of the second of the lower cheek teeth of 30 adult specimens of *Megalocnus rodens*, the giant sloth.

M. r. rodens				*M. r. cassimbae*	
W	L	W	L	W	L
23·8	16	21	15	18·3	15·2
23·2	15·8	23·5	15	18	13·4
23	14·8	22·5	15	19·5	15
22·5	16	21·2	15	21·4	15·2
20·5	15·5	22	14	20	15
19	15	21	15	16.5	14.8
23	15.5	19.8	15.7		
19.5	14.5	23	15.8		
23	16	22	14.5		
20	14·8	21	16		
21·2	15·5	22·5	17		
22·8	15·6	19·5	15·2		

Test the within group variance–covariance matrices for homogeneity. If the result is favourable test whether the two mean vectors are significantly different, thus justifying the classification into subspecies.

2. C. Burt (1950) has provided the following frequencies of characteristics among 100 male residents of Liverpool.

TALL MEN

	Hair colour:					
	Fair		Red		Dark	
Eye colour	Narrow head	Wide head	Narrow head	Wide head	Narrow head	Wide head
Light	8	2	6	2	9	2
Mixed	1	2	2	—	3	2
Brown	—	—	—	—	1	3

SHORT MEN

	Hair colour:					
	Fair		Red		Dark	
Eye colour	Narrow head	Wide head	Narrow head	Wide head	Narrow head	Wide head
Light	4	—	—	—	—	—
Mixed	1	2	1	2	12	8
Brown	—	2	2	—	19	4

By scoring eye and hair colour as two pairs of quantal variates and head width as a further quantal variate (so that, e.g., a light-eyed, fair-haired, narrow-headed man would be scored as 0 0 0 0 0, and a brown-eyed, dark-haired, wide-headed man would be scored 1 0 1 0 1) find the single canonical axis to transform the five-component mean vectors of tall and short men. Are the two transformed mean values significantly different?

3. The following three sets of data (Edwards and Fraccaro, 1960; Edwards, 1961) show the sequences of the first four births in families of four or more. The first set refers to families of Swedish ministers of religion, while the second and third sets were extracted from parish records and maternity stations in Finland.

Birth order	No. 1	No. 2	No. 3
♂ ♂ ♂ ♂	246	742	792
♂ ♂ ♂ ♀	223	677	780
♂ ♂ ♀ ♂	230	671	788
♂ ♂ ♀ ♀	224	695	738
♂ ♀ ♂ ♂	217	595	716
♂ ♀ ♂ ♀	222	647	710
♂ ♀ ♀ ♂	175	677	712
♂ ♀ ♀ ♀	221	655	705
♀ ♂ ♂ ♂	205	656	696
♀ ♂ ♂ ♀	217	600	737
♀ ♂ ♀ ♂	205	627	701
♀ ♂ ♀ ♀	182	561	679
♀ ♀ ♂ ♂	207	680	686
♀ ♀ ♂ ♀	204	659	641
♀ ♀ ♀ ♂	182	654	704
♀ ♀ ♀ ♀	183	734	753
Totals	3,343	10,530	11,538

Ascribing the value unity to a male birth and zero to a female, make a canonical analysis of these data ($p = 4$, $h = 3$).

4. Stower *et al.* (1960) provides the following information about eight populations of the desert locust (E = elytron length; F = femur length; C = head width).

Population	No. of insects	Sex	Mean values (mm) E	F	C	Temperature conditions	Conditions of rearing	Parental conditions
Dik	33	♂	52·267	23·703	7·488	Shade	Dense bands	Dense swarms
	36	♀	57·500	25·522	7·939			
Adarit	110	♂	53·484	24·765	7·503		Dense bands	Loose swarms
	112	♀	60·250	27·214	8·146			
Agamat	90	♂	51·660	23·167	7·152	Cool	Dense bands	Dense swarms
	93	♀	55·809	25·243	7·711			
Zula	18	♂	50·833	25·083	6·517		Low density	Low density
	10	♀	60·440	29·330	7·640			
Shal Shal	13	♂	48·908	24·308	6·423		Low density	Low density
	12	♀	60·592	29·942	7·725			
Akbanazuf	43	♂	49·877	24·635	6·405	Cool	Low density	Low density
	38	♀	61·292	30·287	7·868			
Khasha-Beihan	17	♂	51·071	25·512	6·529	Hot	Low density	Possibly swarming
	9	♀	60·722	30·578	7·433			
Archico	108	♂	51·617	25·464	6·642	Hot	Dense bands	Dense swarms
	107	♀	60·243	29·277	7·460			

The 'between' and 'within' sums of squares and products matrices (the latter not tested for equality by criterion (3)) were given as:

$$\begin{array}{lcc} & \text{d.f.} & \\ \text{'Between'} & 15 & \begin{bmatrix} 13555{\cdot}93 & 6132{\cdot}78 & 1452{\cdot}01 \\ & 3788{\cdot}40 & 381{\cdot}42 \\ & & 243{\cdot}18 \end{bmatrix} \\ \text{'Within'} & 833 & \begin{bmatrix} 3035{\cdot}86 & 1074{\cdot}10 & 258{\cdot}35 \\ & 1520{\cdot}90 & 137{\cdot}71 \\ & & 110{\cdot}21 \end{bmatrix} \end{array}$$

Make a canonical analysis of these data.

5. Blackith and Albrecht (1959) report the measurements made on four groups of 'crowded, laboratory-bred' Red Locusts. The four six-component mean vectors and the 'within' variance–covariance matrix are given on the following page. Make a canonical analysis of the data.

No. of eye stripes	Sex	No. of insects	Z	E	O	F	C	H
			Mean values of characters indicated					
7	♂	35	2·5019	52·7893	3·8879	26·6946	7·2932	8·2100
7	♀	22	3·0337	58·1592	3·9569	29·7762	7·8169	8·8669
8	♂	14	2·5180	53·4581	3·9917	28·0875	7·5858	8·3950
8	♀	21	3·3266	60·7375	4·0744	31·3856	8·2806	9·1881

Variance–covariance matrix

0·102715	0·289420	0·009692	0·169622	0·040382	0·059732
	2·776243	0·064040	0·991217	0·222717	0·251552
		0·008092	0·044762	0·010532	0·010198
			0·771332	0·132497	0·144837
				0·041860	0·036699
					0·049418

Z = weight O = compound eye width C = head width
E = elytron length F = posterior femur length H = pronotal height

6. Experimental data condensed from Claringbold and Sobey (1958) illustrate a neat device for quantifying a single qualitative variate scale. Mice aged from 12 to 20 weeks were sensitized by the injection of alum-precipitated bovine gamma-globulin antigen. Fourteen days later a shocking dose of bovine gamma-globulin was administered. In the original experiment four levels of sensitizing and shocking doses were used but we have amalgamated these in pairs to produce a 'high' and 'low' dose level, respectively. Four lines of mice were used and sex was distinguished. Each subgroup of the original experiment contained two mice and thus each of our subgroups has eight mice in it.

The effect of the shocking dose may range from nothing to death. Three intermediate stages of anaphylaxis can be distinguished: (1) minor disturbance, (2) major disturbance, and (3) partial or complete paralysis. Our purpose is to produce one or more sets of scores which will best discriminate between these five states. If we think of the states as the five possible patterns assumed by four quantal variates x_1, x_2, x_3 and x_4 these patterns could be written as:

State

$$\begin{array}{cccccccccc} & & 0 & & 1 & & 2 & & 3 & & 4 \\ \begin{bmatrix} x_1 \\ x_2 \\ x_3 \\ x_4 \end{bmatrix} & = & \begin{bmatrix} 0 \\ 0 \\ 0 \\ 0 \end{bmatrix} & \text{or} & \begin{bmatrix} 1 \\ 0 \\ 0 \\ 0 \end{bmatrix} & \text{or} & \begin{bmatrix} 0 \\ 1 \\ 0 \\ 0 \end{bmatrix} & \text{or} & \begin{bmatrix} 0 \\ 0 \\ 1 \\ 0 \end{bmatrix} & \text{or} & \begin{bmatrix} 0 \\ 0 \\ 0 \\ 1 \end{bmatrix} \end{array}$$

and the application of a vector of coefficients $\mathbf{c}'$, say, to $\mathbf{x}$ will produce a 'score' for each of the possible states.

Using this device the above-mentioned data can be written in a frequency table:

'Line'	Sex	Antigen	Shock	State 0	1	2	3	4
1	♀	L	L	0	0	7	1	0
			H	0	1	3	2	2
		H	L	1	2	4	1	0
			H	0	4	1	2	1
	♂	L	L	2	3	3	0	0
			H	1	1	4	2	0
		H	L	1	5	2	0	0
			H	0	3	2	2	1
2	♀	L	L	2	2	1	3	0
			H	1	1	2	3	1
		H	L	0	2	4	2	0
			H	0	2	3	2	1
	♂	L	L	6	1	0	1	0
			H	1	0	6	1	0
		H	L	3	0	0	1	4
			H	0	2	3	3	0
3	♀	L	L	3	1	1	3	0
			H	1	1	2	4	0
		H	L	0	1	6	0	1
			H	0	1	0	6	1
	♂	L	L	3	4	0	1	0
			H	2	1	3	2	0
		H	L	3	1	3	1	0
			H	0	2	4	2	0
4	♀	L	L	3	0	0	5	0
			H	1	1	2	3	1
		H	L	0	0	0	6	2
			H	0	1	0	3	4
	♂	L	L	0	2	6	0	0
			H	0	0	3	4	1
		H	L	2	0	2	3	1
			H	1	0	5	2	0

Use the first canonical axis obtained from these data to produce a score $\mathbf{c}'\mathbf{x}$ for each of the five vectors $\mathbf{x}$ given above.

7. In a study of the variability of British birds' eggs, Fisher (1937) used a linear model to 'explain' the logarithms of the variance estimates of the egg-lengths and egg-breadths, respectively, of 161 species of birds for each of which about 100 eggs had been collected. In this model there were, in effect, 26 z-vectors which accounted for: (i) the grand mean, (ii) the differences between the means of the 24 groups into which the species were subdivided, and (iii) the logarithms of the mean egg-length and mean egg-breadth, respectively, of each species.

It was found possible to classify the species in six of the 24 groups into four abundance categories. The pairs of residuals obtained by applying the foregoing model to each of these 68 species are shown in the following table together with their abundance classification. Writing the four abundance categories as three variates in the manner of the foregoing problem we may partition the 5×5 matrix of variances and covariances obtained from these 68 observations in the form

$$\begin{bmatrix} \hat{\mathbf{\Sigma}}_{11} & \hat{\mathbf{\Sigma}}_{12} \\ \hat{\mathbf{\Sigma}}_{21} & \hat{\mathbf{\Sigma}}_{22} \end{bmatrix}$$

where, e.g., $\hat{\mathbf{\Sigma}}_{11}$ is the estimated variance–covariance matrix of the three dummy variates, and $\hat{\mathbf{\Sigma}}_{22}$ is that of the pair of residuals which summarize the variability of each species. (Note that whereas $\hat{\mathbf{\Sigma}}_{11}$ is based on 67 degrees of freedom, $\hat{\mathbf{\Sigma}}_{22}$ – and thus $\hat{\mathbf{\Sigma}}_{12}$ – only has 62 degrees of freedom because of the six within-group restrictions.)

If $\mathbf{x}_1$ is a three-component vector of dummy variates and $\mathbf{x}_2$ is a two-component vector of residual variates – so that

$$\mathbf{x} = \begin{bmatrix} \mathbf{x}_1 \\ \mathbf{x}_2 \end{bmatrix}$$

is an observational quintuplet, of which there are 68 in our problem – we require a pair of linear compounds, say $u = \boldsymbol{\alpha}'\mathbf{x}_1$ and $v = \boldsymbol{\gamma}'\mathbf{x}_2$, such that the variances of u and v are each unity while their correlation is a maximum in comparison with that of other similar pairs of compounds. In terms of our numerical example we wish to find a score u, determined for any species of bird by its abundance category, which is most highly correlated with a linear compound v which synthesizes the variability of that species. This score will enable us to verify the notion that greater abundance and greater variability go together.

It can be shown that the required vector $\boldsymbol{\alpha}$ is given by the solution of the three homogeneous equations

$$(\hat{\mathbf{\Sigma}}_{12}\hat{\mathbf{\Sigma}}_{22}^{-1}\hat{\mathbf{\Sigma}}_{21} - \nu\hat{\mathbf{\Sigma}}_{11})\boldsymbol{\alpha} = \mathbf{0}$$

Rarest species			Less rare species			Less common species			Commonest species		
Shelduck	−17·96	−15·17	Eider	9·07	−3·91	Widgeon	12·57	22·45	Mallard	−2·41	4·25
Graylag goose	17·75	24·03	Scoter	1·52	−6·41	Pochard	−2·01	−16·79	Teal	16·45	−0·49
			Goosander	−30·24	−15·90	Gadwall	−13·43	17·43	Pintail	5·36	28·37
			Red-breasted merganser	−9·63	−13·82	Tufted duck	−8·30	−11·72	Shoveller	21·22	−12·31
Golden eagle	7·08	17·56	Kite	4·78	−15·49	Merlin	−22·86	−14·11	Kestrel	−3·98	−12·27
Sea eagle	10·85	22·77	Honey buzzard	−11·41	−17·10	Peregrine	−11·61	−12·90	Sparrow hawk	27·41	27·42
						Hobby	−13·58	−3·98	Buzzard	−9·19	−0·49
						Hen harrier	22·53	8·61			
Great skua	−0·91	3·91	Great black-backed gull	−21·84	−18·01	Black-headed gull	−3·63	−5·13	Kittiwake	−2·98	−4·20
Arctic skua	−1·44	3·58	Little black-backed gull	18·89	14·69	Common gull	7·61	19·83	Herring gull	4·68	23·16
Roseate tern	−9·86	−15·22	Sandwich tern	−6·95	−17·15	Arctic tern	−1·93	−0·67			
			Little tern	11·52	1·32	Common tern	6·84	−6·15			
Chough	−45·45	−3·54	Jackdaw	−13·57	0·51	Carrion crow	3·15	−15·34	Rook	20·88	−9·34
						Hooded crow	4·22	−10·98	Magpie	36·15	10·90
						Raven	7·42	24·76	Jay	−12·77	3·00
Ring ouzle	−7·21	−9·94	Mistlethrush	5·34	3·75	Redbreast	−9·31	18·88	Blackbird	6·54	27·16
Nightingale	19·15	4·89				Stonechat	−16·05	−8·58	Thrush	0·52	8·18
						Whinchat	−6·55	−18·64	Wheatear	8·63	−18·47
									Redstart	−1·09	−7·28
Dartford warbler	−17·16	−7·52	Reed warbler	−4·71	1·71	Blackcap	−21·95	9·33	Willow warbler	−7·49	−12·76
			Wood warbler	10·26	8·55	Garden warbler	−10·76	4·13	Whitethroat	14·62	7·26
			Marsh warbler	−1·80	8·58	Sedge warbler	6·01	−24·62	Lesser whitethroat	5·93	9·74
			Grasshopper warbler	17·59	1·86	Chiffchaff	9·44	−6·22			

supplemented by the variance condition $\boldsymbol{\alpha}'\hat{\boldsymbol{\Sigma}}_{11}\boldsymbol{\alpha} = 1$. Here ν is the largest of the three roots (all non-negative) of the determinantal equation

$$|\hat{\boldsymbol{\Sigma}}_{12}\hat{\boldsymbol{\Sigma}}_{22}^{-1}\hat{\boldsymbol{\Sigma}}_{21} - \nu\hat{\boldsymbol{\Sigma}}_{11}| = 0$$

and is equal to the (canonical) correlation between $\mathbf{x}_1$ and $\mathbf{x}_2$. Similarly the two components of $\boldsymbol{\gamma}$ are obtained from the equations

$$(\hat{\boldsymbol{\Sigma}}_{21}\hat{\boldsymbol{\Sigma}}_{11}^{-1}\hat{\boldsymbol{\Sigma}}_{12} - \nu\hat{\boldsymbol{\Sigma}}_{22})\boldsymbol{\gamma} = \mathbf{0}$$

with the appropriate variance condition and with ν the same as before (or determined from the second – instead of third – order determinant corresponding to these equations).

Apply the foregoing theory to Fisher's data to obtain the scores for each abundance category and the canonical correlation between abundance and variability.

(*Answer:* 0, 0·51, 0·50, 2·57; and 0·320)

References to the Use of D^2 in Biological Work

BLACKITH, R. E. (1957) 'Polymorphism in some Australian locusts and grasshoppers.' *Biometrics* **13**, 183–196.

BLACKITH, R. E. and ALBRECHT, F. O. (1959) 'Morphometric differences between the eye-stripe polymorphs of the Red Locust.' *Sci. J. R. Coll. Sci.* **27**, 13–27.

BLACKITH, R. E. and ROBERTS, M. I. (1958). 'Farbenpolymorphismus bei einigen Feldheuschrecken.' *Zeit. Vererbungs.* **89**, 328–337.

GILES, E. (1960) 'Multivariate analysis of pleistocene and recent coyotes (*Canis latrans*) from California.' *Univ. Calif. Publ. geol. Sci.* **36**, 369–390.

HUGHES, R. E. and LINDLEY, D. V. (1955) 'Application of biometric methods to problems of classification in ecology.' *Nature, Lond.* **175**, 806–807.

MAJUMDAR, D. N. and RAO, C. R. (1960) *Race Elements in Bengal.* Calcutta.

MUKHERJEE, R., RAO, C. R. and TREVOR, J. C. (1955) *The Ancient Inhabitants of Jebel Moya.* Cambridge.

SOKAL, R. R. (1961) 'Distance as a measure of taxonomic similarity.' *Syst. Zool.* **10**, 70–79.

STOWER, W. J., DAVIES, D. E. and JONES, I. B. (1960) 'Morphometric studies of the desert locust, *Schistocerca gregaria* (Forsk.).' *J. Anim. Ecol.* **29**, 309–339.

TALBOT, P. A. and MULHALL, H. (1962) *The Physical Anthropology of Southern Nigeria: A Biometric Study in Statistical Method.* Cambridge.

References to the Use of Canonical Analysis

ASHTON, E. H., HEALY, M. J. R. and LIPTON, S. (1957) 'The descriptive use of discriminant functions in physical anthropology.' *Proc. Roy. Soc.* B, **146**, 552–572.

CLARINGBOLD, P. J. (1958) 'Multivariate quantal analysis.' *J. Roy. Statist. Soc.* B, **20**, 398–405.

CLIFFORD, H. T. and BINET, F. E. (1954) 'A quantitative study of a presumed hybrid swarm between *Eucalyptus elaeophora* and *E. goniocalyx*.' *Aust. J. Bot.* **2**, 325–336.

JOLICOEUR, P. (1959) 'Multivariate geographical variation in the wolf *Canis lupus* L.' *Evolution* **13**, 283–299.

Other References in Chapter Seven

BARTLETT, M. S. (1938) 'Further aspects of the theory of multiple regression.' *Proc. Camb. Phil. Soc.* **34**, 33–40.

BARTLETT, M. S. (1947) 'Multivariate analysis'. *J. Roy. Statist. Soc. B*, **9**, 176-197.

BARTLETT, M. S. (1952) 'The goodness of fit of a single hypothetical discriminant function in the case of several groups.' *Ann. Eugen., Lond.* **16**, 199–214.

BLACKITH, R. E. (1960) 'A synthesis of multivariate techniques to distinguish patterns of growth in grasshoppers.' *Biometrics* **16**, 28–40.

BURT, C. (1950). 'The factorial analysis of qualitative data.' *Brit. J. Statist. Psychol.* **3**, 166–185.

CLARINGBOLD, P. J. and SOBEY, W. R. (1958) 'Studies in anaphylaxis. III: Re-examination of scores for anaphylaxis using four inbred lines of mice.' *Aust. J. biol. Sci.* **11**, 434–441.

EDWARDS, A. W. F. (1961) 'A factorial analysis of sex ratio data.' *Ann. Hum. Genet., Lond.* **25**, 117–121.

EDWARDS, A. W. F. and FRACCARO, M. (1960) 'Distribution and sequences of sexes in a selected sample of Swedish families.' *Ann. Hum. Genet., Lond.* **24**, 245–252.

FISHER, R. A. (1937) 'The relation between variability and abundance shown by the measurements of the eggs of British nesting birds.' *Proc. Roy. Soc. Lond.* B, **122**, 1–26.

JOLICOEUR, P. and MOSIMANN, J. E. (1960) 'Size and shape variation in the painted turtle. A principal component analysis.' *Growth* **24**, 339–354.

MATTHEW, W. D. and PAULA COUTO, C. DE (1959) 'The Cuban edentates.' *Bull. Amer. Mus. nat. Hist.* **117**, Art. 1.

RAHMAN, N. A. (1962) 'On the sampling distribution of the studentized Penrose measure of distance.' *Ann. Hum. Genet., Lond.* **26**, 97–106.

RAO, C. R. (1952) *Advanced Statistical Methods in Biometric Research*. New York.

REEVE, E. C. R. (1941). 'A statistical analysis of taxonomic differences within the genus *Tamandua* Gray (Xenarthra).' *Proc. zool. Soc. Lond.* A, **111**, 279–302.

REYMENT, R. A. (1962) 'Observations on homogeneity of covariance matrices in paleontologic biometry.' *Biometrics* **18**, 1–11.

CHAPTER EIGHT

Factor Analysis

Factor Analysis (and we deliberately use the capitals) has been described (Burt and Banks, 1947) as 'a statistical technique for reducing a *large* number of *correlated* variables to terms of a *small* number of uncorrelated variables. The correlated variables consist usually of measurements for *observable* traits; the uncorrelated variables (called "factors") are abstract *hypothetical* components' (authors' italics).

This definition by two psychologists may sound suspiciously like a principal components analysis in which p correlated variates are transformed into p uncorrelated (orthogonal) variates in descending order of variability, only the first k being 'significant' in the summarization. However, although this may not have been too clear in the past, Factor Analysis is nowadays distinguished from principal components analysis by two characteristics:

(i) Each of the p original variates is supposed analysable into $m < p$ mutually uncorrelated 'common factors' with an uncorrelated residual ('unique') component which is not correlated with any of the remaining $p-1$ variates;

(ii) The m orthogonal axes of 'common factors' may be rotated to new orthogonal or oblique axes to conform with theoretical ideas underlying the formulation of the model.

The effect of the first of these characteristics is that only a portion of the variances or the unities in the diagonal of the estimated $p \times p$ variance–covariance or correlation matrix, respectively, is regarded as due to the $m < p$ transformed variates. When $m = p$ the residual component vanishes, the whole of the variances (or unities) is accounted for, and we are back at the p-variate orthogonal transformation which we considered in Chapter Six. If only k of these principal axes are used (because of the 'sphericity' of the remaining components) the result is similar (though not identical) to a Factor Analysis with m set equal to k. The two sets of results have, however, been arrived at with different models in mind.

The model

The mathematical form of the model that Factor Analysis assumes is:

$$\underset{(p\times 1)}{\mathbf{x}} = \underset{(p\times 1)}{\boldsymbol{\mu}} + \underset{(p\times m)}{\boldsymbol{\Gamma}}\;\underset{(m\times 1)}{\mathbf{f}} + \underset{(p\times 1)}{\mathbf{u}} \qquad (1)$$

where $\mathbf{x}$ is $N(\boldsymbol{\mu}, \boldsymbol{\Gamma\Gamma}'+\boldsymbol{\Delta})$, $\mathbf{f}$ is $N(\mathbf{0},\mathbf{I})$, $\mathbf{u}$ is $N(\mathbf{0},\boldsymbol{\Delta})$ and is independent of $\mathbf{f}$, and $\boldsymbol{\Delta}$ is a $p \times p$ diagonal matrix with non-negative elements. The matrix $\boldsymbol{\Gamma\Gamma}'$ is required to be of rank $m < p$, that is to say there are $p-m$ linear relations connecting the p rows of this symmetrical matrix.

We note that

$$\begin{aligned}\boldsymbol{\Sigma} &\equiv \mathscr{E}\{(\mathbf{x}-\boldsymbol{\mu})(\mathbf{x}-\boldsymbol{\mu})'\} = \mathscr{E}\{(\boldsymbol{\Gamma}\mathbf{f}+\mathbf{u})(\boldsymbol{\Gamma}\mathbf{f}+\mathbf{u})'\}\\ &= \mathscr{E}\{\boldsymbol{\Gamma}\mathbf{f}(\boldsymbol{\Gamma}\mathbf{f})'+\boldsymbol{\Gamma}\mathbf{f}\mathbf{u}'+\mathbf{u}(\boldsymbol{\Gamma}\mathbf{f})'+\mathbf{u}\mathbf{u}'\}\\ &= \mathscr{E}(\boldsymbol{\Gamma}\mathbf{f}\mathbf{f}'\boldsymbol{\Gamma}')+\mathscr{E}(\mathbf{u}\mathbf{u}') \quad \text{since } \mathscr{E}(\mathbf{u}) = \mathbf{0} = \mathscr{E}(\mathbf{f}) \text{ and } \mathbf{u} \text{ and } \mathbf{f} \text{ are independent with } \mathscr{E}(\mathbf{f}\mathbf{f}') = \mathbf{I}\\ &= \boldsymbol{\Gamma}\mathscr{E}(\mathbf{f}\mathbf{f}')\boldsymbol{\Gamma}'+\boldsymbol{\Delta}\end{aligned}$$

i.e.,

$$\boldsymbol{\Sigma} = \boldsymbol{\Gamma\Gamma}'+\boldsymbol{\Delta} \tag{2}$$

The foregoing model may be compared with the principal component transformation of Chapter Six where

$$\underset{(p\times 1)}{\mathbf{x}} = \underset{(p\times 1)}{\boldsymbol{\mu}} + \underset{(p\times p)}{\mathbf{A}^{-1}}\ \underset{(p\times 1)}{\mathbf{y}} = \boldsymbol{\mu}+\mathbf{A}'\mathbf{y}$$

since $\mathbf{AA}' = \mathbf{I}$. Further, on pre-multiplying by $\mathbf{A}'$, and post-multiplying by $\mathbf{A}$, the relation

$$\mathbf{A}\boldsymbol{\Sigma}\mathbf{A}' = \boldsymbol{\Lambda}$$

we obtain

$$\boldsymbol{\Sigma} = \mathbf{A}'\boldsymbol{\Lambda}\mathbf{A} = (\mathbf{A}'\boldsymbol{\Lambda}^{1/2})(\boldsymbol{\Lambda}^{1/2}\mathbf{A}) = \mathbf{JJ}' \quad \text{(say)} \tag{3}$$

where $\mathbf{J}' = \boldsymbol{\Lambda}^{1/2}\mathbf{A}$.

This comparison shows that the m components of $\mathbf{f}$ replace the p components of $\mathbf{y}$ and that there is a 'residual' $\mathbf{u}$ in the factor analytic model which finds no place in principal components. This vector variate $\mathbf{u}$ 'extracts' $\boldsymbol{\Delta}$ from the diagonal elements of $\boldsymbol{\Sigma}$.

Clearly the usefulness of Factor Analysis lies in the possibility of representing $\mathbf{x}$ (with p components) in terms of the relatively few components of $\mathbf{f}$. The smaller m is the happier we shall be. In fact, in the earliest psychological writings at the beginning of this century m was taken as unity.

The technique of Factor Analysis thus consists of estimating from a p-variate sample of N observations $\mathbf{x}$: (i) $\boldsymbol{\mu}$ (which estimate we will hereafter assume to be $\bar{\mathbf{x}}$, the observational mean vector), (ii) $\boldsymbol{\Gamma}$, the $(p \times m)$ matrix of coefficients known as 'factor loadings' (or 'saturations'), and (iii) $\boldsymbol{\Delta}$, the matrix of variances of the 'unique' variate $\boldsymbol{\mu}$. Note particularly that $\mathbf{f}$ is not generally 'estimated' since it is the m-variate Normal sample value corresponding to an observed p-variate $\mathbf{x}$ and is thus of little consequence when the Normal parameters $\boldsymbol{\mu}$, $\boldsymbol{\Gamma}$, $\boldsymbol{\Delta}$ are known (or estimated). This shows that it is the *structure* of the model that is regarded as of importance. It is thought that the observed $\mathbf{x}$ are samples from a Normal universe specified by the particular parameters mentioned.

The model we have described above has a peculiar indeterminacy. Suppose we simultaneously transform $\mathbf{f}$ and the rows of $\mathbf{\Gamma}$ by the two $(m \times m)$ matrices of coefficients $\mathbf{A}$ and $\mathbf{T}$, respectively, so that $\mathbf{f}$ becomes $\mathbf{f}^*$ and $\mathbf{\Gamma}$ becomes $\mathbf{G}$,
i.e.,

$$\mathbf{f}^* = \mathbf{Af} \quad \text{and} \quad \mathbf{G} = \mathbf{\Gamma T}$$

[Note that we post-multiply a matrix to transform its rows.] Then

$$\begin{aligned}
\mathscr{E}\{(\mathbf{x}-\boldsymbol{\mu})(\mathbf{x}-\boldsymbol{\mu})'\} &= \mathscr{E}\{(\mathbf{Gf}^*+\mathbf{u})(\mathbf{Gf}^*+\mathbf{u})'\} \\
&= \mathbf{G}\mathscr{E}(\mathbf{f}^*\mathbf{f}^{*\prime})\mathbf{G}'+\mathbf{\Delta} \quad \text{the other terms being zero} \\
&= \mathbf{G}\mathscr{E}\{\mathbf{Af}(\mathbf{Af})'\}\mathbf{G}'+\mathbf{\Delta} \\
&= \mathbf{GAA}'\mathbf{G}'+\mathbf{\Delta} \quad \text{since } \mathscr{E}(\mathbf{ff}') = \mathbf{I} \\
&= (\mathbf{\Gamma T})\mathbf{AA}'(\mathbf{\Gamma T})'+\mathbf{\Delta} \\
&= \mathbf{\Gamma TA}(\mathbf{TA})'\mathbf{\Gamma}'+\mathbf{\Delta} \\
&= \mathbf{\Gamma\Gamma}'+\mathbf{\Delta} \quad \textit{provided} \quad \mathbf{TA}(\mathbf{TA})' = \mathbf{I}
\end{aligned}$$

which means that $\mathbf{TA}$ must be orthogonal. If, therefore, the two matrices of the simultaneous transformations of $\mathbf{\Gamma}$ and $\mathbf{f}$ are chosen so that their product $\mathbf{TA}$ is orthogonal then the model is *left unchanged.*

It is this feature of the Factor Analysis model that permits the investigator to rotate the so-called common-factor axes (the columns of $\mathbf{\Gamma}$) to any convenient positions. In other words, having estimated a set of coefficients $\mathbf{\Gamma}$, the Factor Analyst may *arbitrarily* transform them by post-multiplication of $\mathbf{\Gamma}$ by any $(m \times m)$ matrix $\mathbf{T}$. Of course the effect of this transformation is that the original factors $\mathbf{f}$ become a set $\mathbf{f}^*$ which is $N(\mathbf{0}, \mathbf{\Psi})$, where $\mathbf{\Psi}$ is a variance–covariance matrix uniquely determined by the fact that $\mathbf{TA}$ is orthogonal and $\mathbf{T}$ is known. These new 'factors' are thus correlated with one another (but not with $\mathbf{u}$) unless $\mathbf{A}$ is orthogonal (i.e., $\mathscr{E}(\mathbf{f}^*\mathbf{f}^{*\prime}) = \mathbf{AA}' = \mathbf{I}$). When this latter requirement is satisfied $\mathbf{T}$ is also orthogonal (because $\mathbf{TA}$ must be). This means that if we are loath to make a transformation to *correlated factors* by an oblique rotation of the common-factor axes we may nevertheless use an orthogonal transformation (rotation) on $\mathbf{\Gamma}$.

Now, we will avoid this indeterminancy of model (1) by requiring each successive component variate in $\mathbf{f}$ to absorb as much as possible of the variability in $\mathbf{x}$ remaining after that of $\mathbf{u}$ has been 'extracted'. Both the procedures we now describe do this – though in slightly different ways.

Factor Analysis in biology

At the time of writing only a few biologists have published work involving the use of Factor Analysis. Five of these [Kraus and Choi (1958), Teissier (1955), Goodall (1954) – cited in Chapter Six – Bailey (1956), and Teissier (1956)] used standardized **x**-values (so that $\mathbf{\Sigma}$ was the correlation

Article	Values of p	m	Factor method	No. of iterations for $\mathbf{\Delta}$	Rotation
Wright (1932)	5	3		—	
	7	3	General	—	
	7	3	plus	—	None
	6	3	group	—	
Stroud (1953)	14	5	Centroid	2	Oblique
	14	6	Centroid	2	Oblique
Tanner and Burt (1954)	11	4	Centroid†	> 1	None
Wright (1954)‡	6	3	Principal	> 1	None
Ferrari *et al.* (1957)	23	4	Centroid	?	None
Matsakis (1957*a*)	8	3			
	8	3	Centroid	?	None
	8	3			
Matsakis (1957*b*)	8	3	Centroid	?	None
Sokal (1958*b*)	10	4	Principal	?	Oblique
Dagnelie (1960)	9	2	Centroid	4	None
	23	3	Centroid	1	None
	38	2	Centroid	1	None
Morishima and Oka (1960)	16	4	Centroid	1	None
	16	4	Centroid	1	None
Pearce and Holland (1960)‡	6	3	?	?	None
	6	2			
Sokal and Daly (1961)	25	6	Centroid	6	Oblique
Sokal, Daly and Rohlf (1961)	19	5	Principal	3	Oblique
	6	2	Principal	3	Oblique
Rohlf and Sokal (1962)	40	8		6	
	40	8	Centroid	3	Oblique
	23	5		> 1	
Rasch (1962)	13	3	Centroid	2	None
Sokal (1962)	18	3	Centroid	> 1	Oblique
Reyment (1963)	17	10	New§	1	None

† And also by means of the 'general plus group', or bi-factor, method (see, e.g., Harman, 1960).

‡ Cited in Chapter Six.

§ An approximation to maximum likelihood (see below) which avoids iteration by estimating $\mathbf{\Delta}$ as $\alpha\{\text{diag.}\,\hat{\mathbf{\Sigma}}\}^{-1}$ where α is a parameter to be calculated (see Jöreskog, 1963).

matrix) and ignored the diagonal elements of $\mathbf{\Delta}$. From our viewpoint these articles can be regarded as examples of p-variate transformations to be classed with the techniques of Chapter Six. However, in the two last-mentioned articles the authors used *orthogonal* rotations of the component (factor?) axes (namely by means of an orthogonal $\mathbf{T}$) to clarify the biological significance of their results.†

But the momentum has been increasing largely because of the widespread availability of high-speed computers. The foregoing table gives a conspectus of the factorial techniques used in 17 articles in which biological data were analysed. The expression 'centroid method' refers to the Thurstone (1947) approximation to Principal Factor Analysis. This approximate procedure is now really only justified when electronic computers are not available.

Principal Factor Analysis

Our purpose is now to estimate $\mathbf{\Gamma}$ and $\mathbf{\Delta}$ from a sample of N p-variate observations. In view of the Normality assumption we know that this sample can be replaced (without loss of 'information') by the statistics $\hat{\boldsymbol{\mu}}$ and $\hat{\mathbf{\Sigma}}$ calculated therefrom. One difficulty is that we then have to estimate *both* $\mathbf{\Gamma}$ and $\mathbf{\Delta}$ from the relation

$$\mathbf{\Sigma} = \mathbf{\Gamma}\mathbf{\Gamma}' + \mathbf{\Delta}$$

Let us suppose, however, that we can make a reasonable 'guess' at the p diagonal elements of $\mathbf{\Delta}$. If we write these as $\hat{\mathbf{\Delta}}$ we are then left with the estimation of $\mathbf{\Gamma}$ as

$$\underset{(p \times m)}{\hat{\mathbf{\Gamma}}} = \{\mathbf{g}_1 \quad \mathbf{g}_2 \quad \dots \quad \mathbf{g}_m\} \quad \text{(say)}$$

from the relation

$$\hat{\mathbf{\Sigma}} - \hat{\mathbf{\Delta}} = \hat{\mathbf{\Gamma}}\hat{\mathbf{\Gamma}}'$$

This relation reminds us of (3) and suggests that we should estimate $\mathbf{\Gamma}$ in the same way as we obtained $\mathbf{J}$ in (3), namely by principal components analysis. In this case, however, we will be working with the matrix $\hat{\mathbf{\Sigma}} - \hat{\mathbf{\Delta}}$. Each successive eigenvalue of this matrix will 'absorb' as much as possible of the balance of the aggregate variance, namely of the trace‡ of $\hat{\mathbf{\Sigma}} - \hat{\mathbf{\Delta}}$. It should be remembered that any matrix of the form $\mathbf{BB}'$ is symmetric and all its eigenvalues are non-negative, i.e., it is positive semi-definite. If, then, there are negative values among the (largest) m eigenvalues of $\hat{\mathbf{\Sigma}} - \hat{\mathbf{\Delta}}$ it shows that either (i) $\hat{\mathbf{\Delta}}$ is an inappropriate estimate or (ii) $\hat{\mathbf{\Sigma}} - \hat{\mathbf{\Delta}}$ cannot be written as $\hat{\mathbf{\Gamma}}\hat{\mathbf{\Gamma}}'$.

† An article from a related discipline (Imbrie, 1963) advocates oblique rotations after a principal components analysis.

‡ I.e., the sum of the principal diagonal elements.

We will accordingly write

$$|(\hat{\boldsymbol{\Sigma}}-\hat{\boldsymbol{\Delta}})-\kappa\mathbf{I}| = 0 \tag{4}$$

and proceed to calculate the m largest roots $\kappa_1, \kappa_2, \ldots \kappa_m$, the remainder being assumed to be zero since $\boldsymbol{\Gamma}$ has only m columns. Using the ith of these eigenvalues we may obtain the first $\overline{p-1}$ elements of $\mathbf{g}_i$ by solving the first $\overline{p-1}$ of the equations (see (15)′ of Chapter Six)

$$\mathbf{g}_i'(\hat{\boldsymbol{\Sigma}}-\hat{\boldsymbol{\Delta}}) = \kappa_i \mathbf{g}_i' \qquad (i = 1, 2, \ldots m) \tag{5}$$

It is easily confirmed that if we obtained the pth element of $\mathbf{g}_i$ by requiring the sum of the squares of the elements of $\mathbf{g}_i$ to be unity (the procedure we used in Chapter Six) we would then have to multiply each of its elements by $\kappa_i^{1/2}$ in order for $\boldsymbol{\Gamma}\boldsymbol{\Gamma}'$ to be equal to $\hat{\boldsymbol{\Sigma}}-\hat{\boldsymbol{\Delta}}$. We may telescope these steps by requiring

$$\mathbf{g}_i'\mathbf{g}_i = \kappa_i \qquad (i = 1, 2, \ldots m) \tag{6}$$

This equation (making the sum of the squares of the p components of $\mathbf{g}_i$ equal to a non-negative number κ_i) completes the estimation of $\boldsymbol{\Gamma}$ based on the guessed value of $\boldsymbol{\Delta}$.

We must now see if we can improve our first estimate $\hat{\boldsymbol{\Delta}}$ by using our estimate $\hat{\boldsymbol{\Gamma}}$. Let us calculate

$$\hat{\hat{\boldsymbol{\Delta}}} = \text{diag}\,(\hat{\boldsymbol{\Sigma}}-\hat{\boldsymbol{\Gamma}}\hat{\boldsymbol{\Gamma}}') \tag{7}$$

(where, e.g., diag $\mathbf{A}$ stands for the diagonal matrix the elements of which are the same as the diagonal elements of $\mathbf{A}$) and use this as our second estimate of $\boldsymbol{\Delta}$. We then have to repeat the procedure (4), (5) and (6) using $\hat{\boldsymbol{\Sigma}}-\hat{\hat{\boldsymbol{\Delta}}}$ instead of $\hat{\boldsymbol{\Sigma}}-\hat{\boldsymbol{\Delta}}$. This process of solving (4), (5) and (6) must be repeated again and again each time using the estimate of $\boldsymbol{\Delta}$ obtained at the preceding iteration.

This iterative procedure – known as Principal Factor Analysis – must be repeated until two successive estimates of $\boldsymbol{\Gamma}$ agree to a chosen number of significant figures.† The actual elements of any intermediate $\boldsymbol{\Gamma}$-estimate are not required in the calculation of (7) if we adopt a temporary scaling $\mathbf{g}_i'\mathbf{g}_i = 1$ in lieu of (6) so that the subtractive term in (7) becomes $\hat{\boldsymbol{\Gamma}}\mathbf{K}\hat{\boldsymbol{\Gamma}}'$ where $\mathbf{K}$ is the diagonal matrix of eigenvalues κ_i $(i = 1, 2, \ldots m)$. However, if any of the latter are negative in the final iteration (where the proper scaling (6) must be employed to find $\hat{\boldsymbol{\Gamma}}$) the m-value utilized must be abandoned. (The need for iteration of the estimation process explains the column heading 'No. of iterations for $\boldsymbol{\Delta}$' in the table of

† If they ever do. The literature contains mathematically constructed examples of such failure which might just occur in practice.

published biological applications of Factor Analysis on p. 156.) Notice that after completing the iterations

$$\text{diag}\,(\hat{\mathbf{\Gamma}}\hat{\mathbf{\Gamma}}'+\hat{\mathbf{\Delta}}) = \text{diag}\,\hat{\mathbf{\Sigma}}$$

but, in an obvious notation,

$$\text{nondiag}\,\hat{\mathbf{\Gamma}}\hat{\mathbf{\Gamma}}' \neq \text{nondiag}\,\hat{\mathbf{\Sigma}}$$

This circumstance leads to the notion of testing the 'correctness' of m. Essentially we are then asking whether the last $p-m$ roots of the final iteration of (4) are sufficiently close to zero for the differences between $\hat{\mathbf{\Sigma}}$ and $\hat{\mathbf{\Gamma}}\hat{\mathbf{\Gamma}}'+\hat{\mathbf{\Delta}}$ to be the result of sampling variation.

We remark that a given set of data may produce what appear to be perfectly reasonable mathematical solutions of the equations (4), (5) and (6) for *all* assumed values of m, e.g., for $m = 1, 2, \ldots p-1$. Only the statistical test just mentioned can distinguish between these solutions and indicate what is the smallest value of m which will 'fit' the data *given* the hypothesis of Normality.

A special case of the foregoing analysis shows why some authors prefer to discard Factor Analysis, with all its complications, in favour of principal components. Let us suppose that all the elements of $\mathbf{\Delta}$ are the same and that we know δ^2 where

$$\mathbf{\Delta} = \delta^2\mathbf{I}$$

We may picture δ^2 as relatively small since otherwise the m 'common factors' have 'explained' too small a part of $\mathbf{x}$ for the analysis to be helpful.

In this case equation (4) becomes

$$|(\hat{\mathbf{\Sigma}}-\delta^2\mathbf{I})-\kappa\mathbf{I}| = 0$$

i.e.,

$$|\hat{\mathbf{\Sigma}}-(\kappa+\delta^2)\mathbf{I}| = 0$$

But

$$|\hat{\mathbf{\Sigma}}-\lambda\mathbf{I}| = 0$$

showing that

$$\lambda_i = \kappa_i+\delta^2 \qquad (i = 1, 2, \ldots p) \tag{8}$$

Now the principal axes are given by (cf. (15)′ of Chapter Six)

$$\mathbf{a}_i'\hat{\mathbf{\Sigma}} = \lambda_i\mathbf{a}_i' \tag{9}$$

together with

$$\mathbf{a}_i'\mathbf{a}_i = 1 \qquad (i = 1, 2, \ldots p) \tag{10}$$

On the other hand the components of $\hat{\mathbf{\Gamma}}$ are obtained in this case from

$$\mathbf{g}_i'(\hat{\mathbf{\Sigma}}-\delta^2\mathbf{I}) = \kappa_i\mathbf{g}_i'$$

i.e., from

$$\mathbf{g}_i'(\hat{\mathbf{\Sigma}}-\delta^2\mathbf{I}) = (\lambda_i-\delta^2)\,\mathbf{g}_i' \quad \text{by (8)}$$

i.e., from

$$\mathbf{g}_i'\hat{\mathbf{\Sigma}} = \lambda_i\mathbf{g}_i' \tag{11}$$

together with

$$\mathbf{g}_i'\mathbf{g}_i = \kappa_i = \lambda_i-\delta^2 \qquad (i = 1, 2, \dots m) \tag{12}$$

Since equation (9) is the same as equation (11) except for a possible constant multiplier, the only differences between the $\mathbf{a}_i'$ and $\mathbf{g}_i'$ lie (i) in their different (scaling) normalizations (10) and (12), respectively, and (ii) in the fact that we ignore the last $p-m$ **g**-vectors. In this particular case, therefore, principal components and Principal Factor Analysis are likely to give very similar results if m is only a little less than p.

A peculiar feature of the model (1) is that, so long as $m < p$ and $\mathbf{\Delta} \neq \mathbf{0}$, the p-dimensional space of $\mathbf{x}$ (namely, the p-dimensional space of the principal axes) is *not* the same space as that of the m factor-axes. In fact the latter is not even 'embedded' in the former. This has the consequence that although we can envisage $\mathbf{x}$ as a point in a flattened rugby football of points in p dimensions the m **f**-vectors cannot be represented in the football at all. This is very different from the situation in Chapter Six where we left the points *in situ* and rotated the p axes of reference.

Test of adequacy of model (1)

Having estimated $\mathbf{\Gamma}$ and $\mathbf{\Delta}$ our problem is to decide from these estimates whether, in the p-variate Normal universe from which we are sampling,

$$\underset{(p\times p)}{\mathbf{\Sigma}} = \underset{(p\times m)}{\mathbf{\Gamma}}\;\underset{(m\times p)}{\mathbf{\Gamma}'} + \underset{(p\times p)}{\mathbf{\Delta}}$$

This test may be referred to as the test for the correctness of m.

Now the logarithm of the likelihood ratio, namely the ratio of the likelihood of the sample on the basis of the above hypothesis to the likelihood based on an arbitrary $\mathbf{\Sigma}$, can be shown (e.g., Anderson and Rubin, 1956) to be proportional to

$$N \ln\{|\hat{\mathbf{\Gamma}}\hat{\mathbf{\Gamma}}'+\hat{\mathbf{\Delta}}|/|\hat{\mathbf{\Sigma}}|\} \tag{13}$$

If the method of estimation used is efficient – which, in general, means that Canonical Factor Analysis (see below) has been used – this criterion is approximately distributed as χ^2 with $(p-m)(p-m-1)/2$ degrees of freedom. We may use this test as an approximation even when Principal Factor Analysis is the method of estimation used† and also when $\mathbf{\Sigma}_R$, instead of $\mathbf{\Sigma}$, has been operated on.

† It provides maximum likelihood estimates for the case $\mathbf{\Delta}=\delta^2\mathbf{I}$.

Numerical illustration

As illustrations of the technique of Principal Factor Analysis we will apply it to the 8×8 variance and correlation matrices obtained from the Blackith–Roberts grasshopper data utilized in Chapter Six. The matrices analysed were designated matrix (c) (with elements calculated to six decimals) and matrix (d) (with five decimals).

The first step is to choose a reasonably low value of m which we hope will lead to an adequate fit of the data. A rule-of-thumb used in psychometric texts is to choose m equal to the number of groupings of the p-variates which are revealed by the correlation matrix. Reference to p. 118 shows that the variates numbered 2, 3 and 4 are fairly highly correlated and might thus constitute a group. On the other hand the variates 5, 6, 7, 8 and 9 are intercorrelated at a noticeably lower level and might be collected together in a second group. We may thus attempt a Factor Analysis with two 'common factors', i.e., with $m = 2$.

The next step is to make initial 'guesses' about the elements of $\mathbf{\Delta}$. A feature of many iterative procedures is that no matter what starting-values are used the final result is the same. Unfortunately this is not true with Principal Factor Analysis. Using an 11×11 matrix of observed correlations between assessments of primary emotions, Wrigley (1959) has shown that substantially different estimates of $\hat{\mathbf{\Gamma}}$ are produced by the use of (i) zeros, (ii) unities, and (iii) the reciprocals of the corresponding element of the inverse of $\hat{\mathbf{\Sigma}}_R$, in the principal diagonal of $\hat{\mathbf{\Delta}}$. Incidentally his experiment indicated that when m was 4 or more about 100 iterations were required to produce successive values of $\hat{\mathbf{\Gamma}}\hat{\mathbf{\Gamma}}'$ that 'varied only slightly'.

Another disturbing feature of Wrigley's (*loc. cit.*) results was the frequency with which the 'final' estimate of $\mathbf{\Delta}$ contained one or more negative elements. In fact in the two sets of solutions for $m = 1, 2, 3, \ldots 10$ with initial estimates (i) and (iii), respectively, only those for $m = 3$ avoided this failure of model (1) which requires all elements of $\mathbf{\Delta}$ to be non-negative. While in the Wrigley example $m = 3$ was thus the only possible solution the use of the statistical criterion (13) could still result in a judgement of 'bad fit'. This would be an example of the total failure of the factor analytic model.

In our numerical example – and in the computer program outlined in Appendix I – we have chosen to use number (iii) of Wrigley's alternatives for the initial estimate for $\hat{\mathbf{\Delta}}$. This is because it has a rather tenuous validity from a theoretical viewpoint (Harman, 1960, Chapter 5). That is to say, if we are operating on $\hat{\mathbf{\Sigma}}_R$ the first estimate of $\mathbf{\Delta}$ is

$$\hat{\mathbf{\Delta}} = (\operatorname{diag} \hat{\mathbf{\Sigma}}_R^{-1})^{-1}$$

while if we are using $\hat{\mathbf{\Sigma}}$ the corresponding estimate is

$$\hat{\mathbf{\Delta}} = \{\text{diag}\,\hat{\mathbf{\Sigma}}^{-1}\}^{-1}$$

Now with $m = 2$ criterion (13) is approximately distributed as χ^2 with 15 degrees of freedom. The 5% critical value of this distribution is 24·996. Using Principal Factor Analysis on an IBM 709 in the manner outlined in Appendix I, criterion (13) (with $N = 368$) was 33·829 for matrix (c) and 36·667 for matrix (d). Thus two 'common factors' are insufficient to fit the data. With $m = 3$ the χ^2 for the variance–covariance matrix (c) is 17·478 in comparison with a 5% critical value of 18·307 (10 degrees of freedom). But it is only when we reach $m = 4$ that the calculated value of (13) for matrix (d) is below the corresponding critical value of χ^2 (namely, 9·951 and 12·592, respectively). This awkward feature of Principal Factor Analysis, namely that two different factor models apply to one and the same set of data scaled in two different ways, is avoided by the technique to be developed below. We will therefore abstain from reproducing and 'interpreting' the vectors of 'loadings' in the two different $\hat{\mathbf{\Gamma}}$. The table below summarizes the 'fit' of the original matrices by comparing the diagonal (common factor) elements of $\hat{\mathbf{\Gamma}}\hat{\mathbf{\Gamma}}'$ with those of the original matrix.

Original variances and portion accounted for by m common factors in a Principal Factor Analysis

Variate	Matrix (c)		Matrix (d)	
no.	Original	$m = 3$	Original	$m = 4$
2	0·0138	0·0123	1	0·851
3	0·0150	0·0107	1	0·751
4	0·2545	0·1887	1	0·703
5	0·0198	0·0084	1	0·468
6	0·0097	0·0029	1	0·513
7	0·0197	0·0102	1	0·482
8	0·0015	0·0003	1	0·298
9	0·4155	0·1777	1	0·472
All	0·7495	0·4112	8	4·538

It may be mentioned that, with the variance–covariance matrix, it required 18 iterations to produce a $\hat{\mathbf{\Delta}}$, the elements of which did not differ from the preceding $\hat{\mathbf{\Delta}}$ by as much as 5 units in the fifth decimal place. On the other hand with matrix (d) ($m = 4$) after 41 iterations there was still one element in the principal diagonal of $\hat{\mathbf{\Delta}}$ that differed by as much as 2 units in the third decimal place from the corresponding element of the estimate of $\hat{\mathbf{\Delta}}$ immediately preceding. These results, essentially confirming those of Wrigley (1959), lead us to view with some suspicion the published results of Factor Analyses obtained after small numbers of iterations.

A feature of the foregoing numerical procedures was the choice of a small m-value which was only discarded in favour of a larger value because the resulting model did not fit the observations. This means that we have been seeking the model representation (1) with the smallest possible m. In turn this implies that the elements of $\mathbf{\Delta}$, the variances of the u-variates, are to be made as large as possible without overly disturbing the fit.†

The end result is that the m-column matrix $\hat{\mathbf{\Gamma}}$ will necessarily 'discard' into the u-variates a (much) larger portion of the aggregate variance (as measured by the sum of the diagonal elements of $\hat{\mathbf{\Sigma}}$) than the first m columns of the corresponding principal components matrix $\mathbf{J}$.

Furthermore, the number, k, of significantly different eigenvalues (i.e., non-isoclinic variation which lends itself to interpretation) is likely to be larger than the smallest satisfactory value of m. Thus, for example, the $m = 3$ 'common factors' of the Principal Factor Analysis of matrix (c) accounted for 55% of the trace of the original 8×8 matrix. An equal number of eigenvalues of the matrix accounted for 93%, while all eight eigenvalues were deemed to be significantly different. The statistician cannot help feeling dissatisfied with a technique that characterizes as 'unique' to that animal or plant group as much as 45% of its aggregate variability.

Canonical Factor Analysis

The validity of Principal Factor Analysis as a method of estimating $\mathbf{\Gamma}$ and $\mathbf{\Delta}$ may be seriously questioned on the ground that it produces different results when $\mathbf{x}$ is scaled. Reverting to the model relation (1) we note that division of each component of $\mathbf{x}$ by its standard deviation (real or estimated) $\sigma_{jj}^{1/2}$ is equivalent to pre-multiplication of each side of (1) by $(\operatorname{diag}\mathbf{\Sigma})^{-1/2}$. But

$$(\operatorname{diag}\mathbf{\Sigma})^{-1/2}(\boldsymbol{\mu}+\mathbf{\Gamma}\mathbf{f}+\mathbf{u}) = (\operatorname{diag}\mathbf{\Sigma})^{-1/2}\boldsymbol{\mu}+\{(\operatorname{diag}\mathbf{\Sigma})^{-1/2}\mathbf{\Gamma}\}\mathbf{f}+(\operatorname{diag}\mathbf{\Sigma})^{-1/2}\mathbf{u}$$

The first of the three terms of this result shows that each component of $\boldsymbol{\mu}$ is being standardized (as we should expect), while the last term shows that the transformed p-variate $\mathbf{u}$ retains a mean of $\mathbf{0}$ but has a variance matrix $\mathbf{\Delta}_1$, say, given by $\mathbf{\Delta}_1 = \mathbf{\Sigma}^{-1/2}\mathbf{\Delta}\mathbf{\Sigma}^{-1/2}$. Finally, if we are to retain the notion of unit Normal variates for the p components of $\mathbf{f}$, the rows of

† Wrigley (1959) showed that the elements of $\mathbf{\Delta}$ do not necessarily increase for every reduction by unity in the size of m. However, the statement in the text above is broadly correct.

$\mathbf{\Gamma}$ have been scaled by division by $\sigma_{11}^{1/2}$, $\sigma_{22}^{1/2}$, ... $\sigma_{pp}^{1/2}$, respectively. This relationship is far from being satisfied by the Principal Factor solutions (i.e., estimates of $\mathbf{\Gamma}$) of the variance–covariance and correlation matrix, respectively.

We will accordingly outline a preferred technique in which the foregoing scaling relationships hold good between the two solutions. This invariant procedure is obtained as the maximum-likelihood solution of the problem of estimating $\mathbf{\Gamma}$ and $\mathbf{\Delta}$. We will treat it as completely analogous to the canonical analysis of Chapter Seven.

As we may surmise, the non-invariance to scaling of Principal Factor Analysis is because it utilizes $\mathbf{\Sigma}-\mathbf{\Delta}$ instead of $\mathbf{\Delta}^{-1/2}(\mathbf{\Sigma}-\mathbf{\Delta})\mathbf{\Delta}^{-1/2}$. The analogy with Chapter Seven is that the 'residual' or 'within' variance–covariance matrix is now $\mathbf{\Delta}$ and the 'between' variability is represented by $\mathbf{\Sigma}-\mathbf{\Delta}$. We must thus replace equation (4) by

$$|\hat{\mathbf{\Delta}}^{-1/2}(\hat{\mathbf{\Sigma}}-\hat{\mathbf{\Delta}})\hat{\mathbf{\Delta}}^{-1/2}-\nu\mathbf{I}| = 0$$

and $\hat{\mathbf{\Gamma}}$ will be determined from

$$\mathbf{g}_i'\hat{\mathbf{\Delta}}^{-1/2}(\hat{\mathbf{\Sigma}}-\hat{\mathbf{\Delta}})\hat{\mathbf{\Delta}}^{-1/2} = \nu_i\mathbf{g}_i' \qquad (i = 1, 2, \ldots m)$$

together with

$$\mathbf{g}_i'\hat{\mathbf{\Delta}}^{-1}\mathbf{g}_i = \nu_i$$

This solution is essentially the same as that provided by Lawley in his second paper (1942) on this subject. It has been the basis of all published numerical applications since then. In order to simplify the procedure for desk calculators Lawley proposed an iterative solution which avoided the need to solve the above determinantal equation. This was used by Lawley himself in 1943 (reproduced in Thomson, 1951) and by Emmett (1949). It was programmed for an electronic computer by Lord (1956) and by Maxwell (1961). Both these authors report difficulties in the application of the method. Lord (*loc. cit.*) states that to avoid the appearance of imaginary numbers† he, in effect, had to commence with an approximate Centroid solution for $\mathbf{\Gamma}$ with $m = 4$, and work upwards through $m = 5, 6, \ldots 10$, each time using the previous solution with a column of 'guessed' g's appended. His original correlation matrix $\hat{\mathbf{\Sigma}}_R$ was 33×33 and about 30 iterations were required with *each* value of m in order to produce $\hat{\mathbf{\Gamma}}$'s the elements of which did not vary by more than 0·002 'throughout ten successive iterations'. On the other hand Maxwell

† Namely, numbers which when squared produce negative results. It would seem that the possibility of temporarily scaling $\mathbf{g}_i$ by means of the relation $\mathbf{g}_i'\hat{\mathbf{\Delta}}^{-1}\mathbf{g}_i = 1$ was overlooked.

has published (*loc. cit.*) a 10×10 correlation matrix in which the estimates of $\mathbf{\Gamma}$ with $m = 4$ were still not converging after 1100 iterations.†

Howe (1955) proposed an alternative procedure for use with desk calculators but by then Rao (1955) had arranged for a direct computer solution of the foregoing determinantal and vectorial equations. This program was used by Bechtoldt (1961) on a 17×17 correlation matrix with $m = 6$. This author states that he required only five iterations to produce successive estimates of $\mathbf{\Delta}$ which did not differ in any element by more than $\pm 0{\cdot}01$.

But the direct solution of the foregoing equations has the serious disadvantage that if any element of $\hat{\mathbf{\Delta}}$ is nearly zero convergence of the iterative process is likely to be slow or even to fail. We propose, therefore, to rewrite the equations in a different form – although the final estimate of $\mathbf{\Gamma}$ will be unchanged.‡

The above determinantal equation is equivalent to

$$|(\hat{\mathbf{\Sigma}} - \hat{\mathbf{\Delta}}) - \nu\hat{\mathbf{\Delta}}| = 0$$

i.e.,

$$|(\hat{\mathbf{\Sigma}} - \hat{\mathbf{\Delta}}) - \nu(\hat{\mathbf{\Sigma}} - \overline{\hat{\mathbf{\Sigma}} - \hat{\mathbf{\Delta}}})| = 0$$

i.e.,

$$|(1+\nu)(\hat{\mathbf{\Sigma}} - \hat{\mathbf{\Delta}}) - \nu\hat{\mathbf{\Sigma}}| = 0$$

or

$$|(\hat{\mathbf{\Sigma}} - \hat{\mathbf{\Delta}}) - \theta\hat{\mathbf{\Sigma}}| = 0 \qquad (4)'$$

where $\theta = \nu/(1+\nu)$. This is the original form of Lawley's (1940) maximum-likelihood solution.

We now use the m largest roots of $(4)'$ to obtain the columns $\mathbf{g}_i$ of $\mathbf{\Gamma}$, namely

$$\mathbf{g}_i'(\hat{\mathbf{\Sigma}} - \hat{\mathbf{\Delta}}) = \theta_i \mathbf{g}_i'\hat{\mathbf{\Sigma}} \qquad (i = 1, 2, \ldots m) \qquad (5)'$$

together with the normalization

$$\mathbf{g}_i'\hat{\mathbf{\Sigma}}^{-1}\mathbf{g}_i = \theta_i \qquad (6)'$$

Having completed this solution based on a preliminary $\hat{\mathbf{\Delta}}$ we obtain a second, improved estimate $\hat{\hat{\mathbf{\Delta}}}$ from the relation

$$\hat{\hat{\mathbf{\Delta}}} = \operatorname{diag}(\hat{\mathbf{\Sigma}} - \hat{\mathbf{\Gamma}}\hat{\mathbf{\Gamma}}') \qquad (7)'$$

† The writer attempted to reproduce this failure but, after only 56 iterations, the largest difference between the elements of two successive $\hat{\mathbf{\Delta}}$'s was $0{\cdot}0017$, the second largest $0{\cdot}0006$, and all other elements were apparently correct to three decimals. The resulting $\hat{\mathbf{\Gamma}}$-value differed substantially from that of Maxwell (*loc. cit.*). More recently Maxwell (1964) has advocated the use of $(4)'$ for numerical work.

‡ The computer program outlined in Appendix I was applied to Emmett's (1949) 9×9 correlation matrix with $m = 2$ and reproduced the results given in Lawley and Maxwell (1963).

and insert this in lieu of $\hat{\mathbf{\Delta}}$ in (4)′.† Successive iterations are carried out until two estimates of $\mathbf{\Delta}$ agree to the desired accuracy. The final $\hat{\mathbf{\Delta}}$ and the $\hat{\mathbf{\Gamma}}$ that results from its use in (4)′, (5)′ and (6)′ – assuming that no value of θ_i is negative – constitute the Canonical Factor Analysis.

We leave it as an exercise to the reader to prove that when $\mathbf{\Delta} \equiv \delta^2 \mathbf{I}$ (and writing $\kappa_i = \delta^2 \nu_i$) the earlier solution at once reduces to a Principal Factor Analysis of the variance–covariance (*not* the correlation) matrix.

Testing the adequacy of model (1)

When Canonical Factor Analysis has been used to estimate $\mathbf{\Gamma}$ and $\mathbf{\Delta}$ the factor N in criterion (13) can be refined and the second term simplified. The result is

$$\left\{N - m - \frac{2(p-m)+7-2/(p-m)}{6}\right\} \sum_{j=m+1}^{p} \ln(1-\theta_j) \qquad (14)$$

which indicates that it is measuring the deviations from the hypothetical universal zeros of the smallest $p-m$ sample roots of

$$|\hat{\mathbf{\Gamma}}\hat{\mathbf{\Gamma}}' - \theta\hat{\mathbf{\Sigma}}| = 0$$

Numerical illustration

The foregoing techniques were applied to the 8×8 Blackith–Roberts matrix (c) in the manner outlined in Appendix I. As with Principal Factor Analysis, d of the Appendix was chosen as 4 so that the elements of the final $\hat{\mathbf{\Delta}}$ can be assumed correct to four decimal places.

Trial with $m = 2$ resulted in a χ^2-value significant at the 1% level. However, with $m = 3$ the criterion (14) proved non-significant ($\chi^2 = 14{\cdot}484$ with 10 degrees of freedom). The maximum-likelihood (i.e., in a certain sense, the 'best') factor structure of matrix (c) or (d), indifferently, thus agrees with that derived from a Principal Factor Analysis of matrix (c). Very few published Factor Analyses have operated on variance–covariance matrices.

The matrix $\mathbf{\Gamma}$ produced after 23 iterations was

$$\hat{\mathbf{\Gamma}} = \begin{bmatrix} 0{\cdot}1086 & -0{\cdot}0173 & 0{\cdot}0021 \\ 0{\cdot}1011 & -0{\cdot}0202 & -0{\cdot}0033 \\ 0{\cdot}3846 & 0{\cdot}1801 & 0{\cdot}0032 \\ 0{\cdot}0836 & 0{\cdot}0173 & -0{\cdot}0402 \\ 0{\cdot}0504 & -0{\cdot}0195 & 0{\cdot}0048 \\ 0{\cdot}0777 & 0{\cdot}0231 & 0{\cdot}0494 \\ 0{\cdot}0174 & 0{\cdot}0044 & -0{\cdot}0104 \\ 0{\cdot}3371 & 0{\cdot}2799 & 0{\cdot}0104 \end{bmatrix}$$

† Here again the right-hand side of (7)′ can be calculated without solving (6)′.

while the (diagonal) elements of $\hat{\mathbf{\Delta}}$ were 0·0017, 0·0043, 0·0741, 0·0109, 0·0068, 0·0107, 0·0010, and 0·2234, respectively. Since $\text{tr}\,\hat{\mathbf{\Sigma}} = 0{\cdot}749382$ and $\text{tr}\,\hat{\mathbf{\Delta}} = 0{\cdot}33287$ (the last figure being spurious) we see that the common factors 'absorb' 55·6% of the aggregate variance. In our principal components analysis of p. 120 the first three eigenvalues absorbed 95·4% of this variance. It should be clear by now that principal components and Factor Analysis are totally different techniques. It is indeed unfortunate that they have become confused in the literature.

As to the interpretation of the 'loadings' in $\hat{\mathbf{\Gamma}}$ we can only draw the biologist's attention to (i) the 'general factor' and a second (bi-polar) factor in which the hind femoral and the elytron lengths play a dominant role, (ii) the antithetical position taken by the aggregate of the width of the grasshopper's head, its pronotal width, and its prozonal length in relation to the other five measured parts which are weighted differently, and (iii) the importance of the metazonal length and the hind femoral width, offsetting one another, in the third factor. Blackith (1960)† has made a Centroid Factor Analysis of all ten (instead of eight) variates and the reader is referred to that paper for further details.

Rotation

The objectives and techniques associated with the 'rotation' of the m estimated common factor axes into supposedly more meaningful positions occupy a large part of the existing texts on Factor Analysis. Thus one chapter of Burt (1940), three chapters of Thurstone (1947), three of Thomson (1951), six (shorter) chapters of Cattell (1952), two of Adcock (1954), two of Fruchter (1954), four chapters of Harman (1960), and one chapter of Lawley and Maxwell (1963) are devoted specifically to the computational procedures of rotation while other chapters of these books usually contain discussions *pro* and *con*.

Two different types of argument are used to justify the rotation of a set of common factor axes found by some standard computational procedure – usually the Centroid approximation to Principal Factor Analysis. The first of these stems from the psychologist's feeling that he knows what 'factors' are common to certain of the p variates observed (which are usually 'tests' of one kind or another in his case) and which variates do not call these or other 'factors' into play. He can therefore group the variates together in a significant manner and can rotate the factor axes so that the loadings (g-coefficients in our notation) attached to factors that should not appear in the specified group of tests are (approximately) zero.

This argument lost its appeal when it appeared that psychologists had different views on the 'factors' that entered into the various tests used.

† Cited in Chapter Six.

A particularly wide gap existed between those who would allow a 'general' factor to appear (with positive loadings) in all the tests (i.e., the first column of positive elements in $\mathbf{\Gamma}$ would be left unrotated) and those who denied the existence of such a factor in a broad battery of tests. An instructive example of the divergent interpretations that result from these two views is provided in the notes by Burt and Jackson, respectively (1960).†

The second argument rests on Thurstone's (1947) notion of 'simple structure'. Briefly $\mathbf{\Gamma}$ has to be transformed to a matrix $\mathbf{G}$ which has a large number of strategically placed zero elements. Thus each row should have at least one zero (since a test should not evoke all the m 'factors of the mind') and every column of $\mathbf{G}$ should have at least m zeros. Thurstone laid down three other criteria for the zero elements of $\mathbf{G}$ and in 1954 attempted to provide a more automatic rotational procedure as follows.

If we write

$$\underset{(p\times m)}{\mathbf{\Gamma}} = \begin{bmatrix} \mathbf{h}_1' \\ \mathbf{h}_2' \\ \cdot \\ \cdot \\ \cdot \\ \mathbf{h}_p' \end{bmatrix} \quad \text{and } \mathbf{G} = \mathbf{\Gamma T}$$

with

$$\underset{(m\times m)}{\mathbf{T}} = \{\mathbf{t}_1 \quad \mathbf{t}_2 \quad \dots \quad \mathbf{t}_m\}$$

then Thurstone chooses

$$\mathbf{t}_j = (\mathbf{\Gamma}'\mathbf{W}_j\mathbf{\Gamma})^{-1}\mathbf{h}_{k_j}/\{\mathbf{h}_{k_j}'(\mathbf{\Gamma}'\mathbf{W}_j\mathbf{\Gamma})^{-2}\mathbf{h}_{k_j}\}^{1/2}$$

where $\mathbf{W}_j$ is a $(p\times p)$ diagonal matrix of positive weights and the denominator is merely a normalization factor which ensures that the sum of the squares of the components of $\mathbf{t}_j$ is unity.

The weights of $\mathbf{W}_1$ are obtained as follows. Select k_1 as a row of $\mathbf{\Gamma}$ with a number of small elements as well as some large ones, and form the p-component vector $\mathbf{\Gamma h}_{k_1}$. Rank these p components in order of absolute size and ascribe the weight 6 to the smallest one-seventh (i.e., $p/7$ in number) of them; then the weight 5 to the next smallest seventh; and so on until finally the weight 0 is ascribed to the largest seventh. These weights are inserted into the p diagonal cells of $\mathbf{W}_j$ in such a way that each weight corresponds to the element of $\mathbf{x}$ in the same row.

† A biological example is obtained by comparing Tanner and Burt's (1954) re-analysis of Sewall Wright's (1932) hen-bone data by the bi-factor method, and Sokal's (1958*a*) interpretation of these data using 'simple structure'.

Having calculated $\mathbf{t}_1$ the row k_2 is chosen to correspond with an x-variate that has a near-zero component in $\mathbf{t}_1$. The weights of $\mathbf{W}_2$ are then computed as they were in $\mathbf{W}_1$ and these provide $\mathbf{t}_2$. Then k_3 is chosen as the number of an x-variate with near-zero components in *both* $\mathbf{t}_1$ and $\mathbf{t}_2$. And so on.

Note that the rotation produces correlated factors (see p. 155) with variance–covariance matrix

$$\boldsymbol{\Psi} = \mathbf{AA}' = \mathbf{T}^{-1}(\mathbf{TAA}'\mathbf{T}')(\mathbf{T}')^{-1} = \mathbf{T}^{-1}(\mathbf{T}')^{-1} = (\mathbf{T}'\mathbf{T})^{-1}$$

In order to avoid the arbitrary selection of k_1 Sokal (1958*a*) proposed the simultaneous calculation of $\mathbf{t}_j$ for $k_1 = 1, 2, \ldots p$ and the subsequent choice of the m of these vectors which are the most nearly orthogonal to one another. His paper contains five examples of the application of the methods to biological data.

It may be added that a number of other analytical procedures have been designed to effectuate rotations to different forms of 'simple structure' (Harman, 1960, Chapters 14 and 15).

However, it appears to the writer that none of the psychologists' arguments in favour of rotation apply to the biological field. Reading the psychometric literature one is impressed by the widespread view that Factor Analysis of a series of p carefully chosen tests 'extracts' the hidden 'factors of the mind' that are exercised in answering the test questions. In our opinion no such claim can be made when Factor Analysis is applied to biological data. This should be clear to a biologist whose p measurements on an animal or a plant are made because they are convenient (or even the only ones possible) rather than the result of carefully designed 'tests' of that animal's reactions under a wide variety of circumstances. It seems to us, too, that the notion of 'simple structure' does not apply where a given measurement x is merely one of many designed to 'summarize' the animal or plant rather than to utilize one or two of its 'factors'. Readers interested in the various rotational techniques should therefore consult one of the texts cited above.

A note on 'Normality'

Throughout this monograph we have assumed that the sample of N univariate or multivariate observations has been drawn from a Normal universe. When an appreciable degree of skewness is present in the observations, or when variances are functions of the mean, we have supposed that appropriate transformations have been made to secure approximate Normality. In general, directly observed biological measurements and many qualitative characters are distributed in a manner that does not diverge too far from the Normal or can be made to assume this form (see, e.g., Sokal and Daly, 1961, for a number of examples). Furthermore, the distribution of a linear compound of a number of random variables tends towards the Normal as the number of variates increases (unless one or more of the coefficients used dominate the rest).

However, indices constructed from Normally distributed variates may well have distributions that are far from Normal. An immediate example is provided by the sum of the squares of N Normally distributed variates measured from the sample mean. This sum is distributed proportionally to χ^2_{N-1} (the constant of proportionality being σ^2, the variance of the sampled universe), and this distribution only tends to Normality as N becomes large. Another example is the quotient of two Normally distributed variables.

But not all the procedures we have introduced are equally disturbed by a lack of Normality in the observations. The methods of Part A are all 'robust' in the sense that deviations from Normality of the distribution of the residual e are relatively unimportant (Chapter 10 of Scheffé, 1959, cited in Chapter One). However, the tests of Part B are likely to be more closely dependent on the correctness of the multivariate Normality of the observations. Though numerical examples are scarce in the literature on this subject we would think that Bartlett's test of the equivalence of h variance–covariance matrices would be very sensitive to departures from Normality and that the same would be true of the tests of the sizes of k and m in Chapter Six and this chapter, respectively. In fact the whole concept of ellipsoids of variation and the rotation of axes to produce uncorrelated variates is so closely linked with the multivariate Normal distribution that the methods of these two chapters should really only be applied to data of this type.† On the other hand the choice of the directions of the canonical axes has nothing to do with Normality, but the subsequent test of 'how many axes' has. This encourages us to use canonical analysis on quantal variates but leaves the test of its success rather rough and ready.

The use of Factor Analysis and its surrogates in biology

We have mentioned that some biologists have used the terminology of Factor Analysis in describing principal components analyses of multivariate data. Others, understandably, have used simpler techniques to achieve a similar objective. In addition there is a group of biological

† 'Presence' *vs.* 'absence' of p different plant species on N sample quadrats represents the limiting case of a measure of the amount of plant cover which could be Normally distributed. The calculation of a matrix of correlation coefficients (tetrachoric r) from pairs of 2×2 frequency tables could thus be an approximation to the correct matrix. Such matrices have been subjected to Factor Analysis by Burt (1962). For simpler procedures with the same 'factor' objectives, see Goodall (1953), Vries (1954), and Williams and Lambert (1959).

articles in which factor analytic methods have been used to discriminate between species. We will therefore conclude this booklet with a critical review of these and other publications.

At the outset we remind our readers that:

(i) Principal components analysis is intended to achieve a parsimonious summarization of a random sample from a *single* universe of multivariate Normal measurements;
(ii) Canonical analysis is a procedure of discriminating as clearly as possible between *two* or *more* multivariate Normal universes with the *same* variance–covariance matrix; and
(iii) Factor Analysis is an attempt to elicit the underlying Normal multivariate *structure* of a universe that can be sampled with respect to many correlated variates.

While (i) may tend to merge into (iii) when we ignore the smallest $p-k$ eigenvalues of its analysis, conceptually the bases and the computational procedures of the two techniques are (or should be) quite different.

Now suppose we have measured p variates on N_j specimens of a given species of bee ($j = 1, 2, \dots h$); $\sum_{j=1}^{h} N_j = N$. Some of these variates may be qualitative (e.g., the colour of the abdomen), others discrete (e.g., the number of antennal segments), while some will be measured lengths or weights. Possibly some of these measurements will have been transformed by taking their logarithms or their square roots, etc., in order to make them conform more closely to Normal form. The most cogent procedure to discriminate between these h species of bees and to discover their underlying affinities is canonical analysis. It has been described in Chapter Seven.

But, following Bartlett (1948), let us examine the determinantal equation of such an analysis on the supposition that $N \to \infty$ and that p is larger than $h-1$. This equation, namely (14) of Chapter Seven, can be written as

$$|\boldsymbol{\Xi} - \nu\boldsymbol{\Sigma}| = 0$$

and has $h-1$ non-zero (positive) roots. Here $\boldsymbol{\Xi}$ is the 'between species', and $\boldsymbol{\Sigma}$ the 'within species', variance–covariance matrix. Now, if a symmetrical $p \times p$ determinant is of rank $h-1 < p$ its order can be reduced from p to $h-1$ by the same linear operations on its rows and columns. We may therefore rewrite the foregoing determinantal equation as

$$|\boldsymbol{\Xi}^* - \nu\boldsymbol{\Sigma}^*| = 0$$

where both matrices are $(h-1) \times (h-1)$ and symmetric.

We now suppose that the off-diagonal terms of $\mathbf{\Sigma}^*$ are zero (a very severe restriction) and thus replace our equation by

$$|\Xi^* - \nu \,\text{diag}\, \mathbf{\Sigma}^*| = 0$$

In order to reduce the matrix Ξ^* to the form of a correlation matrix we must pre-multiply and post-multiply by $(\text{diag}\,\Xi^*)^{-1/2}$. Doing this to the whole matrix expression results in

$$|\mathbf{R}_P - \nu\,(\text{diag}\,\Xi^*)^{-1/2}\,\text{diag}\,\mathbf{\Sigma}^*\,(\text{diag}\,\Xi^*)^{-1/2}| = 0$$

where

$$\mathbf{R}_P = (\text{diag}\,\Xi^*)^{-1/2}\,\Xi^*\,(\text{diag}\,\Xi^*)^{-1/2}$$

is the $(h-1)\times(h-1)$ correlation matrix between h species with the 'average species' eliminated, and the term which ν multiplies is a diagonal matrix, the typical element of which is the jth diagonal element of $\mathbf{\Sigma}^*$ divided by the jth diagonal element of Ξ^*. Now, if these diagonal elements can be replaced by unities (which is another strong restriction) the determinantal equation reduces to

$$|\mathbf{R}_P - \nu\mathbf{I}| = 0$$

and the canonical analysis is then the equivalent of a principal components analysis of a matrix of *correlation coefficients between individual species of bees*.

The foregoing analysis indicates that if (1) the measured variates are uncorrelated (which could, of course, be achieved by a preliminary principal components analysis of $\mathbf{\Sigma}$), and (2) the corresponding diagonal elements of Ξ and $\mathbf{\Sigma}$ are equal, then a canonical analysis may be replaced by a principal components analysis of correlation coefficients between the different species. We might attempt to estimate $\mathbf{R}_P$ by calculating the $h(h-1)/2$ correlation coefficients between each pair of species of bees, any species being represented by p specified measurements made on *one* of its members.

We have thus seen that the replacement of a canonical analysis by a principal components analysis of a matrix of 'between species' correlation coefficients is plagued by unjustified assumptions. However, it is logically more satisfactory than the concept of drawing a random sample of p h-tuple measurements from an h-variate Normal universe, when p is actually a *carefully chosen* set of characteristics and the h variates are the species that Chance has made conveniently available to the biologist! The arbitrary nature of the subsequent Factor Analysis is emphasized when we try to apply maximum-likelihood and to determine the 'proper' value of m.

Turning, now, to the summary on pp. 174–175 of procedures used by biologists (other than anthropologists) in their Factor Analyses we notice that four articles, namely Matsakis (1957*b*), Sokal (1958*b*), Morishima and Oka (1960), and Rohlf and Sokal (1962), employ the dubious techniques based on between-species correlation coefficients. In all cases of this type we would recommend the replacement of the measurements on a single animal per species by measurements on at least two animals† and the subsequent canonical analysis of the data. If certain of the characters do not vary at all 'within' a species they can be used as distinguishing marks supplementary to the species name.

The attempt to classify animals and plants by means of indices of 'between species' likeness has not been limited to Factor Analysis. Although some of these indices involve correlation coefficients or other statistical measures of similarity none of them regard the measured animals, plants or bacteria as samples from specific universes – as they surely must be. Thus none of these techniques, cited by Sneath and Sokal (1962), can provide any measure of the correctness of their classifications nor can convincing reasons be given for preferring any one method over the others.

There is, however, a case where correlations between observed species have statistical validity. Goodall (1954)‡ has made a principal components analysis of a sample of 32 equal rectangular areas (160×80 m) of virgin mallee scrub vegetation. The sample areas were measured as to their percentage cover by each of 14 ($= p$) species of plants, each percentage reading being transformed by the arcsine-root transformation. The first five principal axes of the resulting 14×14 correlation matrix were found to be 'significant' by Bartlett's criterion. Similarly Dagnelie's (1960) paper, cited in the exhibit, utilized coded qualitative variates in calculating the correlation coefficients between plant species observed in greater or lesser abundance in a sample of 80 beech groves. Another illustration is found in Reyment (1963)§. These papers provide examples where correlations 'between species' are valid parameters of a single p-variate Normal universe of 'areas'. In fact, with this type of material it is hard to see the justification for calculating correlation coefficients between every pair of p areas based on a 'sample' of 20 'chosen' species (Williams and Lambert, 1961).

† Though we cannot test the equality of the variance–covariance matrices for the different species unless we measure at least $p+1$ animals per species.

‡ Cited in Chapter Six.

§ This author ignored the linear restriction on his 17 variates which always add to 600, a matter discussed in detail by Slater (1951).

Author	Populations	No. sampled	Measurements made	Matrix factored	Interpretation of factors found
Wright (1932, 1954)	3 of rabbits and one of hens	370, 27, 112, and 276	5 or 6 lengths of bones and, in two samples, the ear length and the weight	Correlations between the 5, 6 or 7 measurements	A general size factor and group factors for (a) the head, (b) the limbs, and (c) the hindlimbs (wings)
Stroud (1953)	Soldiers and imagoes of 48 and 43 species, respectively, of termites	1 insect per species but 2 in two cases	14 external body-part lengths	Correlations between 14 measurements	A head-volume factor, a leg factor and an antennal factor for soldiers; a head-volume factor for imagoes; other factors non-regional
Tanner and Burt (1954)	2 of dairy cows	67 Shorthorns and 105 Ayrshires	11 external linear body measurements	Correlations between 11 measurements	A general size factor and a factor for linearity of build in both breeds. Factors for limb and body lengths, for body width and depth (Shorthorns), and for breadth of pelvis and body depth (Ayrshires)
Ferrari *et al.* (1957)	3 years' grass yields, separately	50 sites	23 physical and chemical variables	Correlations between 23 measurements	Yield, content and fertilization factors
Matsakis (1957*a*)	The isopod *Ideotea viridis*	92 subdivided by sex	Lengths of body and 7 external parts	Correlations between 8 measurements	A general growth factor; a factor determining the enlargement of the third pereionite among females only; and a factor determining the growth of the flagella and cephalon and inhibiting that of the sixth pereionite
Matsakis (1957*b*)	8 terrestrial isopods	1 isopod of each form (?)	18 external body-part lengths	Correlations between 8 forms of isopod	A general size factor and two non-overlapping group factors which separate the forms into groups of 5, 1 and 2, respectively
Sokal (1958*b*)	10 species of solitary bees	1 bee per species	122 characters coded in 2–8 classes	Correlations between 10 species	Four factors separate the 10 species into overlapping groups of 3, 3, 3 and 3, respectively

Dagnelie (1960)	38 species of plant and 9 ecological variates	80 beech groves	Each species or ecological variate coded in 2–6 classes	Correlations between species and/or ecological variates	Factors are found that group the species and classify the quality of the soils
Morishima and Oka (1960)	16 species of *Oryza*	31 strains (several plants per strain ?)	42 characters of the plant	Correlations between (the means of?) the 16 species	The four factors separate the species into two groups of 5 and 7, respectively, with the remaining 4 outside and not grouped
Pearce and Holland (1960)	Apple and pear trees, separately	Not stated	6 years' crop yields	Correlations between the years	A general cropping factor and a 'biennial' second factor
Sokal *et al.* (1961)	6 types of insect and physical measurements	34–55	19 biological characters and 6 physical	Correlations between the 25 measurements	Factors representing: (1) effect of solar energy, (2) moth larva and beetle reactions, (3) moth larva locomotion, (4) wasp reactions, (5) louse and beetle reactions, and (6) physical changes
Rohlf and Sokal (1962)	67 species of bees	1 bee per species	122 characters (see above)	3 sets of correlations between 40, 40 and 23 species, respectively	Species groupings derived by other methods broadly confirmed
Rasch (1962)	Heifers	107	13 body-part lengths	Correlations between 13 measurements	A height factor and a factor offsetting height against breadth measurements
Sokal (1962)	The aphid *Pemphigus populi-transversus*	345 pairs of alates from 23 different localities each providing 15 galls	12 body-part lengths and 6 enumerative characters	Correlations between 18 measurements	A general size factor, an antennal factor and a relationship between the sixth antennal segment and the tarsus emerged from the 'within gall' (two alates per gall) analysis
Reyment (1963)	Boreholes in Nigeria	28 boreholes each with 600 individual *ostracoda*	Relative frequency of occurrence of 17 species of *ostracoda*	Correlations between 17 species	Five environmental and five non-environmental factors

It may be added that Goodall's (*loc. cit.*) map of the area under study indicated that the nature of the terrain would result in at least two types of plant cover. The author attempted to differentiate between these types by interpreting the coefficients of each of the principal axes in terms of the areal distinctions it implicitly drew. The writer is unconvinced that an objective classification is achieved by contrasting, for example, the 'highs' and the 'lows' of a random sample from a single Normal universe. It appears to him that Goodall's classificatory objective would have been better achieved by separating the area into topologically similar sub-areas and by comparing their plant cover by means of a canonical analysis.

What we would describe as first steps in this direction were taken by Harberd (1962) with a similar type of data. Five sample turves were cut from each of 80 'interesting' sites and were each examined for the presence or absence of $p = 52$ plant species. Making the severely restrictive assumption that there is no correlation between species on any (supposedly uniform) site the author defines a within-site measure of variability which, in our notation, is $2\,\mathrm{tr}\,\hat{\mathbf{\Sigma}}^{(l)}$, $l = 1, 2, \ldots 80$, where $\mathrm{tr}\,\mathbf{A}$ stands for the sum of the diagonal elements of the matrix $\mathbf{A}$ (tr = trace). He then computes a measure of the difference between the first pair of sites ($N_1 = N_2 = 5$) as

$$\left(\frac{1}{N_1}+\frac{1}{N_2}\right)^{-1} \mathrm{tr}\left\{\mathbf{T}-\left(\frac{N_1}{N_1+N_2}\mathbf{W}^{(1)}+\frac{N_2}{N_1+N_2}\mathbf{W}^{(2)}\right)\right\}$$

where $\mathbf{W}^{(l)} = (N_l-1)\hat{\mathbf{\Sigma}}^{(l)}$ is the familiar 'within' sums of squares and products matrix of site l and $\mathbf{T} = \mathbf{W}+\mathbf{P}$. Since $\mathbf{W} = \mathbf{W}^{(1)}+\mathbf{W}^{(2)}$ the elimination of the 'weighting' of $\mathbf{W}^{(1)}$ and $\mathbf{W}^{(2)}$ would result in

$$\left(\frac{1}{N_1}+\frac{1}{N_2}\right)^{-1} \mathrm{tr}\,\mathbf{P} \quad \text{or} \quad \left(\frac{1}{N_1}+\frac{1}{N_2}\right)^{-1} \mathrm{tr}\,\hat{\mathbf{\Xi}}$$

since $\mathbf{P}$ has one degree of freedom. Harberd proceeds to calculate his (weighted) measure for every possible pair of the 80 sites and, in his paper, describes various methods of grouping the results in order to reach an informative arrangement of the corresponding sites. We note that he is essentially comparing summary statements (namely, traces) of matrices of 'between' variances computed for every possible pair of sites. We would naturally prefer to use canonical analysis – if a 'large' computer were available ($p = 52$).

A suggestion of Tukey (1951) was to use Factor Analysis on the point estimates of the 'components' of variance and covariance obtained in genetic experiments. The 'components of variance', or 'random effects', model in the analysis of variance is described in Chapter 7 of Scheffé (1959, cited in Chapter One). In the simple one-way layout with equal numbers of observations in each class, this model causes the 'between' and 'within' sums of squares to have expected values that differ by a multiple of the variance measuring differences between the various 'sub-species' (say). An estimate of this variance can be obtained by equating the sample values to their expectations. Tukey (*loc. cit.*) extended this notion to the multivariate case and showed how closely the first principal component accounted for a 4×4 'between' component variance–covariance matrix of measurements made on nine crosses between lines of corn.

Such an analysis can only be regarded as approximate since the distribution of the difference between two variance–covariance matrices derived from different Normal universes does not have the Wishart distribution (the distribution of $\hat{\mathbf{\Sigma}}$). In particular, some of the variance-component estimates may be negative (which results in 'imaginary' correlation coefficients for a variate with, presumably, a small 'real' variance!) and the covariance-components such that the corresponding correlation coefficients exceed unity. These features – which are the rule rather than the exception – do not encourage us to perform 'structural' analyses of 'component' variance–covariance matrices.

Nevertheless, two authors, Bailey (1956) and Sokal (1962), have used principal components (with subsequent rotation!) and centroid Factor Analysis, respectively, on the 'genetic' and 'environmental' correlation coefficients, respectively, estimated from multivariate analyses of variance of balanced† two-fold nested classifications. The former author obtained one negative variance out of nine 'environmental' variances in his first set of data‡ and chose to use the 'between litters within strains' correlation matrix in lieu. Sokal found one of the 18 'between' variances and four 'between-within' variances non-significant at the 1% level and accordingly deleted the corresponding variates in his component analyses; he mentions that 'some' of the variance components thus discarded were negative. It should be clear to readers why we advise great caution in the interpretation of such analyses.

The other articles on the summary exhibit which have not been mentioned above provide standard examples of factor analytic techniques. Two questions should be borne in mind by those who refer to them: (i) Would the summarization techniques of principal components analysis have produced different interpretations? and (ii) If more efficient estimation procedures had been used would the values of m have been very different? Above all, the reader should remember that any set of

† There was a slight imbalance in one of Bailey's two sets of data.

‡ Details were not provided for the second set.

biological measurements is a (hopefully) random sample from a universe, conceptually infinite, of such measurements. The use of statistical techniques such as Factor Analysis (or numerically simpler surrogates) should thus be accompanied by the appropriate significance tests. It is futile to analyse differences that could easily occur by chance.

In illustration of this warning we will examine the 25×25 correlation matrix published in Sokal and Daly (1961) and subjected to a Factor Analysis. In the procedural paper of Sokal, Daly and Rohlf (1961) it is stated that 'most variables had around 45' observations, that the minimum number was 34 and that the maximum was 55. The matrix was thus not derived by sampling N 25-variate observations although, because of careful variate transformations, the universe can reasonably be assumed multivariate Normal.

Now, if we have a sample of N from a p-variate Normal universe of uncorrelated variates, namely from $N(\boldsymbol{\mu}, \operatorname{diag}\boldsymbol{\Sigma})$, then it can be shown that

$$-\left(N - \frac{2p+11}{6}\right) \ln |\hat{\boldsymbol{\Sigma}}_R|$$

where $\hat{\boldsymbol{\Sigma}}_R$ is the sample correlation matrix, is approximately distributed as χ^2 with $p(p-1)/2$ degrees of freedom. No such statistic is available for the case where the elements of $\hat{\boldsymbol{\Sigma}}_R$ are based on different sample numbers. However, one might guess that the above test statistic could be used with N replaced by an 'average sample number' determined in an appropriate manner. This averaging is likely to give more weight to the smaller samples as would be the case, for example, if N were the harmonic, instead of the arithmetic, mean of the individual sample numbers.

Purely as an illustration of the sensitivity of the above test statistic to changes in N, we will use it on the Sokal and Daly (*loc. cit.*) matrix. A double-precision computer routine for determinants resulted in $|\hat{\boldsymbol{\Sigma}}_R| = 0{\cdot}2065717 \times 10^{-4}$ so that $-\ln |\hat{\boldsymbol{\Sigma}}_R| = 10{\cdot}7898$. We then have:

N	χ^2	$(2\chi^2)^{1/2} - (599)^{1/2}$	Pr ($\chi^2 \geqslant$ value shown)
40	321·896	0·899	0·1843
41	332·685	1·320	0·0934
42	343·475	1·735	0·0414
43	354·265	2·144	0·0160
44	365·055	2·546	0·0054
45	375·845	2·942	0·0016

In the foregoing we have used the fact that for large degrees of freedom $(2\chi^2)^{1/2} - (2f-1)^{1/2}$ is approximately $N(0, 1)$. Note that if the real average

N were 41 or less there would be no justification in making a Factor Analysis of the matrix. Even with an average of 42 or 43 the validity of a Factor Analysis could well be questioned. It is surprising to find the probability level changing so quickly for unit changes in the sample number.

Problems 8

1. Wright's (1954)† Principal Factor Analysis of his hen-bone correlation coefficients (which were reproduced in Problems 6) with $m = 3$ gave the following result

$$\hat{\mathbf{\Gamma}} = \begin{bmatrix} 0{\cdot}685 & 0{\cdot}361 & 0{\cdot}007 \\ 0{\cdot}639 & 0{\cdot}409 & -0{\cdot}030 \\ 0{\cdot}951 & -0{\cdot}083 & 0{\cdot}162 \\ 0{\cdot}946 & -0{\cdot}152 & 0{\cdot}168 \\ 0{\cdot}930 & -0{\cdot}180 & -0{\cdot}166 \\ 0{\cdot}942 & -0{\cdot}124 & -0{\cdot}154 \end{bmatrix}$$

It is proposed to use an orthogonal transformation matrix (Thomson, 1951)

$$\mathbf{T} = \begin{bmatrix} mq & mp & l \\ -lq & -lp & m \\ p & -q & 0 \end{bmatrix} \qquad \begin{aligned} l^2+m^2 &= 1 \\ p^2+q^2 &= 1 \end{aligned}$$

to 'rotate' $\hat{\mathbf{\Gamma}}$ into a matrix approximately of the form

$$\mathbf{G} = \begin{bmatrix} h_1 & 0 & 0 \\ h_2 & 0 & 0 \\ 0 & w_1 & 0 \\ 0 & w_2 & 0 \\ 0 & 0 & l_1 \\ 0 & 0 & l_2 \end{bmatrix}$$

in which the h's are head loadings, the w's wing loadings and the l's leg loadings. Determine the unknowns in $\mathbf{T}$ as follows: form the matrix $\hat{\mathbf{\Gamma}}\mathbf{T}$ and (i) add the elements of cells numbered (1, 3), (2, 3), (3, 3) and (4, 3), equate the result to zero and obtain l and m, (ii) add the elements of all the (eight) other zero cells, equate the result to zero and obtain p and q. Using these results compute the 18 elements of $\mathbf{G}$ and decide whether the simple three-factor interpretation is defensible.

† See references in Chapter Six.

2. Dagnelie has reported the following correlation matrix based on 43 ecological observational septuplets (5th Int. Biometric Conf. 1963):

$$\begin{bmatrix} 1\cdot00 & -0\cdot01 & 0\cdot22 & 0\cdot08 & -0\cdot15 & -0\cdot07 & 0\cdot08 \\ & 1\cdot00 & 0\cdot26 & -0\cdot16 & -0\cdot01 & 0\cdot24 & 0\cdot17 \\ & & 1\cdot00 & 0\cdot53 & -0\cdot18 & 0\cdot06 & 0\cdot34 \\ & & & 1\cdot00 & -0\cdot05 & -0\cdot14 & -0\cdot11 \\ & & & & 1\cdot00 & 0\cdot30 & 0\cdot12 \\ & & & & & 1\cdot00 & 0\cdot67 \\ & & & & & & 1\cdot00 \end{bmatrix}$$

The (coded or transformed) variates measured at each of the 43 stations were: slope, exposure, acidity, organic matter, sand, lime, and clay. Could this matrix have been sampled from a universe with $\mathbf{\Sigma}_R = \mathbf{I}$?

3. The foregoing matrix was subjected by Dagnelie to a Principal Factor Analysis followed by an orthogonal rotation which emphasized the 'textural' and 'chemical' nature of the two 'significant' factors. The two matrices of loadings were:

$$\hat{\mathbf{\Gamma}} = \begin{bmatrix} 0\cdot05 & 0\cdot24 \\ 0\cdot35 & 0\cdot01 \\ 0\cdot41 & 0\cdot73 \\ -0\cdot03 & 0\cdot66 \\ 0\cdot18 & -0\cdot28 \\ 0\cdot73 & -0\cdot29 \\ 0\cdot80 & -0\cdot05 \end{bmatrix} \quad \text{and} \quad \mathbf{G} = \begin{bmatrix} -0\cdot02 & 0\cdot25 \\ 0\cdot33 & 0\cdot10 \\ 0\cdot20 & 0\cdot81 \\ -0\cdot20 & 0\cdot63 \\ 0\cdot24 & -0\cdot23 \\ 0\cdot78 & -0\cdot08 \\ 0\cdot78 & 0\cdot17 \end{bmatrix}$$

(a) How much of the trace of $\hat{\mathbf{\Sigma}}_R$ is 'absorbed' by these two factors?
(b) Is $m = 2$ sufficiently large?
(c) What is the angle of rotation α implied in the use of the transformation matrix

$$\mathbf{T} = \begin{bmatrix} \cos\alpha & \sin\alpha \\ -\sin\alpha & \cos\alpha \end{bmatrix}$$

to produce $\mathbf{G}$ from $\hat{\mathbf{\Gamma}}$?

References in Chapter Eight

ADCOCK, C. J. (1954) *Factorial Analysis for Non-Mathematicians*. Melbourne.

ANDERSON, T. W. and RUBIN, H. (1956) 'Statistical inferences in factor analysis.' *Proc. III Berkeley Symp. Math. Statist. Prob.* **5**, 111–150.

BAILEY, D. W. (1956) 'A comparison of genetic and environmental principal components of morphogenesis in mice.' *Growth* **20**, 63–74.

BARTLETT, M. S. (1948). 'Internal and external factor analysis.' *Brit. J. Statist. Psychol.* **1**, 73–81.

BECHTOLDT, H. P. (1961) 'An empirical study of the factor analysis stability hypothesis.' *Psychometrika* **26**, 405–432.

BURT, C. (1940) *The Factors of the Mind*. London.

BURT, C. (1962) *Mental and Scholastic Tests*. London.

BURT, C. and BANKS, C. (1947) 'A factor analysis of body measurements for British adult males.' *Ann. Eugen., Lond.* **13**, 238–256.

CATTELL, R. B. (1952) *Factor Analysis*. New York.

DAGNELIE, P. (1960) 'Contribution à l'étude des communautés végétales par l'analyse factorielle.' *Bull. Serv. Carte phytogéog. B*, **5**, 7–71, 93–195.

EMMETT, W. G. (1949) 'Factor analysis by Lawley's method of maximum likelihood.' *Brit. J. Statist. Psychol.* **2**, 90–97.

FERRARI, TH. J., PIJL, H. and VENEKAMP, J. T. N. (1957) 'Factor analysis in agricultural research.' *Netherlands J. Agric. Sci.* **5**, 211–221.

FRUCHTER, B. (1954) *Introduction to Factor Analysis*. New York.

GOODALL, D. W. (1953) 'Objective methods for the classification of vegetation. I: The use of positive interspecific correlation.' *Aust. J. Bot.* **1**, 39–63.

HARBERD, D. J. (1962) 'Application of a multivariate technique to ecological survey.' *J. Ecol.* **50**, 1–17.

HARMAN, H. H. (1960) *Modern Factor Analysis*. Chicago.

HOWE, W. G. (1955) *Some Contributions to Factor Analysis*. ORNL 1919, Oak Ridge, Tenn.

IMBRIE, J. (1963) *Factor and Vector Analysis Programs for Analysing Geologic Data*. Tec. Rep. 6, ONR Task No. 389–135.

JACKSON, M. A. and BURT, C. (1960) 'The factor analysis of the Wechsler Scale. I and II (respectively).' *Brit. J. Statist. Psychol.* **13**, 79–87.

JÖRESKOG, K. G. (1963). *Statistical Estimation in Factor Analysis*. Stockholm.

LAWLEY, D. N. (1940) 'The estimation of factor loadings by the method of maximum likelihood.' *Proc. roy. Soc. Edinb.* **60**, 64–82.

LAWLEY, D. N. (1942) 'Further investigations in factor estimation.' *Proc. roy. Soc. Edinb.* **61**, 176–185.

LAWLEY, D. N. and MAXWELL, A. E. (1963) *Factor Analysis as a Statistical Method*. London.

LORD, F. M. (1956) 'A study of speed factors in tests and academic grades.' *Psychometrika* **21**, 31–50.

MATSAKIS, J. (1957*a*) 'Étude par l'analyse factorielle des dimensions du corps des mâles, des femelles et des indifférenciés d'une population d'*Idotea viridis*, Ispode valvifère.' *C. R. Acad. Sci., Paris* **244**, 1082–1084.

MATSAKIS, J. (1957*b*) 'Sur la classification et les affinités de quelques Isopodes terrestres. Arguments biométriques.' *C. R. Acad. Sci., Paris* **245**, 584–586.

MAXWELL, A. E. (1961) 'Recent trends in factor analysis.' *J. R. Statist Soc. A*, **124**, 49–59.

MAXWELL, A. E. (1964) 'Calculating maximum-likelihood factor loadings.' *J. R. Statist. Soc. A*, **127**, 238–241.

MORISHIMA, H. and OKA, H-I. (1960) 'The pattern of interspecific variation in the genus *Oryza*: Its quantitative representation by statistical methods.' *Evolution* **14**, 153–165.

RAO, C. R. (1955) 'Estimation and tests of significance in factor analysis.' *Psychometrika* **20**, 93–111.

RASCH, D. (1962) 'Die Faktoranalyse und ihre Anwendung in der Tierzucht.' *Biom. Z.* **4**, 15–39.

REYMENT, R. A. (1963) 'Multivariate analytical treatment of quantitative species associations: an example from palaeœcology.' *J. Anim. Ecol.* **32**, 535–547.

ROHLF, F. J. and SOKAL, R. R. (1962) 'The description of taxonomic relationships by factor analysis.' *Syst. Zool.* **11** 1–16.

SLATER, P. (1951) 'The transformation of a matrix of negative correlations.' *Brit. J. Statist. Psychol.* **4**, 9–20.

SNEATH, P. H. A. and SOKAL, R. R. (1962). 'Numerical taxonomy.' *Nature* **193**, 855–860.

SOKAL, R. R. (1958*a*) 'Thurstone's analytical method for simple structure and a mass modification thereof.' *Psychometrika* **23**, 237–257.

SOKAL, R. R. (1958*b*) 'Quantification of the systematic relationships and of phylogenetic trends.' *Proc. X Int. Cong. Ent.* **1**, 409–415.

SOKAL, R. R. (1962) 'Variation and covariation of characters of alate *Pemphigus populi-transversus* in eastern North America.' *Evolution* **16**, 227–245.

SOKAL, R. R. and DALY, H. V. (1961) 'An application of factor analysis to insect behavior.' *Univ. Kan. Sci. Bull.* **42**, 1067–1097.

SOKAL, R. R., DALY, H. V. and ROHLF, F. J. (1961) 'Factor analytical procedures in a biological model.' *Univ. Kan. Sci. Bull.* **42**, 1099–1121.

STROUD, C. P. (1953) 'An application of factor analysis to the systematics of *Kalothermes*.' *Syst. Zool.* **2**, 76–92.

TANNER, J. M. and BURT, A. W. A. (1954) 'Physique in the infra-human mammalia: A factor analysis of body measurements of dairy cows.' *J. Genet.* **52**, 36–51.

TEISSIER, G. (1956) 'Analyse factorielle de la variabilité de *Dixippus morosus* aux différents stades de son developpement. *XIV Int. Cong. Zool. 1953 Proc.* 250–252.

THOMSON, G. (1951) *The Factorial Analysis of Human Ability.* London.

THURSTONE, L. L. (1947) *Multiple-Factor Analysis.* Chicago.

THURSTONE, L. L. (1954) 'An analytical method for simple structure.' *Psychometrika* **19**, 173–182.

TUKEY, J. W. (1951) 'Components in regression.' *Biometrics* **7**, 33–69.

VRIES, D. M. DE (with BARETTA, J. P. and HAMMING, G.) (1954) 'Constellation of frequent herbage plants, based on their correlation in occurrence.' *Vegetatio* **5–6**, 105–111.

WILLIAMS, W. T. and LAMBERT, J. M. (1959) 'Multivariate methods in plant ecology. I: Association-analysis in plant communities.' *J. Ecol.* **47**, 83–101.

WILLIAMS, W. T. and LAMBERT, J. M. (1961) 'Multivariate methods in plant ecology. III: Inverse association-analysis.' *J. Ecol.* **49**, 717–729.

WRIGHT, S. (1932) 'General, group and special size factors.' *Genetics* **17**, 603–619.

WRIGLEY, C. (1959) 'The effect upon the communalities of changing the estimate of the number of factors.' *Brit. J. Statist. Psychol.* **12**, 35–54.

APPENDIX I

Useful Computer Routines

It is important to remember that the production of any entirely new computer program is costly. For example, the development *ab initio* of an IBM 709 double-precision program for the canonical analysis described hereafter required 100 hours of a very experienced programmer's (W. E. Wilkinson's) time and several hours on the machine for testing and debugging. At the standard programmer's hourly rate of $10 and machine time at around $200 an hour, such an undertaking is to be viewed cautiously.

On the other hand every high-speed computer centre has a library of sub-routines that can be linked together, if need be, without much difficulty. Such routines include:

(i) Various transformations (e.g., to logs) of original data.
(ii) Computation of the $p \times p$ sums of squares and cross-products matrix from N p-variate observations.
(iii) The computation of (ii) but effected about the sample mean vector.
(iv) The computation of the product of an $(m \times n)$ and an $(n \times p)$ matrix.
(v) The calculation of the value of a given (square) determinant.
(vi) The calculation of the inverse of a given square matrix. [This routine may be 'disguised' under some such title as 'the solution of a set of simultaneous equations'.]

There is one other sub-routine that is fundamental to multivariate statistical calculations, namely the evaluation of the eigenvalues and eigenvectors of a square, symmetric, positive semidefinite matrix. If this is not already available a detailed description (with 'flow chart') of a suitable procedure is given by J. Greenstadt in Ralston, A. and Wilf, H. S. (1960). The biologist is recommended to ask that this program be written in double-precision arithmetic and that the degree of accuracy of the resolution of the given matrix be made available as part of the regular output.

Another useful reference is Cooley, W. W. and Lohnes, P. R. (1962) which provides the actual FORTRAN programs for many of the procedures described in this book. Nevertheless, for completeness, we outline below the five programs which encompass all the major computational problems described in the preceding pages. In general the programming and machine time required to produce these routines (if not already available) should not be excessive. At the worst the links between the successive standard sub-routines can be done by hand.

'Long' matrix multiplications

Two different types of 'long' matrices will be read into the computer from N data cards (where any such 'card' may include one or more 'trailer' cards). It is possible that N may be quite large, e.g., 1000 or more.

The first type of such matrix is $\mathbf{X}$ which is $(N \times p)$, where p is less than 50 – although its maximum size will actually depend on the computer used. We require to calculate and print-out:

(1) The matrix product $\mathbf{X}'\mathbf{X}$ which is $(p \times p)$;
(2) The sums of each of the p columns of $\mathbf{X}$ (call the resulting row vector $\mathbf{t}'$); and
(3) The difference $\mathbf{X}'\mathbf{X} - \mathbf{tt}'/N$ which is $(p \times p)$.

Item (1) is the sums of squares and cross-products (about the origin), while item (3) is the sums of squares and cross-products about the mean vector. This mean vector is given by $\mathbf{t}'/N$ and is likely to be required as a printed-out item.

Sometimes the matrix $\mathbf{X}$ will be partitioned into h sub-matrices so that

$$\mathbf{X} = \begin{bmatrix} \mathbf{X}_1 \\ \mathbf{X}_2 \\ \cdots \\ \cdots \\ \mathbf{X}_h \end{bmatrix}$$

where $\mathbf{X}_1$ is $(N_1 \times p)$, $\mathbf{X}_2$ is $(N_2 \times p)$, etc., and the foregoing three items will be required for all h subdivisions of the data as well as for the whole matrix $\mathbf{X}$.

[Occasionally the numbers N_j $(j = 1, 2, \ldots h)$ are large and the observations $\mathbf{X}_j$ 'replications' from the viewpoint of the Least Squares model. In other words, the model will use the same q z-values for every p-tuple in $\mathbf{X}_j$ and if $h > q$ (instead of $h = q$) there will be a residual from the model which can be compared with a 'within' matrix. This situation allows the use of a 'collapsed' procedure which will save punching and economize on machine time. Having calculated $\mathbf{X}'\mathbf{X}$ and

$$\sum_{j=1}^{h} \mathbf{X}_j'\mathbf{X}_j$$

we thereafter work only with the totals $\mathbf{t}'_j$ so that our new $\mathbf{X}$ is given by

$$\mathbf{X}_0 = \begin{bmatrix} \mathbf{t}'_1 \\ \mathbf{t}'_2 \\ \cdots \\ \cdots \\ \mathbf{t}'_h \end{bmatrix}$$

and the 'within' matrix is

$$\sum_{j=1}^{h} \mathbf{X}'_j \mathbf{X}_j - \mathbf{X}'_0 \mathbf{N}^{-1} \mathbf{X}_0$$

where $\mathbf{N}$ is a diagonal matrix with elements $N_1, N_2, \ldots N_h$, respectively, in its principal diagonal.]

The second type of 'long' matrix will sometimes accompany an $\mathbf{X}$ matrix. We will denote it by $\mathbf{Z}'$ which is $(N \times q)$, q being less than 50 when p is large. In such a case we require to calculate and print-out:

(1) $\mathbf{X}'\mathbf{X}$ which is $(p \times q)$;
(2) $\mathbf{ZZ}'$ which is $(q \times q)$; and
(3) $\mathbf{ZX}$ which is $(q \times p)$.

Note particularly that both p and q may be as small as unity. Furthermore, even when the last $q-1$ columns of $\mathbf{Z}'$ are to add to zero – as we have advocated in the text – only the original components need be punched. The computer can then proceed directly to $\mathbf{ZZ}'$ and $\mathbf{ZX}$ utilizing the correctional device of (3) on p. 184, the column totals for $\mathbf{Z}'$ being retained in 'memory' until the Np individual residuals from Ω are calculated (if they are required).

[If we have 'collapsed' $\mathbf{X}$ in the manner indicated above it means that

$$\mathbf{Z}' = \begin{bmatrix} \mathbf{Z}'_1 \\ \mathbf{Z}'_2 \\ \cdots \\ \cdots \\ \mathbf{Z}'_h \end{bmatrix}$$

where $\mathbf{Z}'_j$ is $(N_j \times q)$ and has identical rows. If this typical row is written $\mathbf{z}$ then we 'collapse' $\mathbf{Z}'$ to

$$\mathbf{Z}'_0 = \begin{bmatrix} \mathbf{z}'_1 \\ \mathbf{z}'_2 \\ \cdots \\ \cdots \\ \mathbf{z}'_h \end{bmatrix}$$

It can then be shown that

$$\mathbf{ZZ}' = \mathbf{Z}_0 \mathbf{N} \mathbf{Z}'_0 \quad \text{and} \quad \mathbf{ZX} = \mathbf{Z}_0 \mathbf{X}_0$$

and the 'residual' matrix calculated in the usual way (see below) will include (or be equal to, if $h = q$) the 'within' matrix given above.]

Notice that the largest matrix that has to be stored in the computer is of order $\max(p,q)$ and that the 'long' matrix multiplications are obtained directly from the punched-card input. The only time we need 'long' matrices in machine memory is if we require to tabulate the N p-tuples of residuals, namely $\mathbf{X}-\mathbf{Z}'\mathbf{B}$ which is $(N \times p)$.

Multivariate Least Squares model

The basic matrices for this technique are:

$$\mathbf{ZZ}' \qquad \mathbf{ZX} \qquad \mathbf{X}'\mathbf{X}$$

and their computation has been described above.

We now require the calculation and print-out of:

(1) $(\mathbf{ZZ}')^{-1}$ which is $(q \times q)$;

(2) the product $(\mathbf{ZZ}')^{-1}(\mathbf{ZX}) = \mathbf{B}$ which is $(q \times p)$;

(3) the difference $\mathbf{X}'\mathbf{X}-\mathbf{B}'(\mathbf{ZZ}')\mathbf{B}$ which is $(p \times p)$, and the determinant of this matrix.

An invariable second stage of this type of problem consists of the *deletion* (on the computer) of a specified set of *rows* of $\mathbf{Z}$ (which merely requires the deletion of the corresponding rows of $\mathbf{ZX}$ and the rows *and* columns of $\mathbf{ZZ}'$) and the recalculation of (1) to (3). In some cases it may be required to *replace* some of the deleted rows of $\mathbf{Z}$ and to *delete* others before recommencing the cycle.

Note that when $p = 1$ this model becomes the well-known univariate model, ANOVA.

Principal components

As mentioned in Chapter Six, a principal components analysis consists of finding the eigenvalues (latent roots, characteristic roots) and eigenvectors of a symmetric, positive definite matrix. The necessary computer routine will be found in Ralston and Wilf (*loc. cit.*).

Canonical analysis

We will term the following sequence of steps a canonical analysis of the two $p \times p$ symmetric matrices $\mathbf{B}$ and $\mathbf{W}$.

(1) Read in the two symmetric $p \times p$ matrices [of sums of squares and cross-products] together with their 'degrees of freedom' $h-1$ and $N-h$, respectively.

(2) Compute the p eigenvalues and corresponding (column) eigenvectors of $\mathbf{W}$. The former will be written as the diagonal matrix $\mathbf{\Lambda}$ and the eigenvectors will be the columns of $\mathbf{E}$.† [Hence $\mathbf{E}'\mathbf{WE} = \mathbf{\Lambda}$.]

† If any of the elements of $\mathbf{\Lambda}$ are small negative numbers (owing to the accuracy limitations of the computer) they must be replaced by zeros. The matrix $\mathbf{E}$ plays the same role as $\mathbf{A}'$ in Chapter Six.

(3) Form the matrix product

$$\mathbf{\Lambda}^{-1/2}\mathbf{E}'\mathbf{B}\mathbf{E}\mathbf{\Lambda}^{-1/2} \equiv \mathbf{C}$$

(4) Find the p eigenvalues (only) of $\mathbf{C}$. Of these $p-(h-1)$ will be zero if $p > h-1$.

(5) For each non-zero eigenvalue (in descending order of size) solve the first $p-1$ equations of the set

$$(\mathbf{B}-\phi\mathbf{W})\boldsymbol{\alpha} = \mathbf{0}$$

where ϕ is the given eigenvalue of $\mathbf{C}$, $\boldsymbol{\alpha}$ is a p-component vector of unknows with the last component set equal to unity.

(6) For each of the p (or $h-1$, if smaller) vectors $\boldsymbol{\alpha}$ compute the normalized equivalent

$$\left(\boldsymbol{\alpha}'\frac{\mathbf{W}}{N-h}\boldsymbol{\alpha}\right)^{-1/2}\boldsymbol{\alpha} \equiv \boldsymbol{\gamma}$$

The p (or $h-1$) vectors $\boldsymbol{\gamma}$ are the required canonical axes.

Principal Factor Analysis (PFA)

We here operate on the variance–covariance matrix, namely

$$(\mathbf{X}'\mathbf{X}-\mathbf{t}\mathbf{t}'/N)/(N-1) = \mathbf{\Sigma}$$

or on the corresponding correlation matrix

$$(\text{diag}\,\mathbf{\Sigma})^{-1/2}\mathbf{\Sigma}\,(\text{diag}\,\mathbf{\Sigma})^{-1/2} = \mathbf{\Sigma}_R$$

where diag $\mathbf{A}$ is the matrix $\mathbf{A}$ with all of its off-diagonal elements replaced by zeros. In either case the computational prcoedure is (with $m < p$ fixed at the outset):

(1) Calculate $\mathbf{\Sigma}^{-1}$ and $\{\text{diag}\,\mathbf{\Sigma}^{-1}\}^{-1} \equiv \mathbf{\Delta}_0$.

(2) Find the eigenvalues, $\mathbf{\Lambda}$, and eigenvectors, $\mathbf{E}$, of $\mathbf{\Sigma}-\mathbf{\Delta}_0$ where the columns of $\mathbf{\Lambda}$ and $\mathbf{E}$ are ordered according to the decreasing size of the eigenvalues.

(3) Write $\mathbf{\Lambda}_m$ for the $(m\times m)$ diagonal matrix of the m largest eigenvalues and $\mathbf{E}_m$ for the corresponding $(p\times m)$ matrix of eigenvectors.

(4) Obtain $\mathbf{\Delta}_1 = \text{diag}\,(\mathbf{\Sigma}-\mathbf{E}_m\mathbf{\Lambda}_m\mathbf{E}_m')$.

(5) Calculate $\mathbf{\Sigma}-\mathbf{\Delta}_1$ and repeat steps (2) through (4).

(6) Continue until two successive $\mathbf{\Delta}$'s agree to the d'th decimal place. Then test whether the first m eigenvalues of the final $\mathbf{\Sigma}-\mathbf{\Delta}$ are all non-negative. If so calculate $\mathbf{\Gamma} = \mathbf{E}_m\mathbf{\Lambda}_m^{1/2}$. If not, recommence step (2) with m increased by unity subject to $m < p$.

(7) Finally print-out: (a) the final m, $\mathbf{\Gamma}$ and $\mathbf{\Delta}$ and the number of iterations required, (b) $\mathbf{\Gamma}\mathbf{\Gamma}'$, (c) $|\mathbf{\Gamma}\mathbf{\Gamma}'+\mathbf{\Delta}|$ and $|\mathbf{\Sigma}|$.

Canonical Factor Analysis (CFA)

The necessary computational steps are as follows:

(1) Same as (1) of PFA.

(2) Set $\mathbf{B} = \mathbf{\Sigma} - \mathbf{\Delta}_0$, $\mathbf{W} = \mathbf{\Sigma}$ and $N - h = 1$.

(3) Make a canonical analysis of this **B** and **W** excluding the normalization of step (6).

(4) Write $\mathbf{A}_m$ for the $(p \times m)$ matrix of vectors $\boldsymbol{\alpha}$ corresponding to the m largest eigenvalues ϕ and let $\mathbf{\Phi}_m$ be the $(m \times m)$ diagonal matrix with the typical element

$$(\boldsymbol{\alpha}_i' \mathbf{W} \boldsymbol{\alpha}_i)^{-1} \phi_i \qquad (i = 1, 2, \ldots m)$$

(5) Calculate $\mathbf{\Delta}_1 = \text{diag}(\mathbf{\Sigma} - \mathbf{W}\mathbf{A}_m \mathbf{\Phi}_m \mathbf{A}_m' \mathbf{W}')$ and recommence the analysis at step (2) above with $\mathbf{\Delta}_1$ in lieu of $\mathbf{\Delta}_0$.

(6) Continue the iterative process until two successive $\mathbf{\Delta}$'s agree to the d'th decimal place. Then test whether the first m eigenvalues of the final **C** are all non-negative. If so calculate $\mathbf{\Gamma} = \mathbf{W}\mathbf{A}_m \mathbf{\Phi}_m^{1/2}$. If not, recommence step (2) with m increased by unity subject to $m < p$.

(7) Same as (7) of PFA.

References in Appendix I

COOLEY, W. W. and LOHNES, P. R. (1962) *Multivariate Procedures for the Behavioral Sciences*. New York.

RALSTON, A. and WILF, H. S. (1960) *Mathematical Methods for Digital Computers*. New York.

APPENDIX II

General Block Designs and Missing Observations

The general solution of the normal equations given in Chapter Four, namely

$$\hat{\boldsymbol{\beta}} = (\mathbf{ZZ}')^{-1}\mathbf{Zx} \tag{1}$$

requires the inversion of a qth order matrix. If an experiment consists of t 'treatments' arranged in b 'blocks' each consisting of k 'plots'† (so that $q = t+b-1$) the size of the matrix to be inverted can be reduced to the tth order. Furthermore, if the design of the experiment satisfies certain conditions (Pearce, 1963) this matrix inversion may even be effected on a desk machine.

The model Ω

In formulating the model Ω for an experiment of the foregoing type ($N = kb$) we will select the $q = t+b-1$ z-vectors to 'explain' the treatment and block effects as follows:

(1) We will absorb the 'general mean' vector into each of the treatment vectors. More specifically the ith treatment vector ($i = 1, 2, \ldots t$) will have a unit wherever treatment i occurs and a zero otherwise‡;

(2) Assuming that we are not interested in separate estimates of the block β's we will require the components of the block vectors to add to zero and the vector products to be zero. In other words we will impose 'spurious' orthogonality on the $b-1$ block-vectors. We will scale each of these vectors in such a way that the sum of the squares of the components equals k, the number of 'plots' per block.

† The more general case of unequal-sized blocks is considered by Freeman *et al.* (1962).

‡ This is thus a case where the components of t of the z-vectors of Ω do not add to zero.

The β-estimates

In order to separate the t treatment and the $b-1$ block vectors, each of which forms a natural group, we will partition the matrix $\mathbf{Z}'$ between the tth and ($t+1$th) column and write

$$\underset{(bk\times q)}{\mathbf{Z}'} = \left[\underset{(bk\times t)}{\mathbf{Z}_1'} \;\vdots\; \underset{(bk\times \overline{b-1})}{\mathbf{Z}_2'}\right] \tag{2}$$

We then obtain

$$\underset{(q\times q)}{\mathbf{ZZ}'} = \left[\begin{array}{c|c} \underset{(t\times t)}{\mathbf{Z}_1\mathbf{Z}_1'} & \underset{(t\times \overline{b-1})}{\mathbf{Z}_1\mathbf{Z}_2'} \\ \hline \underset{(\overline{b-1}\times t)}{\mathbf{Z}_2\mathbf{Z}_1'} & \underset{(\overline{b-1}\times \overline{b-1})}{\mathbf{Z}_2\mathbf{Z}_2'} \end{array}\right] \tag{3}$$

noting that the orthogonality of the block vectors means that

$$\mathbf{Z}_2\mathbf{Z}_2' = k\mathbf{I}_{b-1} \tag{4}$$

Inversion of this partitioned matrix may be effected by means of the following general lemma in which $\mathbf{P}$ and $\mathbf{S}$ are supposed to be square matrices.

Lemma **1**

$$\begin{bmatrix}\mathbf{P} & \mathbf{Q}\\ \mathbf{R} & \mathbf{S}\end{bmatrix}^{-1} \equiv \begin{bmatrix}\mathbf{\Omega} & -\mathbf{\Omega}\mathbf{Q}\mathbf{S}^{-1}\\ -\mathbf{S}^{-1}\mathbf{R}\mathbf{\Omega} & \mathbf{S}^{-1}+\mathbf{S}^{-1}\mathbf{R}\mathbf{\Omega}\mathbf{Q}\mathbf{S}^{-1}\end{bmatrix}$$

where

$$\mathbf{\Omega} = (\mathbf{P}-\mathbf{Q}\mathbf{S}^{-1}\mathbf{R})^{-1}$$

The lemma may be proved by multiplying both sides of its identity by

$$\begin{bmatrix}\mathbf{P} & \mathbf{Q}\\ \mathbf{R} & \mathbf{S}\end{bmatrix}$$

Using relations (1), (2) and (3) and the lemma we may write the vectors of Least Squares β-estimates as

$$\begin{aligned}\hat{\boldsymbol{\beta}} &= \left[\begin{array}{c|c}\mathbf{Z}_1\mathbf{Z}_1' & \mathbf{Z}_1\mathbf{Z}_2'\\ \hline \mathbf{Z}_2\mathbf{Z}_1' & \mathbf{Z}_2\mathbf{Z}_2'\end{array}\right]^{-1}\left[\begin{array}{c}\mathbf{Z}_1\mathbf{x}\\ \hline \mathbf{Z}_2\mathbf{x}\end{array}\right]\\ &= \left[\begin{array}{c|c}\mathbf{\Omega} & -k^{-1}\mathbf{\Omega}\mathbf{Z}_1\mathbf{Z}_2'\\ \hline -k^{-1}\mathbf{Z}_2\mathbf{Z}_1'\mathbf{\Omega} & k^{-1}\mathbf{I}_{b-1}+k^{-2}\mathbf{Z}_2\mathbf{Z}_1'\mathbf{\Omega}\mathbf{Z}_1\mathbf{Z}_2'\end{array}\right]\left[\begin{array}{c}\mathbf{Z}_1\mathbf{x}\\ \hline \mathbf{Z}_2\mathbf{x}\end{array}\right]\\ &= \left[\begin{array}{c}\mathbf{\Omega}(\mathbf{Z}_1\mathbf{x}-k^{-1}\mathbf{Z}_1\mathbf{Z}_2'\mathbf{Z}_2\mathbf{x})\\ \hline k^{-1}\{\mathbf{Z}_2\mathbf{x}-\mathbf{Z}_2\mathbf{Z}_1'\mathbf{\Omega}(\mathbf{Z}_1\mathbf{x}-k^{-1}\mathbf{Z}_1\mathbf{Z}_2'\mathbf{Z}_2\mathbf{x})\}\end{array}\right]\end{aligned} \tag{5}$$

in which

$$\underset{(t\times t)}{\mathbf{\Omega}} = (\mathbf{Z}_1\mathbf{Z}_1'-k^{-1}\mathbf{Z}_1\mathbf{Z}_2'\mathbf{Z}_2\mathbf{Z}_1')^{-1} \tag{6}$$

is the only matrix inversion required. Note that although we have restricted consideration to the univariate case where $\mathbf{x}$ is a bk-component vector, there is nothing to prevent $\mathbf{x}$ being replaced by $\mathbf{X}$, a $(bk \times p)$ matrix of multivariate observations. In fact much of the following analysis will also apply in the multivariate case.

A 'block totalling' matrix

The foregoing results can be vastly simplified. Let us adjoin a further (namely, a bth) column to the $(bk \times \overline{b-1})$ matrix $\mathbf{Z}_2'$. This column is to consist of bk components each equal to $1/\sqrt{b}$. The sum of the squares of these components is equal to $kb/b = k$, i.e., the same as the sum of the squares of the components of each of the $\overline{b-1}$ vectors in $\mathbf{Z}_2'$. Furthermore, since the components of every vector in $\mathbf{Z}_2'$ add to zero the product of the new vector and each of the original vectors is zero. We thus have using (4)

$$\begin{bmatrix} \underset{(\overline{b-1} \times bk)}{\mathbf{Z}_2} \\ \hdashline b^{-1/2}\mathbf{1}_{bk}' \end{bmatrix} [\mathbf{Z}_2' \;\vdots\; b^{-1/2}\mathbf{1}_{bk}] = \begin{bmatrix} k\mathbf{I}_{b-1} & \mathbf{0}_{b-1} \\ \mathbf{0}_{b-1}' & k \end{bmatrix} = k\mathbf{I}_b \tag{7}$$

Let us now introduce a square 'block totalling' matrix $\mathbf{B}$ of order bk. It is easily seen that if any bk-component column vector is pre-multiplied by

$$\underset{(bk \times bk)}{\mathbf{B}} = \begin{bmatrix} \mathbf{1}_k\mathbf{1}_k' & & & & \text{zeros} & \\ & \mathbf{1}_k\mathbf{1}_k' & & & & \\ & & \mathbf{1}_k\mathbf{1}_k' & & & \\ & & & \cdots & & \\ & \text{zeros} & & & \cdots & \\ & & & & & \mathbf{1}_k\mathbf{1}_k' \end{bmatrix} \tag{8}$$

the result is a bk-component column vector in which each of the b consecutive sets of k components of the original vector have been summed and *repeated k times*. We note that if $\mathbf{B}$ is applied to itself

$$\mathbf{BB} = \mathbf{B}^2 = k\mathbf{B} \tag{9}$$

The usefulness of this matrix $\mathbf{B}$ is seen when we consider

$$k[\mathbf{Z}_2' \;\vdots\; b^{-1/2}\mathbf{1}_{bk}] \begin{bmatrix} \mathbf{Z}_2 \\ \hdashline b^{-1/2}\mathbf{1}_{bk}' \end{bmatrix} = [\mathbf{Z}_2' \;\vdots\; b^{-1/2}\mathbf{1}_{bk}](k\mathbf{I}_b) \begin{bmatrix} \mathbf{Z}_2 \\ \hdashline b^{-1/2}\mathbf{1}_{bk}' \end{bmatrix}$$

$$= \left\{ [\mathbf{Z}_2' \;\vdots\; b^{-1/2}\mathbf{1}_{bk}] \begin{bmatrix} \mathbf{Z}_2 \\ \hdashline b^{-1/2}\mathbf{1}_{bk}' \end{bmatrix} \right\}^2$$

by means of (7). On comparing this result with (9) we find that

$$\mathbf{B} = [\mathbf{Z}_2' \mid b^{-1/2}\mathbf{1}_{bk}]\begin{bmatrix}\mathbf{Z}_2 \\ \hdashline b^{-1/2}\mathbf{1}_{bk}'\end{bmatrix} = \mathbf{Z}_2'\mathbf{Z}_2 + b^{-1}\mathbf{1}_{bk}\mathbf{1}_{bk}' \qquad (10)$$

Tocher's matrix

Relation (10) provides us with the simplification of the expressions (5) and (6) which we mentioned above. For on pre-multiplying (10) by $\mathbf{Z}_1$ and post-multiplying it by $\mathbf{Z}_1'$ we obtain, after rearrangement,

$$\mathbf{Z}_1\mathbf{Z}_2'\mathbf{Z}_2\mathbf{Z}_1' = \mathbf{Z}_1\mathbf{B}\mathbf{Z}_1' - b^{-1}(\mathbf{Z}_1\mathbf{1}_{bk})(\mathbf{1}_{bk}'\mathbf{Z}_1') \qquad (11)$$

Now let us introduce a so-called 'incidence matrix' $\mathbf{N}$ the (i, j) element of which is the number of times treatment i appears in block j ($i = 1, 2, 3, \ldots t$; $j = 1, 2, 3, \ldots b$). This number may conveniently be written as n_{ij}. Then, since the ith column of $\mathbf{Z}_1'$ contains a unit only when treatment i appears, we see that

$$\mathbf{1}_{bk}'\mathbf{Z}_1' = \left\{\sum_{j=1}^{b} n_{1j} \; \sum_{j=1}^{b} n_{2j} \ldots \sum_{j=1}^{b} n_{tj}\right\} = \{r_1 \; r_2 \ldots r_t\} = \mathbf{r}'$$

say, where r_i is the total number of 'replications' of treatment i in the whole experiment. Furthermore, $\mathbf{B}\mathbf{Z}_1'$ is a $(bk \times t)$ matrix the ith column of which contains n_{ij} repeated k times for each value of j. It is easily verified that

$$\begin{aligned}\mathbf{Z}_1\mathbf{B}\mathbf{Z}_1' &= \frac{1}{k}\mathbf{Z}_1\mathbf{B}^2\mathbf{Z}_1' \quad \text{using (9)} \\ &= \frac{1}{k}(\mathbf{B}\mathbf{Z}_1')'(\mathbf{B}\mathbf{Z}_1') \\ &= \mathbf{N}\mathbf{N}'\end{aligned}$$

Inserting these results in (11) and substituting into (6) we have

$$\underset{(t \times t)}{\mathbf{\Omega}} = (\mathbf{Z}_1\mathbf{Z}_1' - k^{-1}\mathbf{N}\mathbf{N}' + (bk)^{-1}\mathbf{r}\mathbf{r}')^{-1} \qquad (12)$$

where $\mathbf{Z}_1\mathbf{Z}_1'$ is a diagonal matrix the elements of which are those of the t-component vector $\mathbf{r}$. This relatively simple expression for inversion holds generally for block designs (with equal sized blocks). It first appeared in the literature in Tocher (1952).

The treatment $\hat{\beta}$'s

Turning now to the partitioned vector (5) we need consider only the first t components of $\hat{\boldsymbol{\beta}}$. Writing these in the form

$$\hat{\boldsymbol{\beta}}_1 = \mathbf{\Omega}\mathbf{Z}_1(\mathbf{x} - k^{-1}\mathbf{Z}_2'\mathbf{Z}_2\mathbf{x}) \qquad (13)$$

we see that the expression in parentheses is a bk-component vector each component of which is a linear combination of the observations. A glance at the two relations preceding (5) shows that $\mathscr{V}(\hat{\boldsymbol{\beta}}_1) = \boldsymbol{\Omega}\sigma^2$. As usual, σ^2 will be estimated by $\mathscr{S}^0_\Omega/(bk-q)$.

Now $\mathbf{Z}_1$ applied to a bk-component vector results in a vector of t components, the ith of which is the result of adding r_i components chosen out of the bk to correspond to treatment i. But, by (10),

$$\begin{aligned} k^{-1}\mathbf{Z}_2'\mathbf{Z}_2\mathbf{x} &= k^{-1}\mathbf{Bx}-(bk)^{-1}\mathbf{1}_{bk}\mathbf{1}_{bk}'\mathbf{x} \\ &= k^{-1}\mathbf{Bx}-\mathbf{1}_{bk}\bar{x} \end{aligned} \tag{14}$$

where $\bar{x}$ is the mean of the bk observations. Finally, $\mathbf{Bx}$ is a vector in which the total of the observations in each block is repeated k times; when $\mathbf{Z}_1$ is applied to it each block total is added as many times as treatment i appears in that block. We may thus write

$$k^{-1}\mathbf{Z}_1\mathbf{Z}_2'\mathbf{Z}_2\mathbf{x} = k^{-1}\mathbf{Nb}-\bar{x}\mathbf{r}$$

where $\mathbf{b}$ is the b-component vector of block totals.

Hence the t-component vector $\hat{\boldsymbol{\beta}}_1$ is given by

$$\hat{\boldsymbol{\beta}}_1 = \boldsymbol{\Omega}\mathbf{v} \equiv \boldsymbol{\Omega}(\mathbf{t}-k^{-1}\mathbf{Nb}+\bar{x}\mathbf{r}) \tag{15}$$

where $\mathbf{t}$ is the t-component vector of treatment *totals*.

The residual sums of squares

It remains to determine the two residual sums of squares, namely $\mathscr{S}^0_\Omega$ and $\mathscr{S}^0_\omega$, where the model ω has equated all the treatment β's to zero. We have, from p. 76 of Chapter Four,

$$\begin{aligned} \mathscr{S}^0_\Omega &= \mathbf{x}'\mathbf{x}-\mathbf{x}'[\mathbf{Z}_1' \mid \mathbf{Z}_2']\begin{bmatrix}\hat{\boldsymbol{\beta}}_1 \\ \hline \hat{\boldsymbol{\beta}}_2\end{bmatrix} \\ &= \mathbf{x}'\mathbf{x}-\mathbf{x}'\mathbf{Z}_1'\hat{\boldsymbol{\beta}}_1-\mathbf{x}'\mathbf{Z}_2'\{k^{-1}(\mathbf{Z}_2\mathbf{x}-\mathbf{Z}_2\mathbf{Z}_1'\hat{\boldsymbol{\beta}}_1)\} \quad \text{by (5)} \\ &= \mathbf{x}'\mathbf{x}-(\mathbf{x}'\mathbf{Z}_1'-k^{-1}\mathbf{x}'\mathbf{Z}_2'\mathbf{Z}_2\mathbf{Z}_1')\hat{\boldsymbol{\beta}}_1-k^{-1}\mathbf{x}'\mathbf{Z}_2'\mathbf{Z}_2\mathbf{x} \\ &= \mathbf{x}'\mathbf{x}-\mathbf{v}'\hat{\boldsymbol{\beta}}_1-\mathbf{x}'(k^{-2}\mathbf{B}^2\mathbf{x}-\mathbf{1}_{bk}\bar{x}) \quad \text{by (14) and (9)} \\ &= \mathbf{x}'\mathbf{x}-\mathbf{v}'\boldsymbol{\Omega}\mathbf{v}-k^{-1}\mathbf{b}'\mathbf{b}+bk\bar{x}^2 \end{aligned} \tag{16}$$

while, remembering to introduce a general-mean vector (or, equivalently, to measure all x's about their mean)

$$\begin{aligned} \mathscr{S}^0_\omega &= \mathbf{x}'\mathbf{x}-bk\bar{x}^2-\mathbf{x}'\mathbf{Z}_2'\{(\mathbf{Z}_2\mathbf{Z}_2')^{-1}\mathbf{Z}_2\mathbf{x}\} \\ &= \mathbf{x}'\mathbf{x}-bk\bar{x}^2-k^{-1}\mathbf{x}'\mathbf{Z}_2'\mathbf{Z}_2\mathbf{x} \quad \text{by (4)} \\ &= \mathbf{x}'\mathbf{x}-k^{-1}\mathbf{b}'\mathbf{b} \end{aligned} \tag{17}$$

These two residuals have $bk-t-b+1$ and $bk-b+1$ degrees of freedom, respectively.

Illustrations

As the first example we will use some numbers given by Kramer *et al.* (1957) to illustrate a 'singular group divisible partially balanced incomplete block design with two associate classes'. In the following layout the two-digit figures are the observations and the single digits represent the treatment from which they derive.

					b	**t**	**r**
Block 1:	1, 29	2, 38	3, 40	4, 33	140	76	3
Block 2:	5, 28	6, 37	7, 24	8, 24	113	116	3
Block 3:	1, 20	2, 37	5, 26	6, 33	116	100	3
Block 4:	3, 23	4, 22	7, 24	8, 15	84	81	3
Block 5:	1, 27	2, 41	7, 36	8, 28	132	83	3
Block 6:	3, 37	4, 26	5, 29	6, 37	129	107	3
						84	3
						67	3

$k = 4 \quad b = 6 \quad t = 8$

and $q = 13$

The incidence matrix is

$$\mathbf{N} = \begin{bmatrix} 1 & 0 & 1 & 0 & 1 & 0 \\ 1 & 0 & 1 & 0 & 1 & 0 \\ 1 & 0 & 0 & 1 & 0 & 1 \\ 1 & 0 & 0 & 1 & 0 & 1 \\ 0 & 1 & 1 & 0 & 0 & 1 \\ 0 & 1 & 1 & 0 & 0 & 1 \\ 0 & 1 & 0 & 1 & 1 & 0 \\ 0 & 1 & 0 & 1 & 1 & 0 \end{bmatrix} \quad \text{and} \quad \mathbf{NN}' = \begin{bmatrix} 3 & 3 & 1 & 1 & 1 & 1 & 1 & 1 \\ 3 & 3 & 1 & 1 & 1 & 1 & 1 & 1 \\ 1 & 1 & 3 & 3 & 1 & 1 & 1 & 1 \\ 1 & 1 & 3 & 3 & 1 & 1 & 1 & 1 \\ 1 & 1 & 1 & 1 & 3 & 3 & 1 & 1 \\ 1 & 1 & 1 & 1 & 3 & 3 & 1 & 1 \\ 1 & 1 & 1 & 1 & 1 & 1 & 3 & 3 \\ 1 & 1 & 1 & 1 & 1 & 1 & 3 & 3 \end{bmatrix}$$

while

$$\mathbf{rr}' = 9\mathbf{1}_8\mathbf{1}_8'$$

and $\mathbf{Z}_1\mathbf{Z}_1'$ is a diagonal matrix the diagonal elements of which are the components of $\mathbf{r}$.

The matrix for inversion is thus, from (12),

$$\mathbf{\Omega}^{-1} = \tfrac{1}{8}\begin{bmatrix} 21 & -3 & 1 & 1 & 1 & 1 & 1 & 1 \\ -3 & 21 & 1 & 1 & 1 & 1 & 1 & 1 \\ 1 & 1 & 21 & -3 & 1 & 1 & 1 & 1 \\ 1 & 1 & -3 & 21 & 1 & 1 & 1 & 1 \\ 1 & 1 & 1 & 1 & 21 & -3 & 1 & 1 \\ 1 & 1 & 1 & 1 & -3 & 21 & 1 & 1 \\ 1 & 1 & 1 & 1 & 1 & 1 & 21 & -3 \\ 1 & 1 & 1 & 1 & 1 & 1 & -3 & 21 \end{bmatrix}$$

The original inversion of (1), namely of a matrix of order $q = 13$, has thus been reduced to one of order 8. In this case the symmetry of the elements of $\mathbf{\Omega}^{-1}$ enables us to effect the inversion without using a computer. We will use two lemmas (Tocher, 1952) each of which may be proved by multiplying both sides of the identity by the inverse of the matrix on the left-hand side.

Now

$$\mathbf{\Omega}^{-1} = 3\mathbf{I}_8 - \tfrac{1}{8}\begin{bmatrix} 3 & -1 & -1 & -1 \\ -1 & 3 & -1 & -1 \\ -1 & -1 & 3 & -1 \\ -1 & -1 & -1 & 3 \end{bmatrix} \otimes \begin{bmatrix} 1 & 1 \\ 1 & 1 \end{bmatrix}$$

where the Kronecker product of two matrices, indicated by a $\otimes$ between them, is the product of each *element* of the *first matrix* by the (whole of the) *second matrix*. The first of the two lemmas may be stated as follows:

Lemma **2**

$$(\mathbf{I}_{uv} + \underset{(u\times u)}{\mathbf{A}} \otimes \mathbf{1}_v \mathbf{1}_v')^{-1} = \mathbf{I}_{uv} - \mathbf{A}(\mathbf{I}_u + v\mathbf{A})^{-1} \otimes \mathbf{1}_v \mathbf{1}_v'$$

Applying this to the above expression for $\mathbf{\Omega}^{-1}$ we obtain (with $u = 4$, $v = 2$ and $\mathbf{A} = -\frac{1}{24}\mathbf{K}$)

$$3\mathbf{\Omega} = \mathbf{I}_8 + \tfrac{1}{24}\mathbf{K}(\mathbf{I}_4 - \tfrac{1}{12}\mathbf{K})^{-1} \otimes \mathbf{1}_2 \mathbf{1}_2'$$

where

$$\mathbf{K} = \begin{bmatrix} 3 & -1 & -1 & -1 \\ -1 & 3 & -1 & -1 \\ -1 & -1 & 3 & -1 \\ -1 & -1 & -1 & 3 \end{bmatrix} = 4\mathbf{I}_4 - \mathbf{1}_4 \mathbf{1}_4'$$

and thus

$$\mathbf{I}_4 - \tfrac{1}{12}\mathbf{K} = \tfrac{2}{3}\mathbf{I}_4 + \tfrac{1}{12}\mathbf{1}_4 \mathbf{1}_4'$$

We have thus reduced the order of the inversion to 4. But we can do even better in this case. For this purpose we state:

Lemma **3**

$$(\mathbf{I}_u - \underset{(u\times m)}{\mathbf{C}} \; \underset{(m\times u)}{\mathbf{D}})^{-1} = \mathbf{I}_u + \mathbf{C}(\mathbf{I}_m - \mathbf{DC})^{-1}\mathbf{D}$$

This is particularly useful when m, the order of the matrix to be inverted on the right-hand side, is less than u. In our case $m = 1$ and $u = 4$ so we get

$$\begin{aligned}(\mathbf{I}_4 + \tfrac{1}{8}\mathbf{1}_4 \mathbf{1}_4')^{-1} &= \mathbf{I}_4 - \tfrac{1}{8}\mathbf{1}_4 (\mathbf{I}_1 + \tfrac{1}{8}\mathbf{1}_4' \mathbf{1}_4)^{-1} \mathbf{1}_4' \\ &= \mathbf{I}_4 - \tfrac{1}{12}\mathbf{1}_4 \mathbf{1}_4'\end{aligned}$$

Collecting these results we find

$$\mathbf{\Omega} = \tfrac{1}{3}\mathbf{I}_8 + \tfrac{1}{48}\mathbf{K}(\mathbf{I}_4 - \tfrac{1}{12}\mathbf{1}_4 \mathbf{1}_4') \otimes \mathbf{1}_2 \mathbf{1}_2'$$

which implies

$$48\boldsymbol{\Omega} = 16\mathbf{I}_8 + \begin{bmatrix} 3 & -1 & -1 & -1 \\ -1 & 3 & -1 & -1 \\ -1 & -1 & 3 & -1 \\ -1 & -1 & -1 & 3 \end{bmatrix} \otimes \mathbf{1}_2\mathbf{1}_2'$$

and on multiplying this result for $\boldsymbol{\Omega}$ by $\boldsymbol{\Omega}^{-1}$ we get $\mathbf{I}_8$, as we should.

We leave the rest of the calculations as an exercise for the reader, merely noting that $\mathscr{S}^0_\Omega = 82{\cdot}625$ and $\mathscr{S}^0_\omega = 635{\cdot}5$ with 11 and 19 degrees of freedom, respectively.

Another example of these techniques is provided by the final illustration of Chapter Two. The reader may verify that the design there presented leads to

$$\boldsymbol{\Omega}^{-1} = 2\mathbf{I}_8 + \tfrac{1}{2}\mathbf{I}_2 \otimes \mathbf{1}_4\mathbf{1}_4'$$

and

$$\boldsymbol{\Omega} = \tfrac{1}{2}\mathbf{I}_8 - \tfrac{1}{16}\mathbf{I}_2 \otimes \mathbf{1}_4\mathbf{1}_4'$$

The vector of 'thermometer' $\hat{\beta}$'s is then $\hat{\boldsymbol{\beta}}_1$ where

$$16\hat{\boldsymbol{\beta}}_1' = \{1{\cdot}79 \;\; 3{\cdot}47 \;\; 3{\cdot}35 \;\; 2{\cdot}11 \;\; 2{\cdot}80 \;\; 3{\cdot}20 \;\; 1{\cdot}64 \;\; 3{\cdot}36\}$$

the results being measured from 40·00 degrees.

Missing observations

There is frequent reference in the literature to carefully designed experiments in which one or two of the animals or plants have died with resultant 'loss' of the corresponding measurements. To maintain generality we will suppose that m observations are 'missing' and write our model as

$$\underset{(N\times 1)}{\mathbf{x}} = \begin{bmatrix} \underset{(m\times 1)}{\mathbf{x}_1} \\ \underset{(N-m\times 1)}{\mathbf{x}_2} \end{bmatrix} = \underset{(N\times q)}{\mathbf{Z}'}\;\underset{(q\times 1)}{\boldsymbol{\beta}} + \mathbf{e} = \begin{bmatrix} \underset{(m\times q)}{\mathbf{Z}_1'} \\ \underset{(N-m\times q)}{\mathbf{Z}_2'} \end{bmatrix}\boldsymbol{\beta} + \mathbf{e}$$

It is supposed that the normal equations matrix $\mathbf{ZZ}'$ has a simple form so that it can easily be inverted. Can we still utilize this computational simplicity when the vector $\mathbf{x}_1$ is missing?

Now the estimate of $\boldsymbol{\beta}$ derived from the $N-m$ actual observations is

$$\begin{aligned} \hat{\boldsymbol{\beta}} &= (\mathbf{Z}_2\mathbf{Z}_2')^{-1}\mathbf{Z}_2\mathbf{x}_2 = (\mathbf{ZZ}' - \mathbf{Z}_1\mathbf{Z}_1')^{-1}\mathbf{Z}_2\mathbf{x}_2 \\ &= (\mathbf{ZZ}')^{-1}[\mathbf{I}_q - \mathbf{Z}_1\mathbf{Z}_1'(\mathbf{ZZ}')^{-1}]^{-1}\mathbf{Z}_2\mathbf{x}_2 \end{aligned}$$

Using lemma 3 above with

$$\mathbf{C} = \mathbf{Z}_1 \quad \text{and} \quad \mathbf{D} = \mathbf{Z}_1'(\mathbf{ZZ}')^{-1}$$

we obtain

$$\hat{\boldsymbol{\beta}} = (\mathbf{ZZ}')^{-1}[\mathbf{I}_q + \mathbf{Z}_1\{\mathbf{I}_m - \mathbf{Z}_1'(\mathbf{ZZ}')^{-1}\mathbf{Z}_1\}^{-1}\mathbf{Z}_1'(\mathbf{ZZ}')^{-1}]\,\mathbf{Z}_2\mathbf{x}_2$$

Note that this expression for $\hat{\boldsymbol{\beta}}$ only involves the actual observations $\mathbf{x}_2$ and that, besides the 'simple' inversion of $\mathbf{ZZ}'$, the only other matrix inversion is one of an mth order matrix. Since m is supposed small (e.g., three or less) this inversion may generally be effected on a desk machine.

Having completed the calculation of $\hat{\boldsymbol{\beta}}$ we have

$$\mathscr{S}_{\Omega}^{0} = \mathbf{x}_2'\mathbf{x}_2 - \mathbf{x}_2'\mathbf{Z}_2'\hat{\boldsymbol{\beta}}$$

with $N-m-q$ degrees of freedom.

One further point may be mentioned. Some textbook procedures for one or two missing observations effectively require the calculation of m dummy observations $\hat{\mathbf{x}}_1$ from the formula

$$\hat{\mathbf{x}}_1 = \{\mathbf{I}_m - \mathbf{Z}_1'(\mathbf{ZZ}')^{-1}\mathbf{Z}_1\}^{-1}\mathbf{Z}_1'(\mathbf{ZZ}')^{-1}\mathbf{Z}_2\mathbf{x}_2$$

the right-hand side of which occurs in our expression for $\hat{\boldsymbol{\beta}}$ above. It may be shown, by considering the form of $\mathbf{Z}_1\hat{\mathbf{x}}_1$, that this

$$\hat{\mathbf{x}}_1 \equiv \mathbf{Z}_1'\hat{\boldsymbol{\beta}}$$

Not surprisingly the dummy observations are those we would insert by means of our Least Squares procedure based on $N-m$ actual observations. Using these dummy observational estimates it can also be shown that

$$\mathscr{S}_{\Omega}^{0} = \mathbf{x}'\mathbf{x} - \mathbf{x}'\mathbf{Z}'\hat{\boldsymbol{\beta}}$$

The reader will not need to be warned, as textbook users are, that the whole set of β's will need recalculation when ω is formulated.

Problems to Appendix II

1. Eight blocks with two plots per block have been used to compare four treatments. Treatments a and b occur in each of the first four blocks while treatments c and d occur in each of the remaining four. Show that the inversion of the Tocher matrix is impossible.

2. The weights of 15 swine 17 weeks after reaching 40 lb are provided in the following table (Dunlop, 1933). The animals are shown as deriving from three different litters and they were given three different protein supplements, namely (a) liver, (b) soya bean, and (c) meal and meat meal, respectively, in addition to a basic ration of cereals, soya bean meal and minerals.

14

Litter no.	Treatment		
	a	b	c
1	166	172	170
	170	176	163
2	163	171	162
	173	173	174
3	159	165	163

Complete the experimental layout by assuming three 'missing observations' in litter 3, and make a Least Squares analysis to determine whether the treatments differed. Because litters and treatments are orthogonal to one another the results can be confirmed very easily.

3. The following (Latin Square) arrangement provides the yields of sugar-beet (in pounds) in plots subjected to the application of chalk at a rate (in tons per acre) indicated by the single digit preceding each yield (Yates, 1936). It will be seen that the yields in the control (i.e., 0) plots were considered invalid and they have been eliminated. Because of possible fertility patterns in the soil it will be assumed that there are 'row'

3, 702	1, 571	0, —	4, 722	2, 710
0, —	2, 668	4, 667	1, 546	3, 676
4, 675	3, 612	1, 554	2, 575	0, —
1, 636	0, —	2, 589	3, 573	4, 583
2, 613	4, 606	3. 586	0, —	1, 475

effects and 'column' effects but that these effects do not interact. We must thus allow four β's for rows and another four for columns; with the three β's for treatment differences and the general mean, this implies a total of 12 degrees of freedom accounted for by the model Ω.

If the treatment vectors, which may be made (spuriously) orthogonal to one another, precede the general mean and the 'row' and 'column' vectors we find that $\mathbf{ZZ'}$ can be written in the form

$$\begin{bmatrix} \mathbf{Z}_1\mathbf{Z}_1' & \mathbf{0} \\ \mathbf{0}' & \mathbf{Z}_2\mathbf{Z}_2' \end{bmatrix}$$

where $\mathbf{Z}_1\mathbf{Z}_1'$ is the (3×3) matrix of treatments, and consequently

$$\hat{\boldsymbol{\beta}}_1 = (\mathbf{Z}_1\mathbf{Z}_1')^{-1}\mathbf{Z}_1\mathbf{x}$$

In order to calculate $\mathscr{S}^0_\Omega$ and the $\mathscr{S}^0_\omega$ corresponding to a model in which treatment differences are assumed zero, we require to evaluate $\mathbf{x}'\mathbf{Z}_2'(\mathbf{Z}_2\mathbf{Z}_2')^{-1}\mathbf{Z}_2\mathbf{x}$. Obtain the value of this expression by regarding it as the reduction due to the model in a residual sum of squares based on a randomized incomplete block experiment in which the 'rows' are five blocks and the columns (numbered 1 to 5) are five 'treatments'. Complete the analysis of the sugar-beet experiment by calculating $\hat{\boldsymbol{\beta}}_1$ and its variance–covariance matrix having tested that the treatment effects are, in fact, significant.

References in Appendix II

DUNLOP, G. (1933) 'Methods of experimentation in animal nutrition.' *J. Agric. Sci.* **23**, 580–614.

FREEMAN, G. H. and JEFFERS, J. N. R. (1962) 'Estimation of means and standard errors in the analysis of non-orthogonal experiments by electronic computer.' *J. R. Statist. Soc. B*, **24**, 435–446.

KRAMER, C. Y. and BRADLEY, R. A. (1957) 'Examples of intra-block analysis for factorials in group divisible, partially balanced, incomplete block designs.' *Biometrics* **13**, 197–224.

PEARCE, S. C. (1963) 'The use and classification of non-orthogonal designs (with discussion).' *J. R. Statist. Soc. A*, **126**, 353–377.

TOCHER, K. D. (1952) 'The design and analysis of block experiments (with discussion).' *J. R. Statist. Soc. B*, **14**, 45–100.

YATES, F. (1936) 'Incomplete Latin Squares.' *J. Agric. Sci.* **26**, 301–315.

Addendum

The following material should appear immediately preceding the subheading **The *p*-variate Normal** on p. 115.

The components of any eigenvector $\mathbf{a}_i'$ are actually the *direction cosines* of the ith principal axis, namely the cosines of the p angles this axis makes with the p original axes taken in order. For example, in Fig. 3 the elements of $\mathbf{a}_i'$ are $\cos\alpha$ and $\cos(90° - \alpha) = \sin\alpha$, respectively. In some cases biological theory may prescribe values that these cosines should assume. Thus if the x-values are the logarithms of measurements of length made on an animal the hypothesis of equal relative growth rates of every part measured would imply that each of the components of $\mathbf{a}_1'$ would equal $p^{-1/2}$ (Jolicoeur, 1963). Certain differential growth rate hypotheses would also ascribe values to the components of $\mathbf{a}_1'$ (*loc. cit.*).

An approximate (i.e., large sample) test of the appropriateness of a given (i.e., not derived from the data) eigenvector $\boldsymbol{\alpha}_i'$, where $\boldsymbol{\alpha}_i'\boldsymbol{\alpha}_i = 1$ has been derived by Anderson (1963). He shows that

$$N\{\hat{\lambda}_i \boldsymbol{\alpha}_i'\hat{\boldsymbol{\Sigma}}^{-1}\boldsymbol{\alpha}_i + \hat{\lambda}_i^{-1}\boldsymbol{\alpha}_i'\hat{\boldsymbol{\Sigma}}\boldsymbol{\alpha}_i - 2\} \tag{17}$$

is distributed as χ^2 with $p-1$ degrees of freedom. Note that if $\boldsymbol{\Lambda}$ and $\mathbf{A}$ have been calculated the inverse of $\boldsymbol{\Sigma}$ is easily obtained from the relation

$$\boldsymbol{\Sigma}^{-1} = \mathbf{A}'\boldsymbol{\Lambda}^{-1}\mathbf{A} \tag{18}$$

where the inverse of $\boldsymbol{\Lambda}$ is a diagonal matrix with typical element λ_i^{-1}. [Prove the latter statement by effecting the multiplication $\boldsymbol{\Lambda}\boldsymbol{\Lambda}^{-1} = \mathbf{I}$.]

Solely to illustrate the application of this test we will assume that theory suggests that the first eigenvector of the female painted turtle measurements should be $\boldsymbol{\alpha}_1' = (3^{-1/2}\ 3^{-1/2}\ 3^{-1/2})$. Using relation (18)

$$\hat{\boldsymbol{\Sigma}}^{-1} = \begin{bmatrix} 0{\cdot}06148 & -0{\cdot}05134 & -0{\cdot}07605 \\ & 0{\cdot}12858 & -0{\cdot}06932 \\ & & 0{\cdot}31490 \end{bmatrix}$$

and with $N = 24$ and $\hat{\lambda}_1 = 680{\cdot}40$ the criterion (17) becomes

$$24 \times \{680{\cdot}40 \times 3^{-1} \times 0{\cdot}11154 + 0{\cdot}0014697 \times 3^{-1} \times 1776{\cdot}09 - 2\}$$

where 0·11154 and 1776·09 are the sums of all the elements of $\hat{\boldsymbol{\Sigma}}^{-1}$ and $\hat{\boldsymbol{\Sigma}}$, respectively. The criterion is thus 24·167 and, on the basis of the hypothetical theory, is a value of χ^2 with $p - 1 = 2$ degrees of freedom. This is a highly improbable value to have obtained at random, and the hypothesis is accordingly rejected.

Further References to Chapter Six

ANDERSON, T. W. (1963) 'Asymplotic theory for principal component analysis.' *Ann. Math. Statist.* **34**, 122–148.

JOLICOEUR, P. (1963) 'The degree of generality of robustness in *Martes Americana*.' *Growth* **27**, 1–27.

REYMENT, R. A. (1963) 'Studies on Nigerian Upper Cretaceous and Lower Tertiary *Ostracoda*. Part 2: Danian, Paleocene, and Eocene *Ostracoda*.' *Stockh. Contr. Geol.* **10**.

Author Index

Ordinary figures indicate that a name is to be found in the text or problems. Italic figures indicate that a name is to be found in the reference section at the end of a chapter.

Subject Index